HEREDITARY GENIUS:

AN INQUIRY INTO ITS LAWS AND CONSEQUENCES

HEREDITARY GENIUS:

AN INQUIRY INTO ITS LAWS AND CONSEQUENCES

FRANCIS GALTON

COSIMO CLASSICS

NEW YORK

Cosimo, P.O. Box 416
Old Chelsea Station
New York, NY 10113-0416

or visit our website at:
www.cosimobooks.com

Hereditary Genius: An Inquiry into its Laws and Consequences
originally published by The World Publishing Company in 1869.

Library of Congress Cataloging-in-Publication Data
A catalog record for this book is available from the Library of Congress

Cover design by www.wiselephant.com

ISBN: 1-59605-769-6

Preface to the original edition   23
Prefatory chapter to the edition of 1892   25

I. TREATMENT OF THE PROBLEM
Introductory Chapter   45
Classification of Men According to Their Reputation   49
Classification of Men According to Their Natural Gifts   56
Comparison of the Two Classifications   77
Notation   89

II. RECORDS OF FAMILIES
The Judges of England Between 1660 and 1865   95
Statesmen   149
English Peerages, Their Influence upon Race   177
Commanders   188
Literary Men   216
Men of Science   243
Poets   276
Musicians   291
Painters   301
Divines   312
Senior Classics of Cambridge   353
Oarsmen   359
Wrestlers of the North Country   366

III. CONCLUSIONS: HEREDITY AND EVOLUTION
Comparison of Results   373
The Comparative Worth of Different Races   392
Influences that Affect the Natural Ability of Nations   405
General Considerations   416

Appendix   429
Index   437

PREFACE TO THE ORIGINAL EDITION

The idea of investigating the subject of hereditary genius occurred to me during the course of a purely ethnological inquiry, into the mental peculiarities of different races; when the fact, that characteristics cling to families, was so frequently forced on my notice as to induce me to pay especial attention to that branch of the subject. I began by thinking over the dispositions and achievements of my contemporaries at school, at college, and in after life, and was surprised to find how frequently ability seemed to go by descent. Then I made a cursory examination into the kindred of about four hundred illustrious men of all periods of history, and the results were such, in my own opinion, as completely to establish the theory that genius was hereditary, under limitations that required to be investigated. Thereupon I set to work to gather a large amount of carefully selected biographical data, and in the meantime wrote two articles on the subject, which appeared in *Macmillan's Magazine* in June and in August, 1865. I also attacked the subject from many different sides and sometimes with very minute inquiries, because it was long before the methods I finally adopted were matured. I mention all this to show that the foundation for my theories is broader than appears in the book, and as a partial justification if I have occasionally been betrayed into speaking somewhat more confidently than the evidence I have adduced would warrant.

I trust the reader will pardon a small percentage of error and inaccuracy, if it be so small as not to affect the general value of my results. No one can hate inaccuracy more than myself, or can have a higher idea of what an author owes to his readers, in respect to precision; but, in a subject like this, it is exceedingly difficult to correct every mistake, and still more so to avoid omissions. I have often had to run my eyes over many pages of large biographical dictionaries and volumes of memoirs to arrive at data, destined to be packed into half a dozen lines, in an appendix to one of my many chapters.

The theory of hereditary genius, though usually scouted, has been advocated by a few writers in past as well as in modern times. But I may claim to be the first to treat the subject in a statistical manner, to arrive at numerical results, and to introduce the "law of deviation from an average" into discussions on heredity.

A great many subjects are discussed in the following pages, which go beyond the primary issue,—whether or no genius be hereditary. I could not refuse to consider them, because the bearings of the theory I advocate are too important to be passed over in silence.

PREFATORY CHAPTER TO THE

EDITION OF 1892

This volume is a reprint of a work published twenty-three years ago, which has long been unpurchasable, except at second-hand and at fancy prices. It was a question whether to revise the whole and to bring the information up to date, or simply to reprint it after remedying a few staring errata. The latter course has been adopted, because even a few additional data would have made it necessary to recast all the tabulations, while a thorough reconstruction would be a work of greater labour that I can now undertake.

At the time when the book was written, the human mind was popularly thought to act independently of natural laws, and to be capable of almost any achievement, if compelled to exert itself by a will that had a power of initiation. Even those who had more philosophical habits of thought were far from looking upon the mental faculties of each individual as being limited with as much strictness as those of his body, still less was the idea of the hereditary transmission of ability clearly apprehended. The earlier part of the book should be read in the light of imperfect knowledge of the time when it was written, since what was true in the above respects for the year 1869 does not continue to be true for 1892.

Many of the lines of inquiry that are suggested or hinted at in this book have since been pursued by myself, and the results have been published in various memoirs. They are for the most part epitomised in three volumes—namely, *English Men of Science* (1874), *Human Faculty* (1883), *Natural Inheritance* (1889); also to some small extent in a fourth volume, now about to be published, on *Finger Marks*.

The fault in the volume that I chiefly regret is the choice of its title of *Hereditary Genius*, but it cannot be remedied now.

There was not the slightest intention on my part to use the word genius in any technical sense, but merely as expressing an ability that was exceptionally high, and at the same time inborn. It was intended to be used in the senses ascribed to the word in Johnson's Dictionary, viz. "Mental power or faculties. Disposition of nature by which any one is qualified to some peculiar employment. Nature; disposition." A person who is a genius is defined as—A man endowed with superior faculties. This exhausts all that Johnson has to say on the matter, except as regards the imaginary creature of classical authors called a Genius, which does not concern us, and which he describes as the protecting or ruling power of men, places, or things. There is nothing in the quotations from standard authors with which Johnson illustrates his definitions, that justifies a strained and technical sense being given to the word, nor is there anything of the kind in the Latin word *ingenium*.

Hereditary Genius therefore seemed to be a more expressive and just title than *Hereditary Ability*, for ability does not exclude the effects of education, which genius does. The reader will find a studious abstinence throughout the work from speaking of genius as a special quality. It is freely used as an equivalent for natural ability, in the opening of the chapter on "Comparison of Two Classifications." In the only place, so far as I have noticed on reading the book again, where any distinction is made between them, the uncertainty that still clings to the meaning of the word genius in its technical sense is emphatically dwelt upon (p. 386). There is no confusion of ideas in this respect in the book, but its title seems apt to mislead, and if it could be altered now, it should appear as *Hereditary Ability*.

The relation between genius in its technical sense (whatever its precise definition may be) and insanity, has been much insisted upon by Lombroso and others, whose views of the closeness of the connection between the two are so pronounced, that it would hardly be surprising if one of their more enthusiastic followers were to remark that So-and-So cannot be a genius, because he has never been mad nor is there a single lunatic in his family. I cannot go nearly so far as they, nor accept a moiety of their data, on which the connection between ability of a very high order and insanity is supposed to be established. Still, there is a large residuum of evidence which points to a painfully close relation between the two, and I must add that my own later observations have tended in the same direction, for I have been surprised at finding how often insanity or idiocy has appeared among the near relatives of exceptionally able men. Those who are over eager and extremely active in mind must often possess brains that are more excitable and peculiar than is consistent with soundness. They are likely to become crazy at times, and perhaps to break down altogether. Their inborn excitability and peculiarity may be expected to appear in some of their relatives also, but unaccompanied with an equal dose of preservative qualities, whatever they may be. Those relatives would be "crank," if not insane.

There is much that is indefinite in the application of the word genius. It is applied to many a youth by his contemporaries, but more rarely by biographers, who do not always agree among themselves. If genius means a sense of inspiration, or of rushes of ideas from apparently supernatural sources, or of an inordinate and burning desire to accomplish any particular end, it is perilously near to the voices heard by the insane, to their delirious tendencies, or to their monomanias. It cannot in such cases be a healthy faculty, nor can it be desirable to perpetuate it by inheritance. The natural ability of which this book mainly treats, is such as a modern European possesses in a much greater average share than men of the lower races. There is nothing either in the history of domestic animals or in that of evolution to make us doubt that a race of sane men may be formed, who shall be as much superior mentally and morally to the modern European, as the modern European is to the lowest of the Negro races. Individual departures from this high average level in an upward direction would afford an adequate supply of a degree of ability that is exceedingly rare now, and is much wanted.

It may prove helpful to the reader of the volume to insert in this introductory chapter a brief summary of its data and course of arguments. The primary object was to investigate whether and in what degree natural ability was hereditarily transmitted. This could not be easily accomplished without a preliminary classification of ability according to a standard scale, so the first part of the book is taken up with an attempt to provide one.

The method employed is based on the law commonly known to mathematicians as that of "frequency of error," because it was devised by them to discover the frequency with which various proportionate amounts of error might be expected to occur in astronomical and geodetical operations, and thereby to estimate the value that was probably nearest the truth, from a mass of slightly discordant measures of the same fact.

Its application had been extended by Quételet to the proportions of the human body, on the grounds that the differences, say in stature, between men of the same race might *theoretically* be treated as if they were Errors made by Nature in her attempt to mould individual men of the same race according to the same ideal pattern. Fantastic as such a notion may appear to be when it is expressed in these bare terms, without the accompaniment of a full explanation, it can be shown to rest on a perfectly just basis. Moreover, the theoretical predictions were found by him to be correct, and their correctness in analogous cases under reasonable reservations has been confirmed by multitudes of subsequent observations, of which perhaps the most noteworthy are those of Professor Weldon, on that humble creature the common shrimp (*Proc. Royal Society*, p. 2, vol. 51, 1892).

One effect of the law may be expressed under this form, though it is not that which was used by Quételet. Suppose 100 adult Englishmen to be selected at random, and ranged in the order of their statures in a row; the statures of the 50th and the 51st men would be almost identical, and would represent the average of all the statures. Then the difference, according to the law of frequency, between them and the 63rd man

would be the same as that between the 63rd and the 75th, the
75th and the 84th, the 84th and the 90th. The intervening
men between these divisions, whose numbers are 13, 12, 9,
and 6, form a succession of classes, diminishing as we see in
numbers, but each separated from its neighbours by *equal
grades* of stature. The diminution of the successive classes is
thus far small, but it would be found to proceed at an enormously accelerated rate if a much longer row than that of 100
men were taken, and if the classification were pushed much
further, as is fully shown in this book.

After some provisional verification, I applied this same law
to mental faculties, working it backwards in order to obtain a
scale of ability, and to be enabled thereby to give precision to
the epithets employed. Thus the rank of first in 4,000 or there-
abouts is expressed by the word "eminent." The application
of the law of frequency of error to mental faculties has now
become accepted by many persons, for it is found to accord
well with observation. I know of examiners who habitually
use it to verify the general accuracy of the marks given to many
candidates in the same examination. Also I am informed by
one mathematician that before dividing his examinees into
classes, some regard is paid to this law. There is nothing said
in this book about the law of frequency that subsequent experience has not confirmed and even extended, except that more
emphatic warning is needed against its unchecked application.

The next step was to gain a general idea as to the transmission of ability, founded upon a large basis of homogeneous
facts by which to test the results that might be afterwards
obtained from more striking but less homogeneous data. It was
necessary, in seeking for these, to sedulously guard against
any bias of my own; it was also essential that the group to be
dealt with should be sufficiently numerous for statistical treatment, and again, that the family histories of the persons it
contained should be accessible, and, if possible, already
published.

The list at length adopted for this prefatory purpose was
that of the English Judges since the Reformation. Their

kinships were analysed, and the percentage of their "eminent" relations in the various near degrees were tabulated and the results discussed. These were very striking, and seemed amply sufficient of themselves to prove the main question. Various objections to the validity of the inferences drawn from them may, however, arise; they are considered, and, it is believed, disposed of, in the book.

After doing this, a series of lists were taken in succession, of the most illustrious statesmen, commanders, literary men, men of science, poets, musicians, and painters, of whom history makes mention. To each of these lists were added many English eminent men of recent times, whose biographies are familiar, or, if not, are easily accessible. The lists were drawn up without any bias of my own, for I always relied mainly upon the judgment of others, exercised without any knowledge of the object of the present inquiry, such as the selections made by historians or critics. After the lists of the illustrious men had been disposed of, a large group of eminent Protestant divines were taken in hand—namely, those who were included in Middleton's once well known and highly esteemed biographical dictionary of such persons. Afterwards the Senior Classics of Cambridge were discussed, then the north country oarsmen and wrestlers. In the principal lists all the selected names were inserted, in which those who were known to have eminent kinsmen were printed in *italics*, so the proportion of failures can easily be compared with that of the successes. Each list was followed, as the list of the judges had been, with a brief dictionary of kinships, all being afterwards tabulated and discussed in the same way. Finally the various results were brought together and compared, showing a remarkable general agreement, with a few interesting exceptions. One of these exceptions lay in the preponderating influence of the maternal side in the case of the divines; this was discussed and apparently accounted for.

The remainder of the volume is taken up with topics that are suggested by the results of the former portion, such as the comparative worth of different races, the influences that affect the natural ability of nations, and finally a chapter of general considerations.

If the work were rewritten, the part of the last chapter which refers to Darwin's provisional theory of pangenesis would require revision, and ought to be largely extended, in order to deal with the evidence for and against the hereditary transmission of habits that were not inborn, but had been acquired through practice. Marvellous as is the power of the theory of pangenesis in bringing large classes of apparently different phenomena under a single law, serious objections have since arisen to its validity, and prevented its general acceptance. It would, for example, almost compel us to believe that the hereditary transmission of accidental mutilations and of acquired aptitudes would be the rule and not the exception. But leaving out of the question all theoretical reasons against this belief, such as those which I put forward myself many years ago, as well as the more cogent ones adduced by Weissman in late years,—putting these wholly aside, and appealing to experimental evidence, it is now certain that the tendency of acquired habits to be hereditarily transmitted is at the most extremely small. There may be some few cases, like those of Brown-Séquard's guinea-pigs, in which injury to the nervous substance of the parents affects their offspring; but as a general rule, with scarcely any exception that cannot be ascribed to other influences, such as bad nutrition or transmitted microbes, the injuries or habits of the parents are found to have no effect on the natural form or faculties of the child. Whether very small hereditary influences of the supposed kind, accumulating in the same direction for many generations, may not ultimately affect the qualities of the species, seems to be the only point now seriously in question.

Many illustrations have been offered, by those few persons of high authority who still maintain that acquired habits, such as the use or disuse of particular organs in the parents, admit of being hereditarily transmitted in a sufficient degree to notably affect the whole breed after many generations. Among these illustrations much stress has been laid on the diminishing size of the human jaw, in highly civilised peoples. It is urged that their food is better cooked and more toothsome than that of their ancestors, consequently the masticating apparatus of the race has dwindled through disuse. The truth of the evidence on which this argument rests is questionable, because it is not at all certain that non-European races who have more powerful jaws than ourselves use them more than we do. A Chinaman lives, and has lived for centuries, on rice and spoon-meat, or such over-boiled diet as his chopsticks can deal with. Equatorial Africans live to a great extent on bananas, or else on cassava, which, being usually of the poisonous kind, must be well boiled before it is eaten, in order to destroy the poison. Many of the Eastern Archipelago islanders live on sago. Pastoral tribes eat meat occasionally, but their usual diet is milk or curds. It is only the hunting tribes who habitually live upon tough meat. It follows that the diminishing size of the human jaw in highly civilised people must be ascribed to other causes, such as those, whatever they may be, that reduce the weight of the whole skeleton in delicately nurtured animals.

It seems feasible to subject the question to experiment, whether certain acquired habits, acting during at least ten, twenty, or more generations, have any sensible effects on the race. I will repeat some remarks on this subject which I made two years ago, first in a paper read at a Congress in Paris, and afterwards at the British Association at Newcastle. The position taken was that the experiments ought to be made on a large scale, and upon creatures that were artificially hatched, and therefore wholly isolated from maternal teachings. Fowls, moths, and fish were the particular creatures suggested. Fowls are reared in incubators at very many places on a large scale, especially in France. It seemed not difficult to devise practices associated with peculiar calls to food, with colours connected with food, or with food that was found to be really good though deterrent in appearance, and in certain of the breeding-places to regularly subject the chicks to these practices. Then, after many generations had passed by, to examine whether or no the chicks of the then generation had acquired any instinct for performing them, by comparing their behaviour with that of chicks reared in other places. As regards moths, the silkworm industry is so extensive and well understood that there would be abundant opportunity for analogous experiments with moths, both in France and Italy. The establishments for pisciculture afford another field. It would not be worth while to initiate courses of such experiments unless the crucial value of what they could teach us when completed had first been fully assented to. To my own mind they would rank as crucial experiments so far as they went, and be worth undertaking, but they did not appear to strike others so strongly in the same light. Of course before any such experiments were set on foot, they would have to be considered in detail by many competent minds, and be closely criticised.

Another topic would have been treated at more length if this book were rewritten—namely, the distinction between variations and sports. It would even require a remodelling of much of the existing matter. The views I have been brought to entertain, since it was written, are amplifications of those which are already put forward in pp. 421-2, but insufficiently pushed there to their logical conclusion. They are, that the word variation is used indiscriminately to express two fundamentally distinct conceptions: sports, and variations properly so called. It has been shown in *Natural Inheritance* that the distribution of faculties in a population cannot possibly remain constant, if, *on the average*, the children resemble their parents. If they did so, the giants (in any mental or physical particular) would become more gigantic, and the dwarfs more dwarfish, in each successive generation. The counteracting tendency is what I called "regression." The *filial* centre is not the same as the *parental* centre, but it is nearer to mediocrity; it regresses towards the *racial* centre. In other words, the filial centre (or the fraternal centre, if we change the point of view) is always nearer, on the average, to the racial centre than the parental centre was. There must be an average "regression" in passing from the parental to the filial centre.

B

It is impossible briefly to give a full idea, in this place, either of the necessity or of the proof of regression; they have been thoroughly discussed in the work in question. Suffice it to say, that the result gives precision to the idea of a typical centre from which individual variations occur in accordance with the law of frequency, often to a small amount, more rarely to a larger one, very rarely indeed to one that is much larger, and practically never to one that is larger still. The filial centre falls back further towards mediocrity in a constant proportion to the distance to which the parental centre has deviated from it, whether the direction of the deviation be in excess or in deficiency. All true variations are (as I maintain) of this kind, and it is in consequence impossible that the natural qualities of a race may be permanently changed through the action of selection upon mere variations. The selection of the most serviceable *variations* cannot even produce any great degree of artificial and temporary improvement, because an equilibrium between deviation and regression will soon be reached, whereby the best of the offspring will cease to be better than their own sires and dams.

The case is quite different in respect to what are technically known as "sports." In these, a new character suddenly makes its appearance in a particular individual causing him to differ distinctly from his parents and from others of his race. Such new characters are also found to be transmitted to descendants. Here there has been a change of typical centre, a new point of departure has somehow come into existence, towards which regression has henceforth to be measured, and consequently a real step forward has been made in the course of evolution. When natural selection favours a particular sport, it works effectively towards the formation of a new species, but the favour that it simultaneously shows to mere variations seems to be thrown away, so far as that end is concerned.

There may be entanglement between a sport and a variation which leads to a hybrid and unstable result, well exemplified in the imperfect character of the fusion of different human races. Here numerous pure specimens of their several ancestral types are apt to crop out, notwithstanding the intermixture by marriage that had been going on for many previous generations.

It has occurred to others as well as myself, as to Mr. Wallace and to Professor Romanes, that the time may have arrived when an institute for experiments on heredity might be established with advantage. A farm and garden of a very few acres, with varied exposure, and well supplied with water, placed under the charge of intelligent caretakers, supervised by a biologist, would afford the necessary basis for a great variety of research upon inexpensive animals and plants. The difficulty lies in the smallness of the number of competent persons who are actively engaged in hereditary inquiry, who could be depended upon to use it properly.

The direct result of this inquiry is to make manifest the great and measurable differences between the mental and bodily faculties of individuals, and to prove that the laws of heredity are as applicable to the former as to the latter. Its indirect result is to show that a vast but unused power is vested in each generation over the very *natures* of their successors— that is, over their inborn faculties and dispositions. The brute power of doing this by means of appropriate marriages or abstention from marriage undoubtedly exists, however much the circumstances of social life may hamper its employment.[1] The great problem of the future betterment of the human race is confessedly, at the present time, hardly advanced beyond the stage of academic interest, but thought and action move swiftly nowadays, and it is by no means impossible that a generation which has witnessed the exclusion of the Chinese race from the customary privileges of settlers in two continents, and the deportation of a Hebrew population from a large portion of a third, may live to see other analogous acts performed under sudden socialistic pressure. The striking results of an evil inheritance have already forced themselves so far on the popular mind, that indignation is freely expressed, without any marks of disapproval from others, at the yearly output by unfit

[1] These remarks were submitted in my Presidential Address to the International Congress of Demography, held in London in 1892.

parents of weakly children who are constitutionally incapable of growing up into serviceable citizens, and who are a serious encumbrance to the nation. The questions about to be considered may unexpectedly acquire importance as falling within the sphere of practical politics, and if so, many demographic data that require forethought and time to collect, and a dispassionate and leisurely judgment to discuss, will be hurriedly and sorely needed.

The topics to which I refer are the relative fertility of different classes and races, and their tendency to supplant one another under various circumstances.

The whole question of fertility under the various conditions of civilised life requires more detailed research than it has yet received. We require further investigations into the truth of the hypothesis of Malthus, that there is really no limit to over-population beside that which is afforded by misery or prudential restraint. Is it true that misery, in any justifiable sense of that word, provides the only check which acts automatically, or are other causes in existence, active, though as yet obscure, that assist in restraining the overgrowth of population? It is certain that the productiveness of different marriages differs greatly in consequence of unexplained conditions. The variation in fertility of different kinds of animals that have been captured when wild and afterwards kept in menageries is, as Darwin long since pointed out, most notable and apparently capricious. The majority of those which thrive in confinement, and apparently enjoy excellent health, are nevertheless absolutely infertile; others, often of closely allied species, have their productivity increased. One of the many evidences of our great ignorance of the laws that govern fertility, is seen in the behaviour of bees, who have somehow discovered that by merely modifying the diet and the size of the nursery of any female grub, they can at will cause it to develop, either into a naturally sterile worker, or into the potential mother of a huge hive.

Demographers have, undoubtedly, collected and collated a vast amount of information bearing on the fertility of different nations, but they have mainly attacked the problem in the gross and not in detail, so that we possess little more than mean values that are applicable to general populations, and are very valuable in their way, but we remain ignorant of much else, that a moderate amount of judiciously directed research might, perhaps, be able to tell.

As an example of what could be sought with advantage, let us suppose that we take a number, sufficient for statistical purposes, of persons occupying different social classes, those who are the least efficient in physical, intellectual, and moral grounds, forming our lowest class, and those who are the most efficient forming our highest class. The question to be solved relates to the hereditary permanence of the several classes. What proportion of each class is descended from parents who belong to the same class, and what proportion is descended from parents who belong to each of the other classes? Do those persons who have honourably succeeded in life, and who are presumably, on the whole, the most valuable portion of our human stock, contribute on the aggregate their fair share of posterity to the next generation? If not, do they contribute more or less than their fair share, and in what degree? In other words, is the evolution of man in each particular country, favourably or injuriously affected by its special form of civilisation?

Enough is already known to make it certain that the productiveness of both the extreme classes, the best and the worst, falls short of the average of the nation as a whole. Therefore, the most prolific class necessarily lies between the two extremes, but at what intermediate point does it lie? Taken altogether, on any reasonable principle, are the natural gifts of the most prolific class, bodily, intellectual, and moral, above or below the line of national mediocrity? If above that line, then the existing conditions are favourable to the improvement of the race. If they are below that line, they must work towards its degradation.

These brief remarks serve to shadow out the problem; it would require much more space than is now available, before it could be phrased in a way free from ambiguity, so that its solution would clearly instruct us whether the conditions of life at any period in any given race were tending to raise or to depress its natural qualities.

Whatever other countries may or may not have lost, ours has certainly gained on more than one occasion by the infusion of the breed of selected sub-races, especially of that of the Protestant refugees from religious persecution on the Continent. It seems reasonable to look upon the Huguenots as men who, on the whole, had inborn qualities of a distinctive kind from the majority of their countrymen, and who may, therefore, be spoken of as a sub-type—that is to say, capable, when isolated, of continuing their race without its showing any strong tendency to revert to the form of the earlier type from which it was a well-defined departure. It proved, also, that the cross breed between them and our ancestors was a singularly successful mixture. Consequently, England has been largely indebted to the natural refinement and to the solid worth of the Huguenot breed, as well as to the culture and technical knowledge that the Huguenots brought with them.

The frequency in history with which one race has supplanted another over wide geographical areas is one of the most striking facts in the evolution of mankind. The denizens of the world at the present day form a very different human stock to that which inhabited it a dozen generations ago, and to all appearance a no less difference will be found in our successors a dozen of generations hence. Partly it may be that new human varieties have come into permanent or only into temporary existence, like that most remarkable mixed race of the Normans many centuries ago, in whom, to use well-known words of the late Professor Freeman, the indomitable vigour of the Scandinavians, joined to the buoyant vivacity of the Gaul, produced the conquering and ruling race of Europe. But principally the change of which I spoke is due to great alterations in the proportions of those who belong to the old and well established types. The Negro now born in the United States has much the same natural faculties as his distant cousin who is born in

Africa; the effect of his transplantation being ineffective in changing his nature, but very effective in increasing his numbers, in enlarging the range of his distribution, and in destroying native American races. There are now some 8,000,000 of Negroes in lands where not one of them existed twelve generations ago, and probably not one representative of the race which they displaced remains there; on the other hand, there has been no corresponding diminution of numbers in the parent home of the Negro. Precisely the same may be said of the European races who have during the same period swarmed over the temperate regions of the globe, forming the nuclei of many future nations.

It is impossible, even in the vaguest way, in a brief space, to give a just idea of the magnitude and variety of changes produced in the human stock by the political events of the last few generations, and it would be difficult to do so in such a way as not to seriously wound the patriotic susceptibilities of many readers. The natural temperaments and moral ideals of different races are various, and praise or blame cannot be applied at the discretion of one person without exciting remonstrance from others who take different views with perhaps equal justice. The birds and beasts assembled in conclave may try to pass a unanimous resolution in favour of the natural duty of the mother to nurture and protect her offspring, but the cuckoo would musically protest. The Irish Celt may desire the extension of his race and the increase of its influence in the representative governments of England and America, but the wishes of his Anglo-Saxon or Teuton fellow-subjects may lie in the opposite direction; and so on indefinitely. My object now is merely to urge inquiries into the historical fact whether legislation, which has led to the substitution on a large scale of one race for another, has not often been the outcome of conflicting views into which the question of race hardly entered at all, and which were so nearly balanced that if the question of race had been properly introduced into the discussion the result might have been different. The possibility of such being the case cannot be doubted, and affords strong reason for justly appraising the influence of race, and of hereafter including it at neither more nor less than its real value, among the considerations by which political action will be determined.

The importance to be attached to race is a question that deserves a far larger measure of exact investigation than it receives. We are exceedingly ignorant of the respective ranges of the natural and acquired faculties in different races, and there is too great a tendency among writers to dogmatise wildly about them, some grossly magnifying, others as greatly minimising their several provinces. It seems however possible to answer this question unambiguously, difficult as it is.

The recent attempts by many European nations to utilise Africa for their own purposes gives immediate and practical interest to inquiries that bear on the transplantation of races. They compel us to face the question as to what races should be politically aided to become hereafter the chief occupiers of that continent. The varieties of Negroes, Bantus, Arab half-breeds, and others who now inhabit Africa are very numerous, and they differ much from one another in their natural qualities. Some of them must be more suitable than others to thrive under that form of moderate civilisation which is likely to be introduced into Africa by Europeans, who will enforce justice and order, excite a desire among the natives for comforts and luxuries, and make steady industry almost a condition of living at all. Such races would spread and displace the others by degrees. Or it may prove that the Negroes, one and all, will fail as completely under the new conditions as they have failed under the old ones, to submit to the needs of a superior civilisation to their own; in this case their races, numerous and prolific as they are, will in course of time be supplanted and replaced by their betters.

It seems scarcely possible as yet to assure ourselves as to the possibility of any variety of white men to work, to thrive, and to continue their race in the broad regions of the topics. We could not do so without better knowledge that we now possess of the different capacities of individuals to withstand their malarious and climatic influences. Much more care is taken to select appropriate varieties of plants and animals for plantation in foreign settlements, than to select appropriate types of men. Discrimination and foresight are shown in the one case, an indifference born of ignorance is shown in the other. The importance is not yet sufficiently recognised of a more exact examination and careful record than is now made of the physical qualities and hereditary antecedents of candidates for employment in tropical countries. We require these records to enable us to learn hereafter what are the conditions in youth that are prevalent among those whose health subsequently endured the change of climatic influence satisfactorily, and conversely as regards those who failed. It is scarcely possible to properly conduct such an investigation retrospectively.

In conclusion I wish again to emphasise the fact that the improvement of the natural gifts of future generations of the human race is largely, though indirectly, under our control. We may not be able to originate, but we can guide. The processes of evolution are in constant and spontaneous activity, some pushing towards the bad, some towards the good. Our part is to watch for opportunities to intervene by checking the former and giving free play to the latter. We must distinguish clearly between our power in this fundamental respect and that which we also possess of ameliorating education and hygiene. It is earnestly to be hoped that inquiries will be increasingly directed into historical facts, with the view of estimating the possible effects of reasonable political action in the future, in gradually raising the present miserably low standard of the human race to one in which the Utopias in the dreamland of philanthropists may become practical possibilities.

PART ONE

TREATMENT OF THE
PROBLEM

INTRODUCTORY CHAPTER

I propose to show in this book that a man's natural abilities are derived by inheritance, under exactly the same limitations as are the form and physical features of the whole organic world. Consequently, as it is easy, notwithstanding those limitations, to obtain by careful selection a permanent breed of dogs or horses gifted with peculiar powers of running, or of doing anything else, so it would be quite practicable to produce a highly-gifted race of men by judicious marriages during several consecutive generations. I shall show that social agencies of an ordinary character, whose influences are little suspected, are at this moment working towards the degradation of human nature, and that others are working towards its improvement. I conclude that each generation has enormous power over the natural gifts of those that follow, and maintain that it is a duty we owe to humanity to investigate the range of that power, and to exercise it in a way that, without being unwise towards ourselves, shall be most advantageous to future inhabitants of the earth.

I am aware that my views, which were first published four years ago in *Macmillan's Magazine* (in June and August 1865), are in contradiction to general opinion; but the arguments I then used have been since accepted, to my great gratification, by many of the highest authorities on heredity. In reproducing them, as I now do, in a much more elaborate form, and on a greatly enlarged basis of induction, I feel assured that, inasmuch as what I then wrote was sufficient to earn the acceptance of Mr. Darwin (*Domestication of Plants and Animals*, ii. 7), the increased amount of evidence submitted in the present volume is not likely to be gainsaid.

The general plan of my argument is to show that high

reputation is a pretty accurate test of high ability; next to discuss the relationships of a large body of fairly eminent men —namely, the Judges of England from 1660 to 1868, the States, men of the time of George III, and the Premiers during the last 100 years—and to obtain from these a general survey of the laws of heredity in respect to genius. Then I shall examine, in order, the kindred of the most illustrious Commanders, men of Literature and of Science, Poets, Painters, and Musicians, of whom history speaks. I shall also discuss the kindred of a certain selection of Divines and of modern Scholars. Then will follow a short chapter, by way of comparison, on the hereditary transmission of physical gifts, as deduced from the relationships of certain classes of Oarsmen and Wrestlers. Lastly, I shall collate my results, and draw conclusions.

It will be observed that I deal with more than one grade of ability. Those upon whom the greater part of my volume is occupied, and on whose kinships my argument is most securely based, have been generally reputed as endowed by nature with extraordinary genius. There are so few of these men that, although they are scattered throughout the whole historical period of human existence, their number does not amount to more than 400, and yet a considerable proportion of them will be found to be interrelated.

Another grade of ability with which I deal is that which includes numerous highly eminent, and all the illustrious names of modern English history, whose immediate descendants are living among us, whose histories are popularly known, and whose relationships may readily be traced by the help of biographical dictionaries, peerages, and similar books of reference.

A third and lower grade is that of the English Judges, massed together as a whole, for the purpose of the prefatory statistical inquiry of which I have already spoken. No one doubts that many of the ablest intellects of our race are to be found among the Judges; nevertheless the *average* ability of a Judge cannot be rated as equal to that of the lower of the two grades I have described.

I trust the reader will make allowance for a large and some-what important class of omissions I have felt myself compelled to make when treating of the eminent men of modern days. I am prevented by a sense of decorum from quoting names of their relations in contemporary life who are not recognised as public characters, although their abilities may be highly appreciated in private life. Still less consistent with decorum would it have been, to introduce the names of female relatives that stand in the same category. My case is so overpoweringly strong, that I am perfectly able to prove my point without having recourse to this class of evidence. Nevertheless, the reader should bear in mind that it exists; and I beg he will do me the justice of allowing that I have not overlooked the whole of the evidence that does not appear in my pages. I am deeply conscious of the imperfection of my work, but my sins are those of omission, not of commission. Such errors as I may and must have made, which give a fictitious support to my argu-ments, are, I am confident, out of all proportion fewer than such omissions of facts as would have helped to establish them.

I have taken little notice in this book of modern men of eminence who are not English, or at least well known to Englishmen. I feared, if I included large classes of foreigners, that I should make glaring errors. It requires a very great deal of labour to hunt out relationships, even with the facilities afforded to a countryman having access to persons acquainted with the various families; much more would it have been difficult to hunt out the kindred of foreigners. I should have especially liked to investigate the biographies of Italians and Jews, both of whom appear to be rich in families of high intel-lectual breeds. Germany and America are also full of interest. It is a little less so with respect to France, where the Revolution and the guillotine made sad havoc among the progeny of her abler races.

There is one advantage to a candid critic in my having left so large a field untouched; it enables me to propose a test that any well-informed reader may easily adopt who doubts the fairness of my examples. He may most reasonably suspect that

I have been unconsciously influenced by my theories to select men whose kindred were most favourable to their support. If so, I beg he will test my impartiality as follows:—Let him take a dozen names of his own selection, as the most eminent in whatever profession and in whatever country he knows most about, and let him trace out for himself their relations. It is necessary, as I find by experience, to take some pains to be sure that none, even of the immediate relatives, on either the male or female side, have been overlooked. If he does what I propose, I am confident he will be astonished at the completeness with which the results will confirm my theory. I venture to speak with assurance, because it has often occurred to me to propose this very test to incredulous friends, and invariably, so far as my memory serves me, as large a propro- tion of the men who were named were discovered to have eminent relations, as the nature of my views on heredity would have led us to expect.

CLASSIFICATION OF MEN ACCORDING

TO THEIR REPUTATION

The arguments by which I endeavour to prove that genius is hereditary, consist in showing how large is the number of instances in which men who are more or less illustrious have eminent kinsfolk. It is necessary to have clear ideas on the two following matters before my arguments can be rightly appreciated. The first is the degree of selection implied by the words "eminent" and "illustrious." Does "eminent" mean the foremost in a hundred, in a thousand, or in what other number of men ? The second is the degree to which reputation may be accepted as a test of ability.

It is essential that I, who write, should have a minimum qualification distinctly before my eyes whenever I employ the phrases "eminent" and the like, and that the reader should understand as clearly as myself the value I attach to those qualifications. An explanation of these words will be the subject of the present chapter. A subsequent chapter will be given to the discussion of how far "eminence" may be accepted as a criterion of natural gifts. It is almost needless for me to insist that the subjects of these two chapters are entirely distinct.

I look upon social and professional life as a continuous examination. All are candidates for the good opinions of others, and for success in their several professions, and they achieve success in proportion as the general estimate is large of their aggregate merits. In ordinary scholastic examinations marks are allotted in stated proportions to various specified subjects—so many for Latin, so many for Greek, so many for English history, and the rest. The world, in the same way, but almost unconsciously, allots marks to men. It gives them for originality of conception, for enterprise, for activity and energy, for

administrative skill, for various acquirements, for power of
literary expression, for oratory, and much besides of general
value, as well as for more specially professional merits. It does
not allot these marks acccording to a proportion that can easily
be stated in words, but there is a rough commonsense that
governs its practice with a fair approximation to constancy.
Those who have gained most of these tacit marks are ranked,
by the common judgment of the leaders of opinion, as the
foremost men of their day.

The metaphor of an examination may be stretched much
further. As there are alternative groups in any one of which a
candidate may obtain honours, so it is with reputations—they
may be made in law, literature, science, art, and in a host of
other pursuits. Again: as the mere attainment of a general fair
level will obtain no honours in an examination, no more will it
do so in the struggle for eminence. A man must show conspicuous power in at least one subject in order to achieve a high
reputation.

Let us see how the world classifies people, after examining
each of them, in her patient, persistent manner, during the
years of their manhood. How many men of "eminence" are
there, and what proportion do they bear to the whole community?

I will begin by analysing a very painstaking biographical
handbook, lately published by Routledge and Co., called *Men
of the Time*. Its intention, which is very fairly and honestly
carried out, is to include none but those whom the world honours for the ability. Their catalogue of names is 2,500, and a
full half of it consists of American and Continental celebrities.
It is well I should give in a foot-note[1] an analysis of its contents,

---

[1] *Contents of the "Dictionary of Men of the Time," Ed.* 1865:—

62 actors, singers, dancers, &c.; 7 agriculturists; 71 antiquaries,
archæologists, numismatists, &c.; 20 architects; 129 artists (painters
and designers); 950 authors; 400 divines; 43 engineers and mechan-
icians; 10 engravers; 140 lawyers, judges, barristers, and legists; 94
medical practitioners, physicians, surgeons, and physiologists; 39
merchants, capitalists, manufacturers, and traders; 168 military
officers; 12 miscellaneous; 7 moral and metaphysical philosophers,
logicians; 32 musicians and composers; 67 naturalists, botanists,

in order to show the exhaustive character of its range. The numbers I have prefixed to each class are not strictly accurate, for I measured them off rather than counted them, but they are quite close enough. The same name often appears under more than one head.

On looking over the book, I am surprised to find how large a proportion of the "Men of the Time" are past middle age. It appears that in the cases of high (but by no means in that of the highest) merit, a man must outlive the age of fifty to be sure of being widely appreciated. It takes time for an able man, born in the humbler ranks of life, to emerge from them and to take his natural position. It would not, therefore, be just to compare the numbers of Englishmen in the book with that of the whole adult male population of the British isles; but it is necessary to confine our examination to those of the celebrities who are past fifty years of age, and to compare their number with that of the whole male population who are also above fifty years. I estimate, from examining a large part of the book, that there are about 850 of these men, and that 500 of them are decidedly well known to persons familiar with literary and scientific society. Now, there are about two millions of adult males in the British isles above fifty years of age; consequently, the total number of the "Men of the Time" are as 425 to a million, and the more select part of them as 250 to a million.

The qualifications for belonging to what I call the more select part are, in my mind, that a man should have distinguished himself pretty frequently either by purely original work, or as a leader of opinion. I wholly exclude notoriety obtained by a single act. This is a fairly well-defined line, because there is not room for many men to be eminent. Each interest or idea has its mouthpiece, and a man who has attained and can maintain his position as the representative of a party

zoologists, &c.; 36 naval officers; 40 philologists and ethnologists; 60 poets (but also included in authors); 60 political and social economists and philanthropists; 154 men of science, astronomers, chemists, geologists, mathematicians, &c.; 29 sculptors; 64 sovereigns, members of royal families, &c.; 376 statesmen, diplomatists, colonial governors, &c.; 76 travellers and geographers.

or an idea, naturally becomes much more conspicuous than his coadjutors who are nearly equal but inferior in ability. This is eminently the case in positions where eminence may be won by official acts. The balance may be turned by a grain that decides whether A, B, or C shall be promoted to a vacant post. The man who obtains it has opportunities of distinction denied to the others. I do not, however, take much note of official rank. People who have left very great names behind them have mostly done so through non-professional labours. I certainly should not include mere officials, except of the highest ranks, and in open professions, among my select list of eminent men.

Another estimate of the proportion of eminent men to the whole population was made on a different basis, and gave much the same result. I took the obituary of the year 1868, published in *The Times* on January 1st, 1869, and found in it about fifty names of men of the more select class. This was in one sense a broader, and in another a more rigorous selection than that which I have just described. It was broader, because I included the names of many whose abilities were high, but who died too young to have earned the wide reputation they deserved; and it was more rigorous, because I excluded old men who had earned distinction in years gone by, but had not shown themselves capable in later times to come again to the front. On the first ground, it was necessary to lower the limit of the age of the population with whom they should be compared. Forty-five years of age seemed to be a fair limit, including, as it was supposed to do, a year or two of broken health preceding decease. Now, 210,000 males die annually in the British isles above the age of forty-five; therefore, the ratio of the more select portion of the "Men of the Time" on these data is as 50 to 210,000, or as 238 to a million.

Thirdly, I consulted obituaries of many years back, when the population of these islands was much smaller, and they appeared to me to lead to similar conclusions, viz. that 250 to a million is an ample estimate.

There would be no difficulty in making a further selection out of these, to any degree of rigour. We could select the 200, the 100, or the fifty best out of the 250, without much uncertainty. But I do not see my way to work downwards. If I were asked to choose the thousand per million best men, I should feel we had descended to a level where there existed no sure data for guidance, where accident and opportunity had undue influence, and where it was impossible to distinguish general eminence from local reputation, or from mere notoriety.

These considerations define the sense in which I propose to employ the word "eminent." When I speak of an eminent man, I mean one who has achieved a position that is attained by only 250 persons in each million of men, or by one person in each 4,000. 4,000 is a very large number—difficult for persons to realise who are not accustomed to deal with great assemblages. On the most brilliant of starlight nights there are never so many as 4,000 stars visible to the naked eye at the same time; yet we feel it to be an extraordinary distinction to a star to be accounted as the brightest in the sky. This, be it remembered, is my narrowest area of selection. I propose to introduce no name whatever into my lists of kinsmen (unless it be marked off from the rest by brackets) that is less distinguished.

The mass of those with whom I deal are far more rigidly selected—many are as one in a million, and not a few as one of many millions. I use the term "illustrious" when speaking of these. They are men whom the whole intelligent part of the nation mourns when they die; who have, or deserve to have, a public funeral; and who rank in future ages as historical characters.

Permit me to add a word upon the meaning of a million, being a number so enormous as to be difficult to conceive. It is well to have a standard by which to realise it. Mine will be understood by many Londoners; it is as follows:—One summer day I passed the afternoon in Bushey Park to see the magnificent spectacle of its avenue of horse-chestnut trees, a mile long, in full flower. As the hours passed by, it occurred to me to try to count the number of spikes of flowers facing the drive on one side of the long avenue—I mean all the spikes that were visible in full sunshine on one side of the road.

Accordingly, I fixed upon a tree of average bulk and flower, and drew imaginary lines—first halving the tree, then quartering, and so on, until I arrived at a subdivision that was not too large to allow of my counting the spikes of flowers it included. I did this with three different trees, and arrived at pretty much the same result: as well as I recollect, the three estimates were as nine, ten, and eleven. Then I counted the trees in the avenue, and, multiplying all together, I found the spikes to be just about 100,000 in number. Ever since then, whenever a million is mentioned, I recall the long perspective of the avenue of Bushey Park, with its stately chestnuts clothed from top to bottom with spikes of flowers, bright in the sunshine, and I imagine a similarly continuous floral band, of ten miles in length.

In illustration of the value of the extreme rigour implied by a selection of one in a million, I will take the following instance. The Oxford and Cambridge boat-race excites almost a national enthusiasm, and the men who represent their Universities as competing crews have good reason to be proud of being the selected champions of such large bodies. The crew of each boat consists of eight men, selected out of about 800 students; namely the available undergraduates of about two successive years. In other words, the selection that is popularly felt to be so strict, is only as one in a hundred. Now, suppose there had been so vast a number of universities that it would have been possible to bring together 800 men, each of whom had pulled in a University crew, and that from this body the eight best were selected to form a special crew of comparatively rare merit; the selection of each of these would be as 1 to 10,000 ordinary men. Let this process be repeated, and then, and not till then, do you arrive at a superlative crew, representing selections of one in a million. This is a perfectly fair deduction, because the youths at the Universities are a haphazard collection of men, so far as regards their thews and sinews. No one is sent to a University on account of his powerful muscle. Or, to put the same facts into another form:— it would require a period of no less than 100 years, before either University could furnish eight men, each of whom would have sufficient boating eminence to rank as one of the medium crew. Ten thousand years must elapse before eight men could be furnished, each of whom would have the rank of the superlative crew.

It is, however, quite another matter with respect to brain power, for, as I shall have occasion to show, the Universities attract to themselves a large proportion of the eminent scholastic talent of all England. There are nearly a quarter of a million males in Great Britain who arrive each year at the proper age for going to the University: therefore, if Cambridge, for example, received only one in every five of the ablest scholastic intellects, she would be able, in every period of twenty years, to boast of the fresh arrival of an undergraduate, the rank of whose scholastic eminence was that of one in a million.

CLASSIFICATION OF MEN ACCORDING

TO THEIR NATURAL GIFTS

I have no patience with the hypothesis occasionally expressed, and often implied, especially in tales written to teach children to be good, that babies are born pretty much alike, and that the sole agencies in creating differences between boy and boy, and man and man, are steady application and moral effort. It is in the most unqualified manner that I object to pretensions of natural equality. The experiences of the nursery, the school, the University, and of professional careers, are a chain of proofs to the contrary. I acknowledge freely the great power of education and social influences in developing the active powers of the mind, just as I acknowledge the effect of use in developing the muscles of a blacksmith's arm, and no further. Let the blacksmith labour as he will, he will find there are certain feats beyond his power that are well within the strength of a man of herculean make, even although the latter may have led a sedentary life. Some years ago, the Highlanders held a grand gathering in Holland Park, where they challenged all England to compete with them in their games of strength. The challenge was accepted, and the well-trained men of the hills were beaten in the foot-race by a youth who was stated to be a pure Cockney, the clerk of a London banker.

Everybody who has trained himself to physical exercises discovers the extent of his muscular powers to a nicety. When he begins to walk, to row, to use the dumb bells, or to run, he finds to his great delight that his thews strengthen, and his endurance of fatigue increases day after day. So long as he is a novice, he perhaps flatters himself there is hardly an assignable limit to the education of his muscles; but the daily gain is soon discovered to diminish, and at last it vanishes altogether. His maximum performance becomes a rigidly determinate quantity. He learns to an inch, how high or how far he can jump, when he has attained the highest state of training. He learns to half a pound, the force he can exert on the dynamometer, by compressing it. He can strike a blow against the machine used to measure impact, and drive its index to a certain graduation, but no further. So it is in running, in rowing, in walking, and in every other form of physical exertion. There is a definite limit to the muscular powers of every man, which he cannot by any education or exertion overpass.

This is precisely analogous to the experience that every student has had of the working of his mental powers. The eager boy, when he first goes to school and confronts intellectual difficulties, is astonished at his progress. He glories in his newly-developed mental grip and growing capacity for application, and, it may be, fondly believes it to be within his reach to become one of the heroes who have left their mark upon the history of the world. The years go by; he competes in the examinations of school and college, over and over again with his fellows, and soon finds his place among them. He knows he can beat such and such of his competitors; that there are some with whom he runs on equal terms, and others whose intellectual feats he cannot even approach. Probably his vanity still continues to tempt him, by whispering in a new strain. It tells him that classics, mathematics, and other subjects taught in universities, are mere scholastic specialities, and no test of the more valuable intellectual powers. It reminds him of numerous instances of persons who had been unsuccessful in the competitions of youth, but who had shown powers in after-life that made them the foremost men of their age. Accordingly, with newly furbished hopes, and with all the ambition of twenty-two years of age, he leaves his University and enters a larger field of competition. The same kind of experience awaits him here that he has already gone through. Opportunities occur—they occur to every man—and he finds himself incapable of grasping them. He tries, and is tried in many things. In a few years more, unless he is incurably blinded by self-conceit, he learns precisely of what performances he is capable, and what other enterprises lie beyond his compass. When he reaches mature life, he is confident only within certain limits, and knows, or ought to know, himself just as he is probably judged of by the world, with all his unmistakeable weakness and all his undeniable strength. He is no longer tormented into hopeless efforts by the fallacious promptings of overweening vanity, but he limits his undertakings to matters below the level of his reach, and finds true moral repose in an honest conviction that he is engaged in as much good work as his nature has rendered him capable of performing.

There can hardly be a surer evidence of the enormous difference between the intellectual capacity of men, than the prodigious differences in the numbers of marks obtained by those who gain mathematical honours at Cambridge. I therefore crave permission to speak at some length upon this subject, although the details are dry and of little general interest. There are between 400 and 450 students who take their degrees in each year, and of these, about 100 succeed in gaining honours in mathematics, and are ranged by the examiners in strict order of merit. About the first forty of those who take mathematical honours are distinguished by the title of wranglers, and it is a decidedly creditable thing to be even a low wrangler; it will secure a fellowship in a small college. It must be carefully borne in mind that the distinction of being the first in this list of honours, or what is called the senior wrangler of the year, means a vast deal more than being the foremost mathematician of 400 or 450 men taken at haphazard. No doubt the large bulk of Cambridge men are taken almost at haphazard. A boy is intended by his parents for some profession; if that profession be either the Church or the Bar, it used to be almost requisite, and it is still important, that he should be sent to Cambridge or Oxford. These youths may justly be considered as having been taken at haphazard. But there are many others who have fairly won their way to the Universities, and are therefore selected from an enormous area. Fully one-half of the wranglers have been boys of note at their respective schools, and, conversely, almost all boys of note at schools find their way to the Universities. Hence it is that among their comparatively small number of students, the Universities include the highest youthful scholastic ability of all England. The senior wrangler, in each successive year, is the chief of these as regards mathematics, and this, the highest distinction, is, or was, continually won by youths who had no mathematical training of importance before they went to Cambridge. All their instruction had been received during the three years of their residence at the University. Now, I do not say anything here about the merits or demerits of Cambridge mathematical studies having been directed along a too narrow groove, or about the presumed disadvantages of ranging candidates in strict order of merit, instead of grouping them, as at Oxford, in classes, where their names appear alphabetically arranged. All I am concerned with here are the results; and these are most appropriate to my argument. The youths start on their three years' race as fairly as possible. They are then stimulated to run by the most powerful inducements, namely, those of competition, of honour, and of future wealth (for a good fellowship *is* wealth); and at the end of the three years they are examined most rigorously according to a system that they all understand and are equally well prepared for. The examination lasts five and a half hours a day for eight days. All the answers are carefully marked by the examiners, who add up the marks at the end and range the candidates in strict order of merit. The fairness and thoroughness of Cambridge examinations have never had a breath of suspicion cast upon them.

Unfortunately for my purposes, the marks are not published. They are not even assigned on a uniform system, since each examiner is permitted to employ his own scale of marks; but whatever scale he uses, the results as to proportional merit are the same. I am indebted to a Cambridge examiner for a copy of his marks in respect to two examinations, in which the scales of marks were so alike as to make it easy, by a slight proportional adjustment, to compare the two together. This was, to a certain degree, a confidential communication, so that it would

be improper for me to publish anything that would identify
the years to which these marks refer. I simply give them as
groups of figures, sufficient to show the enormous differences

SCALE OF MERIT AMONG THE MEN WHO OBTAIN
MATHEMATICAL HONOURS AT CAMBRIDGE

The results of two years are thrown into a single table
The total number of marks obtainable in each year was 17,000

Number of marks obtained by candidates	Number of candidates in the two years, taken together, who obtained those marks
Under 500	24
500 to 1,000	74
1,000 to 1,500	38
1,500 to 2,000	21
2,000 to 2,500	11
2,500 to 3,000	8
3,000 to 3,500	11
3,500 to 4,000	5
4,000 to 4,500	2
4,500 to 5,000	1
5,000 to 5,500	3
5,500 to 6,000	1
6,000 to 6,500	0
6,500 to 7,000	0
7,000 to 7,500	0
7,500 to 8,000	1
	200

I have included in this table only the first 100 men in each year. The
omitted residue is too small to be important. I have omitted it lest,
if the precise numbers of honour men were stated those numbers
would have served to identify the years. For reasons already given,
I desire to afford no data to serve that purpose.

of merit. The lowest man in the list of honours gains less than
300 marks; the lowest wrangler gains about 1,500 marks; and
the senior wrangler, in one of the lists now before me, gained
more than 7,500 marks. Consequently, the lowest wrangler has
more than five times the merit of the lowest junior optime, and
less than one-fifth the merit of the senior wrangler.

The precise number of marks obtained by the senior wrangler in the more remarkable of these two years was 7,634; by the second wrangler in the same year, 4,123; and by the lowest man in the list of honours, only 237. Consequently, the senior wrangler obtained nearly twice as many marks as the second wrangler, and more than thirty-two times as many as the lowest man. I have received from another examiner the marks of a year in which the senior wrangler was conspicuously eminent. He obtained 9,422 marks, whilst the second in the same year—whose merits were by no means inferior to those of second wranglers in general—obtained only 5,642. The man at the bottom of the same honour list had only 309 marks, or one-thirtieth the number of the senior wrangler. I have some particulars of a fourth very remarkable year, in which the senior wrangler obtained no less than ten times as many marks as the second wrangler, in the "problem paper." Now, I have discussed with practised examiners the question of how far the numbers of marks may be considered as proportionate to the mathematical power of the candidate, and am assured they are strictly proportionate as regards the lower places, but do not afford full justice to the highest. In other words, the senior wranglers above mentioned had *more* than thirty, or thirty-two times the ability of the lowest men on the lists of honours. They would be able to grapple with problems more than thirty-two times as difficult; or when dealing with subjects of the same difficulty, but intelligible to all, would comprehend them more rapidly in perhaps the square root of that proportion. It is reasonable to expect that marks would do some injustice to the very best men, because a very large part of the time of the examination is taken up by the mechanical labour of writing. Whenever the thought of the candidate outruns his pen, he gains no advantage from his excess of promptitude in conception. I should, however, mention that some of the ablest men have shown their superiority by comparatively little writing. They find their way at once to the root of the difficulty in the problems that are set, and, with a few clean, apposite, powerful strokes, succeed in proving they can overthrow it, and then they go on to another question. Every word they write tells. Thus, the late Mr. H. Leslie Ellis, who was a brilliant senior wrangler in 1840, and whose name is familiar to many generations of Cambridge men as a prodigy of universal genius, did not even remain during the full period in the examination room: his health was weak, and he had to husband his strength.

The mathematical powers of the last man on the list of honours, which are so low when compared with those of a senior wrangler, are mediocre, or even above mediocrity, when compared with the gifts of Englishmen generally. Though the examination places 100 honour men above him, it puts no less than 300 "poll men" below him. Even if we go so far as to allow that 200 out of the 300 refuse to work hard enough to get honours, there will remain 100 who, even if they worked hard, could not get them. Every tutor knows how difficult it is to drive abstract conceptions, even of the simplest kind, into the brains of most people—how feeble and hesitating is their mental grasp—how easily their brains are mazed—how incapable they are of precision and soundness of knowledge. It often occurs to persons familiar with some scientific subject to hear men and women of mediocre gifts relate to one another what they have picked up about it from some lecture—say at the Royal Institution, where they have sat for an hour listening with delighted attention to an admirably lucid account, illustrated by experiments of the most perfect and beautiful character, in all of which they expressed themselves intensely gratified and highly instructed. It is positively painful to hear what they say. Their recollections seem to be a mere chaos of mist and misapprehension, to which some sort of shape and organisation has been given by the action of their own pure fancy, altogether alien to what the lecturer intended to convey. The average mental grasp even of what is called a well-educated audience, will be found to be ludicrously small when rigorously tested.

In stating the differences between man and man, let it not be supposed for a moment that mathematicians are necessarily one-sided in their natural gifts. There are numerous instances

of the reverse, of whom the following will be found, as instances of hereditary genius, in the appendix to my chapter on
SCIENCE. I would especially name Liebnitz, as being universally
gifted; but Ampère, Arago, Condorcet, and D'Alembert, were
all of them very far more than mere mathematicians. Nay, since
the range of examination at Cambridge is so extended as to
include other subjects besides mathematics, the differences of
ability between the highest and the lowest of the successful
candidates is yet more glaring than what I have already
described. We still find, on the one hand, mediocre men,
whose whole energies are absorbed in getting their 237 marks
for mathematics; and, on the other hand, some few senior
wranglers who are at the same time high classical scholars and
much more besides. Cambridge has afforded such instances.
Its lists of classical honours are comparatively of recent date,
but other evidence is obtainable from earlier times of their
occurrence. Thus, Dr. George Butler, the Head Master of
Harrow for very many years, including the period when Byron
was a schoolboy (father of the present Head Master, and of
other sons, two of whom are also head masters of great public
schools), must have obtained that classical office on account of
his eminent classical ability; but Dr. Butler was also senior
wrangler in 1794, the year when Lord Chancellor Lyndhurst
was second. Both Dr. Kaye, the late Bishop of Lincoln, and
Sir E. Alderson, the late judge, were the senior wranglers and
the first classical prizemen of their respective years. Since 1824,
when the classical tripos was first established, the late Mr.
Goulburn (son of the Right Hon. H. Goulburn, Chancellor of
the Exchequer) was second wrangler in 1835, and senior classic
of the same year. But in more recent times, the necessary labour
of preparation, in order to acquire the highest mathematical
places, has become so enormous that there has been a wider
differentiation of studies. There is no longer *time* for a man
to acquire the necessary knowledge to succeed to the first
place in more than one subject. There are, therefore, no instances of a man being absolutely first in both examinations,
but a few can be found of high eminence in both classics and

mathematics, as a reference to the lists published in the *Cambridge Calendar* will show. The best of these more recent degrees appears to be that of Dr. Barry, late Principal of Cheltenham, and now Principal of King's College, London (the son of the eminent architect, Sir Charles Barry, and brother of Mr. Edward Barry, who succeeded his father as architect). He was fourth wrangler and seventh classic of his year.

In whatever way we may test ability, we arrive at equally enormous intellectual differences. Lord Macaulay (*see* under LITERATURE for his remarkable kinships) had one of the most tenacious of memories. He was able to recall many pages of hundreds of volumes by various authors, which he had acquired by simply reading them over. An average man could not certainly carry in his memory one thirty-second—ay, or one hundredth—part as much as Lord Macaulay. The father of Seneca had one of the greatest memories on record in ancient times (*see* under LITERATURE for his kinships). Porson, the Greek scholar, was remarkable for this gift, and, I may add, the "Porson memory" was hereditary in that family. In statesmanship, generalship, literature, science, poetry, art, just the same enormous differences are found between man and man; and numerous instances recorded in this book, will show in how small degree, eminence, either in these or any other class of intellectual powers, can be considered as due to purely special powers. They are rather to be considered in those instances as the result of concentrated efforts, made by men who are widely gifted. People lay too much stress on apparent specialities, thinking over-rashly that, because a man is devoted to some particular pursuit, he could not possibly have succeeded in anything else. They might just as well say that, because a youth had fallen desperately in love with a brunette, he could not possibly have fallen in love with a blonde. He may or may not have more natural liking for the former type of beauty than the latter, but it is as probable as not that the affair was mainly or wholly due to a general amorousness of disposition. It is just the same with special pursuits. A gifted man is often capricious and fickle before he selects his occupation, but when it has been chosen, he devotes himself to it with a truly passionate ardour. After a man of genius has selected his hobby, and so adapted himself to it as to seem unfitted for any other occupation in life, and to be possessed of but one special aptitude, I often notice, with admiration, how well he bears himself when circumstances suddenly thrust him into a strange position. He will display an insight into new conditions, and a power of dealing with them, with which even his most intimate friends were unprepared to accredit him. Many a presumptuous fool has mistaken indifference and neglect for incapacity; and in trying to throw a man of genius on ground where he was unprepared for attack, has himself received a most severe and unexpected fall. I am sure that no one who has had the privilege of mixing in the society of the abler men of any great capital, or who is acquainted with the biographies of the heroes of history, can doubt the existence of grand human animals, of natures pre-eminently noble, of individuals born to be kings of men. I have been conscious of no slight misgiving that I was committing a kind of sacrilege whenever, in the preparation of materials for this book, I had occasion to take the measurement of modern intellects vastly superior to my own, or to criticise the genius of the most magnificent historical specimens of our race. It was a process that constantly recalled to me a once familiar sentiment in bygone days of African travel, when I used to take altitudes of the huge cliffs that domineered above me as I travelled along their bases, or to map the mountainous landmarks of unvisited tribes, that loomed in faint grandeur beyond my actual horizon.

I have not cared to occupy myself much with people whose gifts are below the average, but they would be an interesting study. The number of idiots and imbeciles among the twenty million inhabitants of England and Wales is approximately estimated at 50,000, or as 1 in 400. Dr. Seguin, a great French authority on these matters, states that more than thirty per cent. of idiots and imbeciles, put under suitable instruction, have been taught to conform to social and moral law, and rendered capable of order, of good feeling, and of working like

c

the third of an average man. He says that more than forty per cent. have become capable of the ordinary transactions of life, under friendly control; of understanding moral and social abstractions, and of working like *two-thirds* of a man. And, lastly, that from twenty-five to thirty per cent. come nearer and nearer to the standard of manhood, till some of them will defy the scrutiny of good judges, when compared with ordinary young men and women. In the order next above idiots and imbeciles are a large number of milder cases scattered among private families and kept out of sight, the existence of whom is, however, well known to relatives and friends; they are too silly to take a part in general society, but are easily amused with some trivial, harmless occupation. Then comes a class of whom the Lord Dundreary of the famous play may be considered a representative; and so, proceeding through successive grades, we gradually ascend to mediocrity. I know two good instances of hereditary silliness short of imbecility, and have reason to believe I could easily obtain a large number of similar facts.

To conclude, the range of mental power between—I will not say the highest Caucasian and the lowest savage—but between the greatest and least of English intellects, is enormous. There is a continuity of natural ability reaching from one knows not what height, and descending to one can hardly say what depth. I propose in this chapter to range men according to their natural abilities, putting them into classes separated by equal degrees of merit, and to show the relative number of individuals included in the several classes. Perhaps some person might be inclined to make an offhand guess that the number of men included in the several classes would be pretty equal. If he thinks so, I can assure him he is most egregiously mistaken.

The method I shall employ for discovering all this is an application of the very curious theoretical law of "deviation from an average." First, I will explain the law, and then I will show that the production of natural intellectual gifts comes justly within its scope.

The law is an exceedingly general one. M. Quételet, the

Astronomer-Royal of Belgium, and the greatest authority on vital and social statistics, has largely used it in his inquiries. He has also constructed numerical tables, by which the necessary calculations can be easily made, whenever it is desired to have recourse to the law. Those who wish to learn more than I have space to relate, should consult his work, which is a very readable octavo volume, and deserves to be far better known to statisticians than it appears to be. Its title is *Letters on Probabilities*, translated by Downes. Layton and Co. London: 1849.

So much has been published in recent years about statistical deductions, that I am sure the reader will be prepared to assent freely to the following hypothetical case:—Suppose a large island inhabited by a single race, who intermarried freely, and who had lived for many generations under constant conditions; then the average *height* of the male adults of that population would undoubtedly be the same year after year. Also—still arguing from the experience of modern statistics, which are found to give constant results in far less carefully-guarded examples—we should undoubtedly find, year after year, the same proportion maintained between the number of men of different heights. I mean, if the average stature was found to be sixty-six inches, and if it was also found in any one year that 100 per million exceeded seventy-eight inches, the same proportion of 100 per million would be closely maintained in all other years. An equal constancy of proportion would be maintained between any other limits of height we pleased to specify, as between seventy-one and seventy-two inches; between seventy-two and seventy-three inches; and so on. Statistical experiences are so invariably confirmatory of what I have stated would probably be the case, as to make it unnecessary to describe analogous instances. Now, at this point, the law of deviation from an average steps in. It shows that the number per million whose heights range between seventy-one and seventy-two inches (or between any other limits we please to name) can be *predicted* from the previous datum of the average, and of any one other fact, such as that of 100 per million exceeding seventy-eight inches.

The appended diagram will make this more intelligible. Suppose a million of the men to stand in turns, with their backs against a vertical board of sufficient height, and their heights to be dotted off upon it. The board would then present the appearance shown in the diagram. The line of average height is that which divides the dots into two equal parts, and stands,

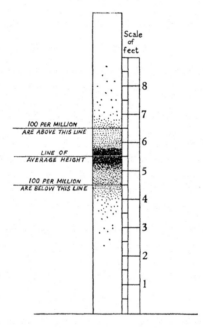

in the case we have assumed, at the height of sixty-six inches. The dots will be found to be ranged so symmetrically on either side of the line of average, that the lower half of the diagram will be almost a precise reflection of the upper. Next, let a hundred dots be counted from above downwards, and let a line be drawn below them. According to the conditions, this line will stand at the height of seventy-eight inches. Using the data afforded by these two lines, it is possible, by the help of the law of deviation from an average, to reproduce, with extra-ordinary closeness, the entire system of dots on the board.

M. Quételet gives tables in which the uppermost line, in-stead of cutting off 100 in a million, cuts off only one in a million. He divides the intervals between that line and the line of average, into eighty equal divisions, and gives the number of dots that fall within each of those divisions. It is easy, by the help of his tables, to calculate what would occur under any other system of classification we pleased to adopt.

This law of deviation from an average is perfectly general in its application. Thus, if the marks had been made by bullets fired at a horizontal line stretched in front of the target, they would have been distributed according to the same law. Wherever there is a large number of similar events, each due to the resultant influences of the same variable conditions, two effects will follow. First, the average value of those events will be constant; and, secondly, the deviations of the several events from the average, will be governed by this law (which is, in principle, the same as that which governs runs of luck at a gaming-table).

The nature of the conditions affecting the several events must, I say, be the same. It clearly would not be proper to combine the heights of men belonging to two dissimilar races, in the expectation that the compound results would be gov-erned by the same constants. A union of two dissimilar systems of dots would produce the same kind of confusion as if half of the bullets fired at a target have been directed to one mark, and the other half to another mark. Nay, an examination of the dots would show to a person, ignorant of what had occurred, that such had been the case, and it would be possible, by aid of the law, to disentangle two or any moderate number of superimposed series of marks. The law may, therefore, be used as a most trustworthy criterion, whether or no the events of which an average has been taken, are due to the same or to dissimilar classes of conditions.

I selected the hypothetical case of a race of men living on an island and freely intermarrying, to ensure the conditions under which they were all supposed to live, being uniform in character. It will now be my aim to show there is sufficient uniformity in the inhabitants of the British Isles to bring them fairly within the grasp of this law.

For this purpose, I first call attention to an example given in Quételet's book. It is of the measurements of the circumferences of the chests of a large number of Scotch soldiers. The Scotch are by no means a strictly uniform race, nor are they exposed to identical conditions. They are a mixture of Celts, Danes, Anglo-Saxons, and others, in various proportions, the Highlanders being almost purely Celts. On the other hand, these races, though diverse in origin, are not very dissimilar in character. Consequently, it will be found that their deviations from the average follow theoretical computations with remarkable accuracy. The instance is as follows. M. Quételet obtained his facts from the thirteenth volume of the *Edinburgh Medical Journal*, where the measurements are given in respect to 5,738 soldiers, the results being grouped in order of magnitude, proceeding by differences of one inch. Professor Quételet compares these results with those that his tables give, and here is the result. The marvellous accordance between fact and theory must strike the most unpractised eye. I should say that, for the sake of convenience, both the measurements and calculations have been reduced to per thousands:

Measures of the chest in inches	Number of men per 1,000 by experience	Number of men per 1,000 by calculation	Measures of the chest in inches	Number of men per 1,000 by experience	Number of men per 1,000 by calculation
33	4	7	41	1,628	1,675
34	31	29	42	1,148	1,096
35	141	110	43	645	560
36	322	323	44	160	221
37	732	732	45	87	69
38	1,305	1,333	46	38	16
39	1,867	1,838	47	7	3
40	1,882	1,987	48	2	1

I will now take a case where there is a greater dissimilarity in the elements of which the average has been taken. It is the height of 100,000 French conscripts. There is fully as much variety in the French as in the English, for it is not very many generations since France was divided into completely independent kingdoms. Among its peculiar races are those of Normandy, Brittany, Alsatia, Provence, Bearne, Auvergne—each with their special characteristics; yet the following table shows a most striking agreement between the results of experience compared with those derived by calculation, from a purely theoretical hypothesis:

Height of Men (Inches)	Number of Men	
	Measured	Calculated
Under 61·8	28,620	26,345
61·8 to 62·9	11,580	13,182
62·9 to 63·9	13,990	14,502
63·9 to 65·0	14,410	13,982
65·0 to 66·1	11,410	11,803
66·1 to 67·1	8,780	8,725
67·1 to 68·2	5,530	5,527
68·2 to 69·3	3,190	3,187
Above 69·3	2,490	2,645

The greatest differences are in the lowest ranks. They include the men who were rejected from being too short for the army. M. Quételet boldly ascribes these differences to the effect of fraudulent returns. It certainly seems that men have been improperly taken out of the second rank and put into the first, in order to exempt them from service. Be this as it may, the coincidence of fact with theory is, in this instance also, quite close enough to serve my purpose.

I argue from the results obtained from Frenchmen and

from Scotchmen, that, if we had measurements of the adult males in the British Isles, we should find those measurements to range in close accordance with the law of deviation from an average, although our population is as much mingled as I described that of Scotland to have been, and although Ireland is mainly peopled with Celts. Now, if this be the case with stature, then it will be true as regards every other physical feature—as circumference of head, size of brain, weight of grey matter, number of brain fibres, &c.; and thence, by a step on which no physiologist will hesitate, as regards mental capacity.

This is what I am driving at—that analogy clearly shows there must be a fairly constant average mental capacity in the inhabitants of the British Isles, and that the deviations from that average—upwards towards genius, and downwards towards stupidity—must follow the law that governs deviations from all true averages.

I have, however, done somewhat more than rely on analogy, by discussing the results of those examinations in which the candidates had been derived from the same classes. Most persons have noticed the lists of successful competitors for various public appointments that are published from time to time in the newspapers, with the marks gained by each candidate attached to his name. These lists contain far too few names to fall into such beautiful accordance with theory, as was the case with the Scotch soldiers. There are rarely more than 100 names in any one of these examinations, while the chests of no less than 5,700 Scotchmen were measured. I cannot justly combine the marks of several independent examinations into one fagot, for I understand that different examiners are apt to have different figures of merit; so each examination was analysed separately. The following is a calculation I made on the examination last before me; it will do as well as any other. It was for admission into the Royal Military College at Sandhurst, December 1868. The marks obtained were clustered most thickly about 3,000, so I take that number as representing the average ability of the candidates. From this datum, and from the fact that no candidate obtained more than 6,500 marks, I computed the column B in the following table, by the help of Quételet's numbers. It will be seen that column B accords with column A quite as closely as the small number of persons examined could have led us to expect.

Number of marks obtained by the Candidates	Number of Candidates who obtained those marks	
	A According to fact	B According to theory
6,500 and above	0	0
5,800 to 6,500	1	1
5,100 to 5,800	3	5
4,400 to 5,100	6	8
3,700 to 4,400	11 } 73	13 } 72
3,000 to 3,700	22	16
2,300 to 3,000	22	16
1,600 to 2,300	8	13
1,100 to 1,600	*Either did not venture to compete, or were plucked*	8
400 to 1,100		5
Below 400		1

The symmetry of the descending branch has been rudely spoilt by the conditions stated at the foot of column A. There is, therefore, little room for doubt, if everybody in England had to work up some subject and then to pass before examiners who employed similar figures of merit, that their marks would be found to range, according to the law of deviation from an average, just as rigorously as the heights of French conscripts, or the circumferences of the chests of Scotch soldiers.

The number of grades into which we may divide ability is purely a matter of option. We may consult our convenience by sorting Englishmen into a few large classes, or into many small ones. I will select a system of classification that shall be easily comparable with the numbers of eminent men, as determined in the previous chapter. We have seen that 250 men per million become eminent; accordingly, I have so contrived the classes in the following table that the two highest, F and G, together with X (which includes all cases beyond G, and which are unclassed), shall amount to about that number —namely to 248 per million:

It will, I trust, be clearly understood that the numbers of men in the several classes in my table depend on no uncertain hypothesis. They are determined by the assured law of devia-tions from an average. It is an absolute fact that if we pick out of each million the one man who is naturally the ablest, and also the one man who is the most stupid, and divide the remaining 999,998 men into fourteen classes, the average ability in each being separated from that of its neighbours by *equal grades*, then the numbers in each of those classes will, on the average of many millions, be as is stated in the table. The table may be applied to special, just as truly as to general ability. It would be true for every examination that brought out natural gifts, whether held in painting, in music, or in statesmanship. The proportions between the different classes would be identical in all these cases, although the classes would be made up of different individuals, according as the examination differed in its purport.

It will be seen that more than half of each million is con-tained in the two mediocre classes a and A; the four mediocre classes a, b, A, B, contain more than four-fifths, and the six mediocre classes more than nineteen-twentieths of the entire population. Thus, the rarity of commanding ability, and the vast abundance of mediocrity, is no accident, but follows of necessity, from the very nature of these things.

The meaning of the word "mediocrity" admits of little doubt. It defines the standard of intellectual power found in most provincial gatherings, because the attractions of a more stirring life in the metropolis and elsewhere, are apt to draw away the abler classes of men, and the silly and the imbecile

CLASSIFICATION OF MEN ACCORDING TO THEIR NATURAL GIFTS

Grades of natural ability, separated by equal intervals		Numbers of men comprised in the several grades of natural ability, whether in respect to their general powers, or to special aptitudes							
Below average	Above average	Proportionate, viz. one in	In each million of the same age	In total male population of the United Kingdom, say 15 millions, of the undermentioned ages:					
				20–30	30–40	40–50	50–60	60–70	70–80
a	A	4	256,791	641,000	495,000	391,000	268,000	171,000	77,000
b	B	6	161,279	409,000	312,000	246,000	168,000	107,000	48,000
c	C	16	63,563	161,000	123,000	97,000	66,000	42,000	19,000
d	D	64	15,696	39,800	30,300	23,900	16,400	10,400	4,700
e	E	413	2,423	6,100	4,700	3,700	2,520	1,600	729
f	F	4,300	233	590	450	355	243	155	70
g	G	79,000	14	35	27	21	15	9	4
x all grades below g	X all grades above G	1,000,000	1	3	2	2	2	—	—
On either side of average		1,000,000	500,000	1,268,000	964,000	761,000	521,000	332,000	149,000
Total, both sides			1,000,000	2,536,000	1,928,000	1,522,000	1,042,000	664,000	298,000

The proportions of men living at different ages are calculated from the proportions that are true for England and Wales. (Census 1861, Appendix, p. 107.)

Example.—The class F contains 1 in every 4,300 men. In other words, there are 233 of that class in each million of men. The same is true of class f. In the whole United Kingdom there are 590 men of class F (and the same number of f) between the ages of 20 and 30; 450 between the ages of 30 and 40; and so on.

do not take a part in the gatherings. Hence, the residuum that forms the bulk of the general society of small provincial places, is commonly very pure in its mediocrity.

The class C possesses abilities a trifle higher than those commonly possessed by the foreman of an ordinary jury. D includes the mass of men who obtain the ordinary prizes of life. E is a stage higher. Then we reach F, the lowest of those yet superior classes of intellect, with which this volume is chiefly concerned.

On descending the scale, we find by the time we have reached f, that we are already among the idiots and imbeciles. We have seen in p. 65, that there are 400 idiots and imbeciles, to every million of persons living in this country; but that 30 per cent. of their number, appear to be light cases, to whom the name of idiot is inappropriate. There will remain 280 true idiots and imbeciles, to every million of our population. This ratio coincides very closely with the requirements of class f. No doubt a certain proportion of them are idiotic owing to some fortuitous cause, which may interfere with the working of a naturally good brain, much as a bit of dirt may cause a first-rate chronometer to keep worse time than an ordinary watch. But I presume, from the usual smallness of head and absence of disease among these persons, that the proportion of accidental idiots cannot be very large.

Hence we arrive at the undeniable, but unexpected conclusion, that eminently gifted men are raised as much above mediocrity as idiots are depressed below it; a fact that is calculated to considerably enlarge our ideas of the enormous differences of intellectual gifts between man and man.

I presume the class F of dogs, and others of the more intelligent sort of animals, is nearly commensurate with the f of the human race, in respect to memory and powers of reason. Certainly the class G of such animals is far superior to the g of humankind.

COMPARISON OF THE TWO

CLASSIFICATIONS

Is reputation a fair test of natural ability? It is the only one I can employ—am I justified in using it? How much of a man's success is due to his opportunities, how much to his natural power of intellect?

This is a very old question, on which a great many commonplaces have been uttered that need not be repeated here. I will confine myself to a few considerations, such as seem to me amply adequate to prove what is wanted for my argument.

Let it clearly be borne in mind, what I mean by reputation and ability. By reputation, I mean the opinion of contemporaries, revised by posterity—the favourable result of a critical analysis of each man's character, by many biographers. I do not mean high social or official position, nor such as is implied by being the mere lion of a London season; but I speak of the reputation of a leader of opinion, of an originator, of a man to whom the world deliberately acknowledges itself largely indebted.

By natural ability, I mean those qualities of intellect and disposition, which urge and qualify a man to perform acts that lead to reputation. I do not mean capacity without zeal, nor zeal without capacity, nor even a combination of both of them, without an adequate power of doing a great deal of very laborious work. But I mean a nature which, when left to itself, will, urged by an inherent stimulus, climb the path that leads to eminence, and has strength to reach the summit—one which, if hindered or thwarted, will fret and strive until the hindrance is overcome, and it is again free to follow its labour-loving instinct. It is almost a contradiction in terms, to doubt that such men will generally become eminent. On the other hand, there is plenty of evidence in this volume to show that few have won high reputations without possessing these peculiar gifts. It follows that the men who achieve eminence, and those who are naturally capable, are, to a large extent, identical.

The particular meaning in which I employ the word ability, does not restrict my argument from a wider application; for, if I succeed in showing—as I undoubtedly shall do—that the concrete triple event, of ability combined with zeal and with capacity for hard labour, is inherited, much more will there be justification for believing that any one of its three elements, whether it be ability, or zeal, or capacity for labour, is similarly a gift of inheritance.

I believe, and shall do my best to show, that, if the "eminent" men of any period, had been changelings when babies, a very fair proportion of those who survived and retained their health up to fifty years of age, would, notwithstanding their altered circumstances, have equally risen to eminence. Thus— to take a strong case—it is incredible that any combination of circumstances, could have repressed Lord Brougham to the level of undistinguished mediocrity.

The arguments on which I rely are as follow. It will limit their application for the present to men of the pen and to artists. First, it is a fact, that numbers of men rise, before they are middle-aged, from the humbler ranks of life to that worldly position, in which it is of no importance to their future career, how their youth has been passed. They have overcome their hindrances, and thus start fair with others more fortunately reared, in the subsequent race of life. A boy who is to be care- fully educated is sent to a good school, where he confessedly acquires little useful information, but where he is taught the art of learning. The man of whom I have been speaking has contrived to acquire the same art in a school of adversity. Both stand on equal terms, when they have reached mature life. They compete for the same prizes, measure their strength by efforts in the same direction, and their relative successes are thenceforward due to their relative natural gifts. There are many such men in the "eminent" class, as biographies abundantly show. Now, if the hindrances to success were very great, we should expect all who surmounted them to be prodigies of genius. The hindrances would form a system of natural selection, by repressing all whose gifts were below a certain very high level. But what is the case? We find very many who have risen from the ranks, who are by no means prodigies of genius; many who have no claim to "eminence," who have risen easily in spite of all obstacles. The hindrances undoubtedly form a system of natural selection that represses mediocre men, and even men of pretty fair powers—in short, the classes below D; but many of D succeed, a great many of E, and I believe a very large majority of those above.

If a man is gifted with vast intellectual ability, eagerness to work, and power of working, I cannot comprehend how such a man should be repressed. The world is always tormented with difficulties waiting to be solved—struggling with ideas and feelings, to which it can give no adequate expression. If, then, there exists a man capable of solving those difficulties, or of giving a voice to those pent-up feelings, he is sure to be welcomed with universal acclamation. We may almost say that he had only to put his pen to paper, and the thing is done. I am here speaking of the very first-class men—prodigies—one in a million, or one in ten millions, of whom numbers will be found described in this volume, as specimens of hereditary genius.

Another argument to prove that the hindrances of English social life are not effectual in repressing high ability is, that the number of eminent men in England, is as great as in other countries where fewer hindrances exist. Culture is far more widely spread in America, than with us, and the education of their middle and lower classes far more advanced; but, for all that, America most certainly does not beat us in first-class works of literature, philosophy, or art. The higher kind of books, even of the most modern date, read in America, are principally the work of Englishmen. The Americans have an immense amount of the newspaper-article-writer, or of the member-of-congress stamp of ability; but the number of their really eminent authors is more limited even than with us. I argue that, if the hindrances to the rise of genius, were removed from English society as completely as they have been removed from that of America, we should not become materially richer in highly eminent men.

People seem to have the idea that the way to eminence is one of great self-denial, from which there are hourly temptations to diverge: in which a man can be kept in his boyhood, only by a schoolmaster's severity or a parent's incessant watchfulness, and in after life by the attractions of fortunate friendships and other favourable circumstances. This is true enough of the great majority of men, but it is simply not true of the generality of those who have gained great reputations. Such men, biographies show to be haunted and driven by an incessant instinctive craving for intellectual work. If forcibly withdrawn from the path that leads towards eminence, they will find their way back to it, as surely as a lover to his mistress. They do not work for the sake of eminence, but to satisfy a natural craving for brain work, just as athletes cannot endure repose on account of their muscular irritability, which insists upon exercise. It is very unlikely that any conjunction of circumstances should supply a stimulus to brain work commensurate with what these men carry in their own constitutions. The action of external stimuli must be uncertain and intermittent, owing to their very nature; the disposition abides. It keeps a man ever employed—now wrestling with his difficulties, now brooding over his immature ideas—and renders him a quick and eager listener to innumerable, almost inaudible teachings, that others less keenly on the watch, are sure to miss.

These considerations lead to my third argument. I have shown that social hindrances cannot impede men of high ability, from becoming eminent. I shall now maintain that social advantages are incompetent to give that status to a man of moderate ability. It would be easy to point out several men of fair capacity, who have been pushed forward by all kinds of help, who are ambitious, and exert themselves to the utmost, but who completely fail in attaining eminence. If great peers, they may be lord-lieutenants of counties; if they belong to great county families, they may become influential members of parliament and local notabilities. When they die, they leave a blank for a while in a large circle, but there is no Westminster Abbey and no public mourning for them—perhaps barely a biographical notice in the columns of the daily papers.

It is difficult to specify two large classes of men, with equal social advantages, in one of which they have high hereditary gifts, while in the other they have not. I must not compare the sons of eminent men with those of non-eminent, because much which I should ascribe to breed, others might ascribe to parental encouragement and example. Therefore, I will compare the sons of eminent men with the adopted sons of Popes and other dignitaries of the Roman Catholic Church. The practice of nepotism among ecclesiastics is universal. It consists in their giving those social helps to a nephew, or other more distant relative, that ordinary people give to their children. Now, I shall show abundantly in the course of this book, that the nephew of an eminent man has far less chance of becoming eminent than a son, and that a more remote kinsman has far less chance than a nephew. We may therefore make a very fair comparison, for the purposes of my argument, between the success of the sons of eminent men and that of the nephews or more distant relatives, who stand in the place of sons to the high unmarried ecclesiastics of the Romish Church. If social help is really of the highest importance, the nephews of the Popes will attain eminence as frequently, or nearly so, as the sons of other eminent men; otherwise, they will not.

Are, then, the nephews, &c., of the Popes, on the whole, as highly distinguished as are the sons of other equally eminent men? I answer, decidedly not. There have been a few Popes who were offshoots of illustrious races, such as that of the Medici, but in the enormous majority of cases the Pope is the ablest member of his family. I do not profess to have worked up the kinships of the Italians with any especial care, but I have seen amply enough of them, to justify me in saying that the individuals whose advancement has been due to nepotism, are curiously undistinguished. The very common combination of an able son and an eminent parent, is not matched, in the case of high Romish ecclesiastics, by an eminent nephew and an eminent uncle. The social helps are the same, but hereditary gifts are wanting in the latter case.

To recapitulate: I have endeavoured to show in respect to literary and artistic eminence—

1. That men who are gifted with high abilities—even men of class E—easily rise through all the obstacles caused by inferiority of social rank.

2. Countries where there are fewer hindrances than in England, to a poor man rising in life, produce a much larger proportion of persons of culture, but not of what I call eminent men.

3. Men who are largely aided by social advantages, are unable to achieve eminence, unless they are endowed with high natural gifts.

It may be well to add a few supplementary remarks on the small effects of a good education on a mind of the highest order. A youth of abilities G, and X, is almost independent of ordinary school education. He does not want a master continually at his elbow to explain difficulties and select suitable lessons. On the contrary, he is receptive at every pore. He learns from passing hints, with a quickness and thoroughness that others cannot comprehend. He is omnivorous of intellectual work, devouring a vast deal more than he can utilise, but extracting a small percentage of nutriment, that makes, in the aggregate, an enormous supply. The best care that a master can take of such a boy is to leave him alone, just directing a little here and there, and checking desultory tendencies.

It is a mere accident if a man is placed in his youth in the profession for which he has the most special vocation. It will consequently be remarked in my short biographical notices, that the most illustrious men have frequently broken loose from the life prescribed by their parents, and followed, careless of cost, the paramount dictation of their own natures: in short, they educate themselves. D'Alembert is a striking instance of this kind of self-reliance. He was a foundling (afterwards shown to be well bred as respects ability), and put out to nurse as a pauper baby, to the wife of a poor glazier. The child's indomitable tendency to the higher studies, could not be repressed by his foster-mother's ridicule and dissuasion, nor by the taunts of his schoolfellows, nor by the discouragements of his schoolmaster, who was incapable of appreciating him, nor even by the reiterated deep disappointment of finding that his ideas, which he knew to be original, were not novel, but long previously discovered by others. Of course, we should expect a boy of this kind, to undergo ten or more years of apparently hopeless strife, but we should equally expect him to succeed at last; and D'Alembert did succeed in attaining the first rank of celebrity, by the time he was twenty-four. The reader has only to turn over the pages of my book, to find abundant instances of this emergence from obscurity, in spite of the utmost discouragement in early youth.

A prodigal nature commonly so prolongs the period when a man's receptive faculties are at their keenest, that a faulty education in youth, is readily repaired in after life. The education of Watt, the great mechanician, was of a merely elementary character. During his youth and manhood he was engrossed with mechanical specialities. It was not till he became advanced in years, that he had leisure to educate himself, and yet by the time he was an old man, he had become singularly well-read and widely and accurately informed. The scholar who, in the eyes of his contemporaries and immediate successors, made one of the greatest reputations, as such, that any man has ever made, was Julius Cæsar Scaliger. His youth was, I believe, entirely unlettered. He was in the army until he was twenty-nine, and then he led a vagrant professional life, trying everything and sticking to nothing. At length he fixed himself upon Greek. His first publications were at the age of forty-seven, and between that time and the period of a somewhat early death, he earned his remarkable reputation, only exceeded by that of his son. Boyhood and youth—the period between fifteen and twenty-two years of age, which afford to the vast majority of men, the only period for the acquirement of intellectual facts and habits—are just seven years—neither more nor less important than other years—in the lives of men of the highest order. People are too apt to complain of their imperfect education, insinuating that they would have done great things if they had been more fortunately circumstanced in youth. But if their power of learning is materially diminished by the time they have discovered their want of knowledge, it is very probable that their abilities are not of a very high description, and that, however well they might have been educated, they would have succeeded but little better.

Even if a man be long unconscious of his powers, an opportunity is sure to occur—they occur over and over again to every man—that will discover them. He will then soon make up for past arrears, and outstrip competitors with very many years' start, in the race of life. There is an obvious analogy between the man of brains and the man of muscle, in the unmistakable way in which they may discover and assert their claims to superiority over less gifted, but far better educated, competitors. An average sailor climbs rigging, and an average Alpine guide scrambles along cliffs, with a facility that seems like magic to a man who has been reared away from ships and mountains. But if he have extraordinary gifts, a very little trial will reveal them, and he will rapidly make up for his arrears of education. A born gymnast would soon, in his turn, astonish the sailors by his feats. Before the voyage was half over, he would outrun them like an escaped monkey. I have witnessed an instance of this myself. Every summer, it happens that some young English tourist who had never previously planted his foot on crag or ice, succeeds in Alpine work to a marvellous degree.

Thus far, I have spoken only of literary men and artists, who, however, form the bulk of the 250 per million, that attain to eminence. The reasoning that is true for them, requires large qualifications when applied to statesmen and commanders.

Unquestionably, the most illustrious statesmen and commanders belong, to say the least, to the classes F and G of ability; but it does not at all follow that an English cabinet minister, if he be a great territorial lord, should belong to those classes, or even to the two or three below them. Social advantages have enormous power in bringing a man into so prominent a position as a statesman, that it is impossible to refuse him the title of "eminent," though it may be more than probable that if he had been changed in his cradle, and reared in obscurity he would have lived and died without emerging from humble life. Again, we have seen that a union of three separate qualities—intellect, zeal, and power of work—are necessary to raise men from the ranks. Only two of these qualities, in a remarkable degree, namely intellect and power of work, are required by a man who is pushed into public life; because when he is once there, the interest is so absorbing, and the competition so keen, as to supply the necessary stimulus to an ordinary mind. Therefore, many men who have succeeded as statesmen, would have been nobodies had they been born in a lower rank of life: they would have needed zeal to rise. Talleyrand would have passed his life in the same way as other grand seigneurs, if he had not been ejected from his birthright, by a family council, on account of his deformity, and thrown into the vortex of the French Revolution. The furious excitement of the game overcame his inveterate indolence, and he developed into the foremost man of the period, after Napoleon and Mirabeau. As for sovereigns, they belong to a peculiar category. The qualities most suitable to the ruler of a great nation, are not such as lead to eminence in private life. Devotion to particular studies, obstinate perseverance, geniality and frankness in social relations, are important qualities to make a man rise in the world, but they are unsuitable to a sovereign. He has to view many interests and opinions with an equal eye; to know how to yield his favourite ideas to popular pressure, to be reserved in his friendships and able to stand alone. On the other hand, a sovereign does not greatly need the intellectual powers that are essential to the rise of a common man, because the best brains of the country are at his service. Consequently, I do not busy myself in this volume with the families of merely able sovereigns only with those few whose military and administrative capacity is acknowledged to have been of the very highest order.

As regards commanders, the qualities that raise a man to a peerage, may be of a peculiar kind, such as would not have raised him to eminence in ordinary times. Strategy is as much a speciality as chess-playing, and large practice is required to develop it. It is difficult to see how strategical gifts, combined with a hardy constitution, dashing courage, and a restless disposition, can achieve eminence in times of peace. These qualities are more likely to attract a man to the hunting-field, if he have enough money; or if not, to make him an unsuccessful speculator. It consequently happens that generals of high, but not the very highest order, such as Napoleon's marshals and Cromwell's generals, are rarely found to have eminent kinsfolk. Very different is the case, with the most illustrious commanders. They are far more than strategists and men of restless dispositions; they would have distinguished themselves under any circumstances. Their kinships are most remarkable, as will be seen in my chapter on commanders, which includes the names of Alexander, Scipio, Hannibal, Cæsar, Marlborough, Cromwell, the Princes of Nassau, Wellington, and Napoleon.

Precisely the same remarks are applicable to demagogues. Those who rise to the surface and play a prominent part in the transactions of a troubled period, must have courage and force of character, but they need not have high intellectual powers. Nay, it is more appropriate that the intellects of such men should be narrow and one-sided, and their dispositions moody and embittered. These are not qualities that lead to eminence in ordinary times. Consequently, the families of such men, are mostly unknown to fame. But the kinships of popular leaders of the highest order, as of the two Gracchi, of the two Arteveldts, and of Mirabeau, are illustrious.

I may mention a class of cases that strikes me forcibly as a proof, that a sufficient power of command to lead to eminence in troublous times, is much less unusual than is commonly supposed, and that it lies neglected in the course of ordinary life. In beleaguered towns, as, for example, during the great Indian mutiny, a certain type of character very frequently made its appearance. People rose into notice who had never previously distinguished themselves, and subsided into their former way of life, after the occasion for exertion was over; while during the continuance of danger and misery, they were the heroes of their situation. They were cool in danger, sensible in council, cheerful under prolonged suffering, humane to the wounded and sick, encouragers of the faint-hearted. Such people were formed to shine only under exceptional circumstances. They had the advantage of possessing too tough a fibre to be crushed by anxiety and physical misery, and perhaps in consequence of that very toughness, they required a stimulus of the sharpest kind, to goad them to all the exertions of which they were capable.

The result of what I have said, is to show that in statesmen and commanders, mere "eminence" if by no means a satisfactory criterion of such natural gifts as would make a man distinguished under whatever circumstances he had been reared. On the other hand, statesmen of a high order, and commanders of the very highest, who overthrow all opponents, must be prodigiously gifted. The reader himself must judge the cases quoted in proof of hereditary gifts, by their several merits. I have endeavoured to speak of none but the most illustrious names. It would have led to false conclusions, had I taken a larger number, and thus descended to a lower level of merit.

In conclusion, I see no reason to be dissatisfied with the conditions of accepting high reputation as a very fair test of high ability. The nature of the test would not have been altered, if an attempt had been made to readjust each man's reputation according to his merits, because this is what every biographer does. If I had possessed the critical power of a Ste. Beuve, I should have merely thrown into literature another of those numerous expressions of opinion, by the aggregate of which all reputations are built.

To conclude: I feel convinced that no man can achieve a very high reputation without being gifted with very high abilities; and I trust that reason has been given for the belief, that few who possess these very high abilities can fail in achieving eminence.

NOTATION

I entreat my readers not to be frightened at the first sight of the notation I employ, for it is really very simple to understand and easy to recollect. It was impossible for me to get on without the help of something of the sort, as I found our ordinary nomenclature far too ambiguous as well as cumbrous for employment in this book.

For example, the terms "uncle," "nephew," "grand-father," and "grandson," have each of them two distinct meanings. An uncle may be the brother of the father, or the brother of the mother; the nephew may be the son of a brother, or the son of a sister; and so on. There are four kinds of first cousins, namely, the sons of the two descriptions of uncles and those of the two corresponding aunts. There are sixteen kinds of first cousins "once removed," for either A. may be the son of any one of the four descriptions of male or of the four female cousins of B., or B. may bear any one of those relationships to A. I need not quote more instances in illustration of what I have said, that unbounded confusion would have been introduced had I confined myself in this book, to our ordinary nomenclature.

The notation I employ gets rid of all this confused and cumbrous language. It disentangles relationships in a marvellously complete and satisfactory manner, and enables us to methodise, compare, and analyse them in any way we like.

Speaking generally, and without regarding the type in which the letters are printed, F. stands for Father; G. for Grandfather; U. for Uncle; N. for Nephew; B. for Brother; S. for Son; and P. for Grandson (*Petit-fils* in French).

These letters are printed in capitals when the relationship to be expressed has passed through the male line, and in small type when through the female line. Therefore U. is the paternal uncle; G. the paternal grandfather; N. is a nephew that is son of a brother; P. a grandson that is the child of a son. So again,

u. is the maternal uncle; g. the maternal grandfather; n. a nephew that is son of a sister; p. a grandson that is the child of a daughter.

Precisely the same letters, in the form of *Italics*, are employed for the female relations. For example in correspondence with U. there is *U.* to express an aunt that is the sister of a father; and to u. there is *u.* to express an aunt that is the sister of a mother.

It is consequence of this system of notation, that F. and B. and S. are always printed in capitals, and that their correlatives for mother, sister, and daughter are always expressed in small italicised type, as *f.*, *b.*, and *s.*

The reader must mentally put the word *his* before the letter denoting kinship, and *was* after it. Thus:

ADAMS, John; second President of the United States.

S. John Quincey Adams, sixth President.

P. C. F. Adams, American Minister in England; author.

would be read—

His (*i.e.* John Adams') son *was* John Quincey Adams.
His   „   „   grandson *was* C. F. Adams.

The following table comprises the whole of this notation:—

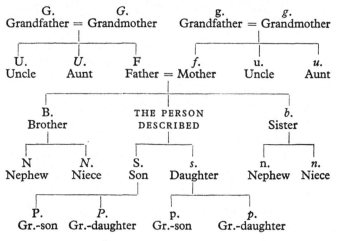

The last explanation I have to make, is the meaning of brackets [ ] when they enclose a letter. It implies that the person to whose name the letter in brackets is annexed has not achieved sufficient public reputation to be ranked, in statistical deductions, on equal terms with the rest.

For facility of reference I give lists, in alphabetical order, of all the letters, within the limits of two letters, that I employ. Thus I always use GF. for great-grandfather, and not FG., which means the same thing.

F.	Father	*F.*	Mother
B.	Brother	*b.*	Sister
S.	Son	*s.*	Daughter

GRANDFATHERS		GRANDMOTHERS	
G.	Father's father	*G.*	Father's mother
g.	Mother's father	*g.*	Mother's mother

GRANDSONS		GRANDDAUGHTERS	
P.	Son's son	*P.*	Son's daughter
p.	Daughter's son	*p.*	Daughter's daughter

UNCLES		AUNTS	
U.	Father's brother	*U.*	Father's sister
u.	Mother's brother	*u.*	Mother's sister

NEPHEWS		NIECES	
N.	Brother's son	*N.*	Brother's daughter
n.	Sister's son	*n.*	Sister's daughter

GREAT-UNCLES		GREAT-AUNTS	
GB.	Father's father's brother	G*b*.	Father's father's sister
gB.	Mother's father's brother	g*b*.	Mother's father's sister
*G*B.	Father's mother's brother	*Gb*.	Father's mother's sister
*g*B.	Mother's mother's brother	*gb*.	Mother's mother's sister

GREAT-GRANDFATHERS		GREAT-GRANDMOTHERS	
GF.	Father's father's father	G*f*.	Father's father's mother
gF.	Mother's father's father	g*f*.	Mother's father's mother
*G*F.	Father's mother's father	*Gf*.	Father's mother's mother
*g*F.	Mother's mother's father	*gf*.	Mother's mother's mother

GREAT-NEPHEWS

NS. Brother's son's son
nS. Sister's son's son
*N*S. Brother's daughter's son

*n*S. Sister's daughter's son

GREAT-NIECES

N*s*. Brother's son's daughter
n*s*. Sister's son's daughter
Ns. Brother's daughter's daughter
ns. Sister's daughter's daughter

GREAT-GRANDSONS

PS. Son's son's son
pS. Daughter's son's son
*P*S. Son's daughter's son
*p*S. Daughter's daughter's son

GREAT-GRANDDAUGHTERS

P*s*. Son's son's daughter
p*s*. Daughter's son's daughter
Ps. Son's daughter's daughter
ps. Daughter's daughter's daughter

FIRST COUSINS, MALE

US. Father's brother's son

uS. Mother's brother's son

*U*S. Father's sister's son
*u*S. Mother's sister's son

FIRST COUSINS, FEMALE

U*s*. Father's brother's daughter
u*s*. Mother's brother's daughter
Us. Father's sister's daughter
us. Mother's sister's daughter

GREAT-GREAT-
GRANDFATHERS

(G, g, *G* or *g*) followed by (G or g)

GREAT-GREAT-
GRANDMOTHERS

(G, g, *G* or *g*) followed by (*G* or *g*)

FIRST COUSINS, MALE
ONCE REMOVED

ASCENDING

(G, g, *G* or *g* (followed by (N or n)

DESCENDING

(U, u, *U* or *u*) followed by (P or p)

FIRST COUSINS, FEMALE
ONCE REMOVED

ASCENDING

(G, g, *G* or *g*) followed by (*N* or *n*)

DESCENDING

(U, u, *U* or *u*) followed by (*P* or *p*)

GREAT-GREAT UNCLES

(G, g, *G* or *g*) followed by (U or u)

GREAT-GREAT AUNTS

(G, g, *G* or *g*) followed by (*U* or *u*)

GREAT-GREAT-
GRANDSONS

(P or *p*) followed by (P or p)

GREAT-GREAT-
GRANDDAUGHTERS

(P or *p*) followed by (*P* or *p*)

PART TWO

RECORDS OF

FAMILIES

THE JUDGES OF ENGLAND BETWEEN

1660 AND 1865

The Judges of England, since the restoration of the monarchy in 1660, form a group peculiarly well adapted to afford a general outline of the extent and limitations of heredity in respect to genius. A judgeship is a guarantee of its possessor being gifted with exceptional ability; the Judges are sufficiently numerous and prolific to form an adequate basis for statistical inductions, and they are the subjects of several excellent biographical treatises. It is therefore well to begin our inquiries with a discussion of their relationships. We shall quickly arrive at definite results, which subsequent chapters, treating of more illustrious men, and in other careers, will check and amplify.

It is necessary that I should first say something in support of my assertion, that the office of a judge is really a sufficient guarantee that its possessor is exceptionally gifted. In other countries it may be different to what it is with us, but we all know that in England, the Bench is never spoken of without reverence for the intellectual power of its occupiers. A seat on the Bench is a great prize, to be won by the best men. No doubt there are hindrances, external to those of nature, against a man getting on at the Bar and rising to a judgeship. The attorneys may not give him briefs when he is a young barrister; and even if he becomes a successful barrister, his political party may be out of office for a long period, at a time when he was otherwise ripe for advancement. I cannot, however, believe that either of these are serious obstacles in the long run. Sterling ability is sure to make itself felt, and to lead to practice; while as to politics, the changes of party are sufficiently frequent to give a fair chance to almost every generation. For every man who is a judge, there may possibly be two other lawyers of the same standing, equally fitted for the post, but it is hard to believe there can be a larger number.

If not always the foremost, the Judges are therefore among the foremost, of a vast body of legal men. The Census speaks of upwards of 3,000 barristers, advocates, and special pleaders; and it must be recollected that these do not consist of 3,000 men taken at haphazard, but a large part of them are already selected, and it is from these, by a second process of selection, that the judges are mainly derived. When I say that a large part of the barristers are selected men, I speak of those among them who are of humble parentage, but have brilliant natural gifts—who attracted notice as boys, or, it may be, even as children, and were therefore sent to a good school. There they won exhibitions and fitted themselves for college, where they supported themselves by obtaining scholarships. Then came fellowships, and so they ultimately found their way to the Bar. Many of these have risen to the Bench. The parentage of the Lord Chancellors justifies my statement. There have been thirty of them within the period included in my inquiries. Of these, Lord Hardwicke was the son of a small attorney at Dover, in narrow circumstances; Lord Eldon (whose brother was the great Admiralty Judge, Lord Stowell) was son of a "coal fitter"; Lord Truro was son of a sheriff's officer; and Lord St. Leonards (like Lord Tenterden, the Chief Justice of Common Pleas) was son of a barber. Others were sons of clergymen of scanty means. Others have begun life in alien professions, yet, notwithstanding their false start, have easily recovered lost ground in after life. Lord Erskine was first in the navy and then in the army, before he became a barrister. Lord Chelmsford was originally a midshipman. Now a large number of men with antecedents as unfavourable to success as these, and yet successful men, are always to be found at the Bar, and therefore I say the barristers are themselves a selected body; and the fact of every judge having been taken from the foremost rank of 3,000 of them, is proof that his exceptional ability is of an enormously higher order than if the 3,000 barristers had been conscripts, drawn by lot from the general mass of their countrymen. I therefore need not trouble myself with quoting passages from biographies, to prove that each of the Judges whose name I have occasion to mention, is a highly gifted man. It is precisely in order to avoid the necessity of this tedious work, that I have selected the Judges for my first chapter.

In speaking of the English Judges, I have adopted the well-known *Lives of the Judges*, by Foss, as my guide. It was published in 1865, so I have adopted that date as the limit of my inquiries. I have considered those only as falling under the definition of "judges" whom he includes as such. They are the Judges of the Courts of Chancery and Common Law, and the Master of the Rolls, but not the Judges of the Admiralty nor of the Court of Canterbury. By the latter limitation, I lose the advantage of counting Lord Stowell (brother of the Lord Chancellor Eldon), the remarkable family of the Lushingtons, that of Sir R. Phillimore, and some others. Through the limitation as regards time, I lose, by ending with the year 1865, the recently-created judges, such as Judge Selwyn, brother of the Bishop of Lichfield, and also of the Professor of Divinity at Cambridge. But I believe, from cursory inquiries, that the relations of these latter judges, speaking generally, have not so large a share of eminence as we shall find among those of the judges in my list. This might have been expected, for it is notorious that the standard of ability in a modern judge is not so high as it used to be. The number of exceptionally gifted men being the same, it is impossible to supply the new demand for heads of great schools and for numerous other careers, now thrown open to able youths, without seriously limiting the field whence alone good judges may be selected. By beginning at the Restoration, which I took for my commencement, because there was frequent jobbery in earlier days, I lose a Lord Keeper (of the same rank as a Lord Chancellor), and his still greater son, also a Lord Chancellor, namely, the two Bacons. I state these facts to show that I have not picked out the period in question, because it seemed most favourable to my argument, but simply because it appeared the most suitable

D

to bring out the truth as to hereditary genius, and was, at the same time, most convenient for me to discuss.

There are 286 judges within the limits of my inquiry; 109 of them have one or more eminent relations, and three others have relations whom I have noticed, but they are marked off with brackets, and are therefore not to be included in the following statistical deductions. As the readiest method of showing, at a glance, the way in which these relations are distributed, I give a table below in which they are all compactly registered. This table is a condensed summary of the Appendix to the present chapter, which should be consulted by the reader whenever he desires fuller information.

TABLE I

SUMMARY OF RELATIONSHIPS OF 109 JUDGES, GROUPED INTO 85 FAMILIES

One relation (or two in family)

Abney	U.
Alibone	G.
Bedingfield	U.
Best (Lord Wynford)	g.
Bickersteth (Lord Langdale)	u.
Bramston	F.
Browne	uS.
Brougham, Lord	gB.
Campbell, Lord	N.
Cooper (Earl of Shaftesbury)	P.
Copley (Lord Lyndhurst)	F.
De Grey (Lord Walsingham)	S.
Erle	B.
2. Eyre, Sir R. and father	F.
Forster	F.
Gurney	S.
Harcourt, Lord	G.
Heath	S.
Henley (E. of Northington)	F.
Hotham	B.
Keating	F.
King, Lord	u.
Lawrence	F.

One relation (or two in family)—cont.

Lee	B.
Mansfield, Lord	P.
Milton	B.
Patteson	S.
2. Powis, Sir L. and brother	B.
2. Raymond, Lord, and father	F.
2. Reynolds, Sir J. and nephew	N.
Romilly, Lord[1]	S.
Scott (Earl Eldon)	B.
Sewell	p.
Thesiger (Lord Chelmsford)	S.
Thurlow, Lord	B.
Treby	S.
(Twisden, *see* Finch)	
Verney	g.
Wigram	B.
Wood (Lord Hatherley)	F.

Two and three relations (or three and four in family)

Alderson	F. U*s*.
(Bathurst, Earl, *see* Buller)	
Blackburn	B. g.
Blackstone	S. N.
2. Buller and Bathurst, Earl	U. u. N.
Burnet	G. F.
Churchill[2]	UP. n.
Clarke	B. u.
2. Clive, Sir E. and uncle	U. UP.
2. Cowper, Earl, and brother	B. NS.
Dampier	F. B.
Dolben	S. B. gB.
2. Erskine, Lord, and son	B. S.
2. Gould, Sir H. and grandson	P. p.
Hewitt (Lord Lifford)	2 S.
2. Jeffreys, Lord, and Trevor	G. *US*.
Jervis	F. GN.
Lechmere	P. u.
Lovell	pS. p*P*.
Nares	S. B.
Parker (E. of Macclesfield) and Sir Thomas	S. UP.
Pepys (E. of Cottenham)	G. g. B.

[1] The kinship is reckoned from Sir Samuel Romilly.
[2] The kinship is reckoned from the Great Duke of Marlborough.

Two and three relations (or three and four in family)—cont.

Pollock	2 B. S.
Rolfe (Lord Cranworth)	*G*N. gF.
Scarlett (Lord Abinger)	2 S.
Spelman	F. GF.
Sutton (Lord Manners)	B. N.
Talbot, Lord	F. N.
Turner	2 U.
2. Wilde, Lord Truro, and nephew	B. N.
2. Willes, Sir J. and son	B. S.
Willmot	P. PS.
2. Windham, Sir W. and brother	B. P. *G*N.

Four or more relations (or five and more in family)

4. Atkyns, Sir R. and three others	G. F. B. p.
Coleridge[1]	S. s. 3 N. P. NS.
Denison	4 NS.
Denman	F. S. uS. uP.
3. Viz. Finch (Earl of Nottingham), Twisden, and Legge	F. 2 S. *U*S. GN. *P*S. (? g*N*)
2. Herbert, Lord Keeper, and son	2 S. 2 US.
3. Hyde, Earl Clarendon, and cousin	2 U. 3 US. S.
Law (Lord Ellenborough)	F. 2 S. 2 B.
(Legge, *see* Finch)	
Lyttleton[2]	B. F. u. g. pS.
3. Viz. 2 Montagu[3] and 1 North (Lord Guilford)	G. B. 2S. 2N. 2P. NS. 5*N*.
(North, *see* Montagu)	
2. Pratt, Earl Camden, and Sir J.	F. S. n. nS.
Somers, Earl (*but see* Yorke)	2 *N*S. 2 *N*P.
Trevor, Lord	g. F. S. U. GB.
(Trevor, Master of the Rolls, *see* Jeffreys)	
Vaughan	3 B. 2 N. p.
2. Yorke, Earl Hardwicke, and son; also, in part, Earl Somers	2 S. 2 P. PS.

[1] The kinship is reckoned from Coleridge the Poet.
[2] Ditto, from the Lord Keeper.
[3] Ditto, from Chief Justice the first Earl of Manchester; the two nephews are William, Ch.B.E., and the Earl of Sandwich; the two grandsons, the Earl of Halifax and James, Ch.B.E. The genealogical table in the Appendix to this chapter, will explain these and the other kinships of the Montagu family.

Several remarkable features in the contents of this table will catch the eye at once. I will begin by shortly alluding to them, and will enter more into details a little further on. First, it will be observed, that the Judges are so largely interrelated, that 109 of them are grouped into only 85 families. These are seventeen doublets, among the Judges, two triplets, and one quadruplet. In addition to these, might be counted six other sets, consisting of those whose ancestors sat on the Bench previously to the accession of Charles II, namely, Bedingfield, Forster, Hyde, Finch, Windham, and Lyttleton. Another fact to be observed, is the nearness of the relationships in my list. The single letters are far the most common. Also, though a man has twice as many grandfathers as fathers, and probably more than twice as many grandsons as sons, yet the Judges are found more frequently to have eminent fathers than grandfathers, and eminent sons than grandsons. In the third degree of relationship, the eminent kinsmen are yet more rare, although the number of individuals in those degrees is increased in a duplicate proportion. When a judge has no more than one eminent relation, that relation is nearly always to be found in the first or second degree. Thus in the first section of the table, which is devoted to single relationships, though it includes as many as thirty-nine entries, there are only two among them (viz. Browne and Lord Brougham) whose kinships extend beyond the second degree. It is in the last section of the table, which treats of whole families, largely gifted with ability, that the distant kinships are chiefly to be found. I annex a table (TABLE II) extracted from the preceding one, which exhibits these facts with great clearness. Column A contains the facts just as they were observed, and column D shows the percentage of individuals, in each degree of kinship to every 100 judges, who have become eminent.

TABLE II also gives materials for judging of the comparative influence of the male and female lines, in conveying ability. Thanks to my method of notation, it is perfectly easy to separate the two lines in the way I am about to explain. I do not attempt to compare relations in the first degree of

TABLE II

	Degrees of Kinship							
	Name of the degree	Corresponding letter			A	B	C	D	E
1 degree	22 F.	...	...	...	22	26	100	26·0	9·1
	30 B.	...	...	...	30	35	150	23·3	8·2
	31 S.	...	...	...	31	36	100	36·0	12·6
2 degrees	7 G.	6 g.	...	...	13	15	200	7·5	2·6
	9 U.	6 u.	...	...	15	18	400	4·5	1·6
	14 N.	2 n.	...	...	16	19	400	4·75	1·7
	11 P.	5 p.	...	...	16	19	200	9·5	3·7
3 degrees	1 GF.	1 gF.	0 gF.		2	2	400	0·5	0·2
	1 GB.	2 gB.	0 gB.		3	4	800	0·5	0·2
	5 US.	2 uS.	1 uS.		9	11	800	1·4	0·5
	7 NS.	1 nS.	0 nS.		15	17	800	2·1	0·7
	2 PS.	2 pS.	0 pS.		5	6	400	1·5	0·5
All more remote	...	...			12	14		0·0	0·0

Name of the degree	Corresponding letter
Father	
Brother	
Son	
Grandfather	
Uncle	
Nephew	
Grandson	
Great-grandfather	
Great-uncle	
First-cousin	
Great-nephew	
Great-grandson	
All more remote	

A. Number of eminent men in each degree of kinship to the most eminent man of the family (85 families).

B. The preceding column raised in proportion to 100 families.

C. Number of individuals in each degree of kinship to 100 men.[1]

D. Percentage of eminent men in each degree of kinship to the most eminent member of distinguished families; it was obtained by dividing B and C and multiplying by 100.

E. Percentages of the previous column reduced in the proportion of (286–24[2] or) 242 to 85, in order to apply to families generally.

[1] These are estimated averages for all except direct ancestors.

[2] That is to say, 286 Judges, less 24, who are included as subordinate members of the 85 families.

kinship—namely, fathers with mothers, sons with daughters, or brothers with sisters, because there exists no criterion for a just comparison of the natural ability of the different sexes. Nay, even if there were means for testing it, the result would be fallacious. A mother transmits masculine peculiarities to her male child, which she does not and cannot possess; and, similarly, a woman who is endowed with fewer gifts of a masculine type than her husband, may yet contribute in a larger degree to the masculine intellectual superiority of her son. I therefore shift my inquiry from the first, to the second and third degrees of kinship. As regards the second degree, I compare the paternal grandfather with the maternal, the uncle by the father's side with the the uncle by the mother's, the nephew by the brother's side with the nephew by the sister's, and the grandson by the son with the grandson by the daughter. On the same principle I compare the kinships in the third degree: that is to say, the father of the father's father with the father of the mother's mother, and so on. The whole of the work is distinctly exposed to view in the following compact table:—

IN THE SECOND DEGREE

    7 G. + 9 U. + 14 N. + 11 P. = 41 kinships through males

    6 g. + 6 u. + 2 n. + 5 p. = 19 kinships through females

IN THE THIRD DEGREE

    1 GF. + 1 GB. + 5 US. + 7 NS. + 2 PS. = 19 kinships through males

    0 gF. + 0 gB. + 1 uS. + 0 nS. + 0 pS. = 1 kinship through females

Total, 60 through males, 20 through females

The numbers are too small to warrant any very decided conclusion; but they go far to prove that the female influence is inferior to that of the male in conveying ability. It must, however, be observed, that the difference between the totals in the second degree is chiefly due to the nephews—a relationship difficult to trace on the female side, because, as a matter of fact, biographers do not speak so fully of the descendants of the sisters of their hero as of those of his brothers. As regards the third degree, the relationships on the female side are much more difficult to ferret out than those on the male, and I have no doubt I have omitted many of them. In my earlier attempts, the balance stood still more heavily against the female side, and it has been reduced exactly in proportion to the number of times I have revised my data. Consequently, though I first suspected a large residuum against the female line, I think there is reason to believe the influence of females but little inferior to that of males, in transmitting judicial ability.

It is, of course, a grief to me, in writing this book, that circumstances make it impossible to estimate the influence of the individual peculiarities of the mother—for good or for bad—upon her offspring. They appear to me, for the reasons stated, to be as important elements in the inquiry as those of the father, and yet I am obliged to completely ignore them in a large majority of instances, on account of the lack of reliable information. Nevertheless, I have numerous arguments left to prove that genius is hereditary.

Before going further, I must entreat my readers to abandon an objection which very likely may present itself to their minds, and which I can easily show to be untenable. People who do not realize the nature of my arguments have constantly spoken to me to this effect: "It is of no use your quoting successes unless you take failures into equal account. Eminent men may have eminent relations, but they also have very many who are ordinary, or even stupid, and there are not a few who are either eccentric or downright mad." I perfectly allow all this, but it does not in the least affect the cogency of my arguments. If a man breeds from strong, well-shaped dogs, but of mixed pedigree, the puppies will be sometimes, but rarely, the equals of their parents. They will commonly be of a mongrel, nondescript type, because ancestral peculiarities are apt to crop out in the offspring. Yet notwithstanding all this, it is easy to develop the desirable characteristics of individual dogs into the assured heirloom of a new breed. The breeder selects the puppies that most nearly approach the wished-for type, generation after generation, until they have no ancestor, within many degrees, that has objectionable peculiarities. So it is with men and women. Because one or both of a child's parents are able, it does not in the least follow as a matter of necessity, but only as one of moderately unfavourable odds, that the child will be able also. He inherits an extraordinary mixture of qualities displayed in his grandparents, great-grandparents, and more remote ancestors, as well as from those of his father and mother. The most illustrious and so-called "well-bred" families of the human race, are utter mongrels as regards their natural gifts of intellect and disposition.

What I profess to prove is this: that if two children are taken, of whom one has a parent exceptionally gifted in a high degree—say as one in 4,000, or as one in a million—and the other has not, the former child has an enormously greater chance of turning out to be gifted in a high degree, than the other. Also, I argue that, as a new race can be obtained in animals and plants, and can be raised, to so great a degree of purity that it will maintain itself, with moderate care in preventing the more faulty members of the flock from breeding, so a race of gifted men might be obtained, under exactly similar conditions.

I must apologise for anticipating, in this off-hand and very imperfect manner, the subject of a future chapter by these few remarks; but I am really obliged to do so, knowing from experience how pertinaciously strangers to the reasoning by which the laws of heredity are established, are inclined to prejudge my conclusions, by blindly insisting that the objection to which I have referred has overbearing weight.

I will now proceed with an examination of what may be learnt from the relationships of the Judges. First, I would ask, are the abler judges more rich in eminent relations than those who are less able? There are two ways of answering this question: the one is to examine into the relationships of the law lords as compared with that of the puisne judges, or of the chancellors compared with that of the judges generally; and the other is to determine whether or no the persons whose names are entered in the third column of TABLE I are above the average of judges in respect to ability. Here are a few of the Lord Chancellors. There are only 30 of those high legal officers within the limits of my inquiry, yet 24 of these have eminent relations; whereas out of the (286 – 30 or) 256 other judges, only (114 – 24 or) 90 have eminent relations. There are therefore 80 per cent. of the chancellors, as compared to 36 per cent. of the rest of the judges, that have eminent relations. The proportion would have been greater if I had compared the chancellors, or the chancellors and the other law lords, with the puisne judges.

The other test I proposed, is equally satisfactory. There can be no doubt of the exceptionally eminent ability of the men whose names appear in the third column. To those who object to my conclusion because Lord Chancellors have more opportunities of thrusting relatives, by jobbery, into eminence than are possessed by the other judges, I can do no more than refer them to what I have already said about reputation being a test of ability, and by giving a short list of the more remarkable cases of relations to the Lord Chancellors, which I think will adequately meet their objection. They are—

1. Earl Bathurst and his daughter's son, the famous judge, Sir F. Buller. 2. Earl Camden and his father, Chief Justice Pratt. 3. Earl Clarendon and the remarkable family of Hyde, in which were two uncles and one cousin, all English judges, besides one Welsh judge, and many other men of distinction. 4. Earl Cowper, his brother the judge, and his great-nephew the poet. 5. Earl Eldon and his brother Lord Stowell. 6. Lord Erskine, his eminent legal brother the Lord Advocate of Scotland, and his son the judge. 7. Earl Nottingham and the most remarkable family of Finch. 8, 9, 10. Earl Hardwicke and his son, also a Lord Chancellor, who died suddenly, and that son's great-uncle, Lord Somers, also a Lord Chancellor. 11. Lord Herbert, his son a judge, his cousins Lord Herbert of Cherbury and George the poet and divine. 12. Lord King and his uncle John Locke the philosopher. 13. The infamous

but most able Lord Jeffreys had a cousin just like him, namely, Sir J. Trevor, Master of the Rolls. 14. Lord Guilford is member of a family to which I simply despair of doing justice, for it is linked with connexions of such marvellous ability, judicial and statesmanlike, as to deserve a small volume to describe it. It contains thirty first-class men in near kinship, including Montagus, Sydneys, Herberts, Dudleys, and others. 15. Lord Truro had two able legal brothers, one of whom was Chief Justice at the Cape of Good Hope; and his nephew is an English judge, recently created Lord Penzance. I will here mention Lord Lyttleton, Lord Keeper of Charles I, although many members of his most remarkable family do not fall within my limits. His father, the Chief Justice of North Wales, married a lady, the daughter of Sir J. Walter, the Chief Justice of South Wales, and also sister of an English judge. She bore him Lord Keeper Lyttleton, also Sir Timothy, a judge. Lord Lyttleton's daughters' son (she married a cousin) was Sir T. Lyttleton, the Speaker of the House of Commons.

There is, therefore, abundant reason to conclude that the kinsmen of Lord Chancellors are far richer in natural gifts than those of the other judges.

I will now take another test of the existence of hereditary ability. It is a comparison of the number of entries in the columns of TABLE I. Supposing that natural gifts were due to mere accident, unconnected with parentage, then the entries would be distributed in accordance with the law that governs the distribution of accidents. If it be a hundred to one against some member of any family, within given limits of kinship, drawing a lottery prize, it would be a million to one against three members of the same family doing so (nearly, but not exactly, because the size of the family is limited), and a million millions to one against six members doing so. Therefore, if natural gifts were due to mere accident, the first column of TABLE I would have been enormously longer than the second column, and the second column enormously longer than the third; but they are not so. There are nearly as many cases of two or three eminent relations as of one eminent relation; and as a set-off against the thirty-nine cases that appear in the first column, there are no less than fifteen cases in the third.

It is therefore clear that ability is not distributed at haphazard, but that it clings to certain families.

We will proceed to a third test.

If genius be hereditary, as I assert it to be, the characteristics that mark a judge ought to be frequently transmitted to his descendants. The majority of judges belong to a strongly-marked type. They are not men who are carried away by sentiment, who love seclusion and dreams, but they are prominent members of a very different class, one that Englishmen are especially prone to honour for at least the six lawful days of the week. I mean that they are vigorous, shrewd, practical, helpful men; glorying in the rough-and-tumble of public life, tough in constitution and strong in digestion, valuing what money brings, aiming at position and influence, and desiring to found families. The vigour of a judge is testified by the fact that the average age of their appointment in the last three reigns has been fifty-seven. The labour and responsibility of the office seem enormous to lookers-on, yet these elderly men continue working with ease for many more years; their average age of death is seventy-five, and they commonly die in harness. Now are these remarkable gists and peculiarities inherited by their sons ? Do the judges often have sons who succeed in the same career, where success would have been impossible if they had not been gifted with the special qualities of their fathers ? The best answer is a list of names. They will be of much interest to legal readers; others can glance them over, and go on to the results.

JUDGES OF ENGLAND, AND OTHER HIGH LEGAL OFFICERS, BETWEEN 1660 AND 1865, WHO WERE, OR ARE, RELATED

I mark those cases with an asterisk (*) where both relations are English Judges

FATHERS	SONS
*Atkyns, Sir Edward, B.E. (Chas. II)	{ Sir Robert, Chief Just. C.P. { Sir Edward, B.E. (Jas. II)
Atkyns, Sir Richard, Chief Just. N. Wales	Sir Edward, B.E. (Chas. II)

FATHERS	SONS
*Bramston, Sir Francis, Chief K.B. (Chas. I)[1]	Sir Francis, B.E. (Chas. II)
Coleridge, Sir John, Just. Q.B. (Vict.)	Sir John Duke, Solic.-Gen.
Dolben, Sir Wm., Just. K.B. (Will. III)	Sir Gilbert, Just. C.P. Ireland; cr. Bart.
*Erskine, T.; cr. Lord Erskine; Lord Chan.	Hon. Sir Thomas, Just. C.P. (Vict.)
*Eyre, Sir Samuel, Just. K.B. (Will. III)	Sir Robert, Chief Just. C.P. (Geo. II)
Finch, Heneage, L.Ch.; cr. E. of Nottingham	Heneage, Solic.-Gen.; cr. Earl Aylesford
Finch, Sir Heneage, Recorder of London	Heneage, Ld. Chan.; cr. E. of Nottingham
*Forster, Sir James, Just. C.P. (Chas. I)	Sir Robert, Chief Just. K.B. (Chas. II)
Gurney, Sir John, B.E. (Vict.)	Rt. Hon. Russell Gurney, Recorder of London
*Herbert, Sir Edw., Lord Keeper (Chas. II)	Sir Edward, Chief Just. K.B. (Jas. II)
Hewitt, James; cr. Ld. Lifford; Just. K.B.	Joseph, Just. K. B. Ireland
Jervis, ——, Chief Just. of Chester	Sir John, Chief Just. C.P. (Vict.)
Law, Edw.; cr. Ld. Ellenborough; Ch. K.B.	Chas. Ewan, M.P., Recorder of London
*Pratt, Sir John, Chief Just. K.B. (Geo. II)	Earl Camden, Lord Chanc. (Geo. III)
*Raymond, Sir Thomas, Just. C.B.	Robert; cr. Ld. Raymond; Ch. K.B. (Geo. II)
Romilly, Sir Samuel, Solic.-Gen.	Cr. Lord Romilly, Master of Rolls (Vict.)
*Willes, Sir John, Chief Just. C.P. (Geo. III)	Sir Edward, Just. K.B. (Geo. III)
*Yorke, Philip, Ld. Chanc.; cr. E. Hardwicke	Hon. Charles, Lord Chanc. (Geo. III)

BROTHERS

*Atkyns, Sir Robert, Chief C.P. (Will. III)	Sir Edward, B.E. (Jas. II)
*Cowper, Wm.; cr. Earl Cowper; Ld. Chanc.	Sir Spencer, Just. C.P. (Geo. II)

[1] I count the fathers of the judges of Charles II because the judges of the present reign are too young to have judges for sons.

BROTHERS

Erskine, T.; cr. Lord Erskine; Lord Chanc.	Henry, twice Lord Advocate, Scotland
Hyde, Sir Robert, Chief K.B. (Chas. II)	Sir Frederick, a Judge in S. Wales Judge of Admiralty
Lee, Sir William, Chief K.B. (Geo. II)	George, Dean of Arches, &c.
*Lyttleton, Lord, Lord Keeper (Chas. I)	Sir Timothy, B.E. (Chas. II)
North, F.; cr. Earl of Guilford; Ld. Chanc.	Roger, Attorney-Gen. to Queen
Pollock, Sir F. Chief B.E. (Vict.)	Sir David, Chief Just. Bombay
*Powis, Sir Lyttleton, Just. K.B. (Geo. I)	Sir Thomas, Just K.B. (Geo. I)
Scarlett, Sir J.; cr. Ld. Abinger; Ch.B.E.	Sir Wm. Ch. Just. Jamaica
Scott, John; cr. Earl of Eldon; Lord Chanc.	William; cr. Lord Stowell; Judge Adm.
Wilde, T.; cr. Lord Truro; Lord Chanc.	Sir ——, Ch. Just. Cape of Good Hope
*Wynham, Sir Hugh, B.E. (Chas. II)	Sir Wadham, B.E. (Chas. II)

GRANDFATHERS	GRANDSONS
*Atkyns, Sir Robt. Chief C.P. (Will. III)	Sir J. Tracy (assumed name of Arkyns), Cursitor B.E. (Geo. III)
Burnet, ——, Scotch Judge; Lord Cramond	Sir Thomas Burnet, Just. C.P.
*Gould, Sir Henry, Just. Q.B. (Anne)	Sir Henry Gould, Just. C.P. (Geo. III)
Jeffreys ,——, Judge in N. Wales	Jeffreys, Lord, Lord Chanc. (Jas. II)
Finch, H. Solic.-Gen.; cr. E. Aylesford	Hon. H. Legge, B.E. (Geo. II)
Walter, Sir E. Chief Just. S. Wales	Lyttleton, Sir T. B. E. (Chas. II)
*Heath, Sir R. Chief K.B. (Chas. I)	Verney, Hon. Sir J. Master of Rolls

Out of the 286 Judges, more than *one in every nine* of them have been either father, son, or brother to another judge, and the other high legal relationships have been even more numerous. There cannot, then, remain a doubt but that the peculiar type of ability that is necessary to a judge is often transmitted by descent.

The reader must guard himself against the supposition, that because the Judges have so many legal relations, therefore they have few other relations of eminence in other walks of life. A long list might be made out of those who had bishops and archbishops for kinsmen. No less than ten judges—of whom one, Sir Robert Hyde, appeared in the previous list—have a bishop or an archbishop for a brother. Of these, Sir William Dolben was brother to one Archbishop of York and son of the sister of another, namely of John Williams, who was also the Lord Keeper to James I. There are cases of Poet-relations, as Cowper, Coleridge, Milton, Sir Thomas Overbury, and Waller. There are numerous relatives who are novelists, physicians, admirals, and generals. My lists of kinsmen at the end of this chapter are very briefly treated, but they include the names of many great men, whose deeds have filled large volumes. It is one of my most serious drawbacks in writing this book, to feel that names, which never now present themselves to my eye without associations of respect and reverence, for the great qualities of those who bore them, are likely to be insignificant and meaningless to the eyes of most of my readers—indeed to all of those who have never had occasion to busy themselves with their history. I know how great was my own ignorance of the character of the great men of previous generations, before I occupied myself with biographies, and I therefore reasonably suspect that many of my readers will be no better informed about them than I was myself. A collection of men that I have learned to look upon as an august Valhalla, is likely to be regarded, by those who are strangers to the facts of biographical history, as an assemblage of mere respectabilities.

The names of North and Montagu, among the Judges, introduce us to a remarkable breed of eminent men, set forth at length in the genealogical tree of the Montagus, and again in that of the Sydneys (see the chapter on LITERARY MEN),

to whose natural history—if the expression be permitted—a
few pages may be profitably assigned. There is hardly a name
in those pedigrees which is not more than ordinarily eminent:
many are illustrious. They are closely tied together in their
kinship, and they extend through ten generations. The main
roots of this diffused ability lie in the families of Sydney and
Montagu, and, in a lesser degree, in that of North.

The Sydney blood—I mean that of the descendants of Sir
William Sydney and his wife—had extraordinary influence in
two different combinations. First with the Dudleys, producing
in the first generation, Sir Philip Sydney and his eminent
brother and sister; in the second generation, at least one
eminent man; and in the third generation, Algernon Sydney,
with his able brother and much be-praised sister. The second
combination of the Sydney blood was with the Harringtons,
producing in the first generation a literary peer, and Elizabeth
the mother of the large and most remarkable family that forms
the chief feature in my genealogical table.

The Montagu blood, as represented by Sir Edward, who
died in the Tower, 1644, is derived from three distinct sources.
His great-grandfather (*g*F.) was Sir John Finnieux, Chief
Justice of the King's Bench; his grandfather (g.) was John
Roper, Attorney-General to Henry VIII; and his father—by
far the most eminent of the three—was Sir Edward Montagu,
Chief Justice of the King's Bench. Sir Edward Montagu, son
of the Chief Justice, married Elizabeth Harrington, of whom
I have just spoken, and had a large family, who in themselves
and in their descendants became most remarkable. To mention
only the titles they won: in the first generation they obtained
two peerages, the earldom of Manchester and the barony of
Montagu; in the second they obtained two more, the earldom
of Sandwich and the barony of Capel; in the third five more,
the dukedom of Montagu, earldoms of Halifax and of Essex,
the barony of Guilford, and a new barony of Capel (second
creation); in the fourth one more, the dukedom of Manchester
(the Premier in 1701); in the fifth one more, the earldom of
Guilford. The second Earl of Guilford, the Premier of

George III (best known as Lord North), was in the sixth generation.

It is wholly impossible for me to describe the characteristics of all the individuals who are jotted down in my genealogical tree. I could not do it without giving a vast deal more room than I can spare. But this much I can do, and ought to do; namely, to take those who are most closely linked with the Judges, and to show that they possessed sterling ability, and did not hold their high positions by mere jobbery, nor obtain their reputations through the accident of birth or circumstances. I will gladly undertake to show this, although it happens in the present instance to put my cause in a peculiarly disadvantageous light, because Francis North, the Lord Keeper, the first Baron Guilford, is the man of all others, in that high position (identical, or nearly so, with that of a Lord Chancellor), whom modern authorities vie in disparaging and condemning. Those who oppose my theories might say, the case of North being Lord Keeper shows it is impossible to trust official rank as a criterion of ability; he was promoted by jobbery, and jobbed when he was promoted; he inherited family influence, not natural intellectual gifts: and the same may be said of all the members of this or of any other pedigree. As I implied before, there is enough truth in this objection to make it impossible to meet it by a flat contradiction, based on a plain and simple statement. It is necessary to analyse characters, and to go a little into detail. I will do this, and when it is concluded I believe many of my readers will better appreciate than they did before, how largely natural intellectual gifts are the birthright of some families.

Francis North, the Lord Keeper, was one of a family of five brothers and one sister. The lives of three of the brothers are familiarly known to us through the charming biographies written by another brother, Roger North. Their position in the Montagu family is easily discovered by means of the genealogical tree. They fall in the third of those generations I have just described—the one in which the family gained one dukedom, two earldoms, and two baronies. Their father was of a.

literary stock, continued backwards in one line during no less than five generations. The first Lord North was an eminent lawyer in the time of Queen Elizabeth, and his son—an able man and an ambassador—married the daughter of Lord Chancellor Rich. His son again—who did not live to enjoy the peerage—married the daughter of a Master of the Court of Requests, and his great-great-grandsons—the intermediate links being more or less distinguished, but of whose marriages I know little—were the brothers North, of whom I am about to speak.

The father of these brothers was the fourth Baron North. He was a literary man, and, among other matters, wrote the life of the founder of his family. He was an "economical" man, and "exquisitely virtuous and sober in his person." The style of his writings was not so bright as that of his father, the second baron, who was described as full of spirit and flame, and who was an author both in prose and verse; his poems were praised by Walpole. The mother of the brothers, namely, Anne Montagu, is described by her son as a compendium of charity and wisdom. I suspect it was from the fourth Baron North that the disagreeable qualities in three of the brothers North were derived—such as the priggishness of the Lord Keeper, and that curious saving, mercantile spirit that appeared under different forms in the Lord Keeper, the Financier, and the Master of Trinity College. I cannot avoid alluding to these qualities, for they are prominent features in their characters, and find a large place in their biographies.

In speaking of the Lord Keeper, I think I had better begin with the evil part of his character. When that has been admitted and done with, the rest of my task will be pleasant and interesting. In short, the Lord Keeper is mercilessly handled in respect to his public character. Lord Campbell calls him the most odious man that ever held the Great Seal, and says that throughout his whole life he sought and obtained advancement by the meanest arts. Bishop Burnet calls him crafty and designing. Lord Macaulay accuses him of selfishness, cowardice, and meanness. I have heard of no writer who commends his public character except his brother, who was tenderly attached to him. I should say, that even Lord Campbell acknowledges the Lord Keeper to have been extremely amiable in all his domestic relations, and that nothing can be more touching than the account we have of the warm and steady affection between him and his brother, who survived to be his biographer. I am, however, no further concerned with the Lord Keeper's public character than to show that, notwithstanding his most unworthy acts to obtain advancement, and notwithstanding he had relatives in high offices to help him, his own ability and that of his brothers were truly remarkable.

Bishop Burnet says of him that he had not the virtues of his predecessor (Lord Nottingham), but he had parts far beyond him. However, Lord Campbell dissents from this and remarks that "a Nottingham does not arise above once in a century." (I will here beg the reader not to be unmindful of the marvellous hereditary gifts of the Nottingham or Finch family.) Macaulay says his intellect was clear, his industry great, his proficiency in letters and science respectable, and his legal learning more than respectable. His brother Roger writes thus of the Lord Keeper's youth:—

> It was singular and remarkable in him that, together with the study of the law, which is thought ordinarily to devour the whole studious time of a young gentleman, he continued to pursue his inquiries into all ingenious arts, history, humanity, and languages; whereby he became not only a good lawyer, but a good historian, politician, mathematician, natural philosopher, and, I must add, musician in perfection.

The Hon. Sir Dudley North, his younger brother, was a man of exceedingly high abilities and vigour. He went as a youth to Smyrna, where his good works are not yet forgotten, and where he made a large fortune; then, returning to England, he became at once a man of the highest note in Parliament as a financier. There was an unpleasant side to his character when young, but he overmastered and outgrew it. Namely, he first showed a strange bent to traffic when at school; afterwards he cheated sadly, and got into debts; then he cheated his parents to pay the debts. At last he made a vigorous effort, and wholly reformed himself, so that his brother concludes his biography in this way:—

> If I may be so free as to give my thoughts of his morals, I must allow that, as to all the mercantile arts and stratagems of trade which could be used to get money from those he dealt with, I believe he was no niggard; but as for falsities . . . . he was as clear as any man living.

It seems, from the same authority, that he was a very forward, lively, and beautiful child. At school he did not get on so well with his books, as he had an excessive desire for action; still, his ability was such that a little application went a long way with him, and in the end he came out a moderate scholar. He was a great swimmer, and could live in the water for a whole afternoon. (I mention this, because I shall hereafter have occasion to speak of physical gifts not unfrequently accompanying intellectual ones.) He sometimes left his clothes in charge of a porter below London Bridge, then ran naked upon the mud-shore of the Thames up almost as high as Chelsea, for the pleasure of swimming down to his clothes with the tide, and he loved to end by shooting the cascade beneath old London Bridge. I often marvel at his feat, when I happen to be on the river in a steamer.

I will now quote Macaulay's description of his first appearance, in his after life, on the stage of English politics. Speaking, in his *History of England,* of the period immediately following the accession of James II, Macaulay says—

"The person on whom devolved the task of devising ways and means was Sir Dudley North, younger brother of the Lord Keeper. Dudley North was one of the ablest men of his time. He had early in life been sent to the Levant, where he had long been engaged in mercantile pursuits. Most men would, in such a situation, have allowed their faculties to rust; for at Smyrna and Constantinople there were few books and few intelligent companions. But the young factor had one of those vigorous understandings which are independent of external aids. In his solitude he meditated deeply on the philosophy of trade, and thought out, by degrees, a complete and admirable theory—substantially the same with that which a hundred years later was expounded by Adam Smith." North was brought into Parliament for Banbury; and, though a new member, was the person on whom the Lord Treasurer chiefly relied for the conduct of financial business in the Lower House. "North's ready wit and perfect knowledge of trade prevailed, both in the Treasury and the Parliament, against all opposition. The old members were amazed at seeing a man who had not been a fortnight in the House, and whose life had been chiefly passed in foreign countries, assume with confidence, and discharge with ability, all the functions of a Chancellor of the Exchequer." He was forty-four years old at the time.

Roger North describes the financial theories of his brother, thus: "One is, that trade is not distributed, as government, by nations and kingdoms, but is one throughout the whole world; as the main sea, which cannot be emptied or replenished in one part, but the whole more or less will be affected." Another was "concerning money; that no nation could want money (specie), and they would not abound in it. . . . For if a people want money, they will give a price for it; and then merchants, for gain, bring it and lay it down before them."

Roger North, speaking of Sir Dudley and of the Lord Keeper, says: "These brothers lived with extreme satisfaction in each other's society; for both had the skill and knowledge of the world, as to all affairs relating to their several professions, in perfection, and each was an Indies to the other, producing always the richest novelties, of which the best understandings are greedy."

The Hon. Dr. John North, Master of Trinity College, Cambridge, differed in some respects from his brothers, and resembled them in others:—

"When he was very young, and also as he grew up, he was of a nice and tender constitution—not so vigorous and athletic as most of his brothers were." "His temper was always reserved and studious. . . . If anything so early seemed amiss in him, it was a non-natural gravity, which in youths is seldom a good sign, for it argues imbecility of body and mind, or both; but his lay wholly in the former, for his mental capacity was vigorous, as none more."

Thus he became devoted to study, and the whole of his expenditure went to books; in other respects he was penurious and hoarding. Consequently, as his brother says, "he was over-much addicted to thinking, or else he performed it with more labour and intenseness than other men ordinarily do. . . . He was, in a word, the most intense and passionate thinker that ever lived, and was in his right mind." This ruined his health. "His flesh was strangely flaccid and soft; his going weak and shuffling, often crossing his legs as if he were tipsy; his sleep seldom or never easy, but interrupted with unquiet and painful dreams—the reposes he had were short and by snatches; his active spirit had rarely any settlement or rest."

It is evident that he played foolish tricks with his brain, and the result was that he had a stroke, and utterly broke up, decaying more and more in mind and body until death relieved him, æt. 38.

There is no doubt that Dr. John North deserved more reputation than he has obtained, partly owing to his early death, and partly to his exceeding sensitiveness in respect to posthumous criticism. He left peremptory orders that all his MSS should be burnt. He appears to have been especially skilled in Greek and Hebrew scholarship.

The Lord Keeper and the Master of Trinity resembled each other in their painfully shy dispositions and studious tastes. The curious money-saving propensities were common to all three brothers. The indolent habits of the Master of Trinity were shared by Sir Dudley after his return to England, who would take no exercise whatever, but sat all day either at home, or else steering a little sailing-vessel on the Thames. The Lord Keeper was always fanciful about his health.

The Hon. Mary North, afterwards Lady Spring, was the

sister of these brothers, and no less gifted than they. Roger North says—

"Besides the advantage of her person, she had a superior wit, prodigious memory, and was most agreeable in conversation." She used to rehearse "by heart prolix romances, with the substance of speeches and letters, as well as passages; and this with little or no hesitation, but in a continual series of discourse—the very memory of which is to me at this day very wonderful."

She died not long after the birth of her first child, and the child died not long after her.

Roger North, the biographer of his brothers, from whom I have quoted so much, was the author of other works, and among them is a memoir on Music, showing that he shared the musical faculty that was strongly developed in the Lord Keeper. Little is known of his private life. He was Attorney-General to the consort of James II. There can be no doubt as to his abilities. The *Lives of the Norths* is a work of no ordinary writer. It is full of touches of genius and shrewd perception of character. Roger North seems to have been a most loving and loveable man.

Charles, the fifth Lord North, was the eldest of the family, and succeeded to the title; but he did not, so far as I am aware, show signs of genius. However, he had a daughter whose literary tastes were curiously similar to those of her uncle, Dr. John. She was a Dudley North, who, in the words of Roger, "emaciated herself with study, whereby she had made familiar to her not only the Greek and Latin, but the Oriental languages." She died early, having collected a choice library of Oriental works.

I will conclude this description of the family with a characteristically quaint piece of their biographer's preface: "Really, the case is memorable for the happy circumstance of a flock so numerous and diffused as this of the last Dudley Lord North's was, and no one scabby sheep in it."

The nearest collateral relation of the North family by the Montagu side is Charles Hatton, their first cousin. He is

alluded to three times in Roger North's *Lives*, and each time
with the same epithet—"the incomparable Charles Hatton."
Why he was so distinguished there is no information, but it is
reasonable to accept Roger North's estimate of his merits, so
far as to classify him among the gifted members of the Montagu
family.

I will mention only four more of the kinsmen of the Norths.
The first is their great-uncle, Sir Henry Montagu, Chief
Justice of the King's Bench, and created Earl of Manchester,
who was grandfather to James Montagu, Ch. B.E. (Geo. III)
and uncle of William, Ch. B.E. (Jas. II), both of whom are
included in my list. Lord Clarendon says of Sir Henry, that
he was a "a man of great industry and sagacity in business,
which he delighted in exceedingly; and preserved so great a
vigour of mind, even to his death, that some who had known
him in his younger years did believe him to have much quicker
parts in his age than before."

The second Earl of Manchester, gN. to the Norths, was the
Baron Kimbolton, of Marston Moor, and, as Lord Campbell
says, "one of the most distinguished men who appeared in the
most interesting period of our history; having, as Lord
Kimbolton, vindicated the liberties of his country in the
Senate, as Earl of Manchester in the field, and having afterwards mainly contributed to the suppression of anarchy by the
restoration of the royal line."

The first Earl of Sandwich, also gN. to the Norths, was the
gallant High Admiral of England in the time of Charles II.
He began life as a soldier, when only eighteen years of age, with
a Parliamentary regiment that he himself had raised; and he
ended it in a naval battle against the Dutch in Southwold
Bay. He also translated a Spanish work on Metallurgy. I do
not know that the book is of any value, but the fact is worthy
of notice as showing that he was more than a mere soldier or
sailor.

The last of the eminent relations of the Norths of whom I
shall speak at length, was the great-grandson of the eldest
brother, who became the famous Premier—the Lord North—

of the time of the American war. Lord Brougham says that all contemporaries agree in representing his talents as having shone with a great and steady lustre during that singularly trying period. He speaks of a wit that never failed him, and a suavity of temper that could never be ruffled, as peculiar qualities in which he, and indeed all his family (his immediate family), excelled most other men. The admirable description of Lord North by his daughter, Lady Charlotte Lindsay, that is appended to his biography by Lord Brougham, is sufficient proof of that lady's high ability.

There is yet another great legal family, related to the Norths, whose place in the pedigree I do not know: it is that of the Hydes, and includes the illustrious first Earl of Clarendon. It appears that the Lord Chief Justice Hyde used to take kindly notice of the Lord Keeper, Francis North, when a young rising barrister, and allude to his kinship, and call him "cousin."

It is want of space, not want of material, that compels me to conclude the description of the able relatives of the Norths and Montagus. But I am sure I have said enough to prove the assertion with which I prefaced it, that natural gifts of an exceedingly high order were inherited by a very large number of the members of the family, and that these owed their reputations to their abilities, and not to family support.

Another test of the truth of the hereditary character of ability is to see whether the near relations of very eminent men are more frequently eminent than those who are more remote. TABLE II (p. 102) answers this question with great distinctness in the way I have already explained. It shows that the near relations of the Judges are far richer in ability than the more remote—so much so, that the fact of being born in the fourth degree of relationship is of no sensible benefit at all. The data from which I obtained column c of that table are as follows:— I find that 23 of the Judges are reported to have had "large families," say consisting of four adult sons in each; 11 are simply described as having "issue," say at the rate of $1\frac{1}{2}$ sons each; and that the number of the sons of others are specified as amounting between them to 186; forming thus far a total of 294. In addition to these, there are 9 reported marriages of judges in which no allusion is made to children, and there are 31 judges in respect to whom nothing is said about marriage at all. I think we are fairly justified, from these data, in concluding that each judge is father, on an average, to not less than one son who lives to an age at which he might have distinguished himself, if he had the ability to do so. I also find the (adult) families to consist on an average of not less than $2\frac{1}{2}$ sons and $2\frac{1}{2}$ daughters each, consequently each judge has an average of $1\frac{1}{2}$ brothers and $2\frac{1}{2}$ sisters.

From these data it is perfectly easy to reckon the number of kinsmen in each order. Thus the nephews consist of the brothers' sons and the sisters' sons: now 100 judges are supposed to have 150 brothers and 250 sisters, and each brother and each sister to have, on the average, only one son; consequently the 100 judges will have (150 + 250, or) 400 nephews.

I need not trouble the reader with more figures; suffice it to say, I have divided the total numbers of eminent kinsmen to 100 judges by the number of kinsmen in each degree, and from that division I obtained the column D in TABLE II, which I now project into a genealogical tree in TABLE III.

It will be observed that TABLE III refers only to distinguished *families*. If we modified it to correspond with column E of TABLE II, in which all the Judges, whether they have distinguished relations or no, are considered, the proportion between the eminent kinsmen in each different degree would be unchanged, though their absolute numbers would be reduced to about one-third of their value.

TABLE III shows in the most unmistakable manner the enormous odds that a near kinsman has over one that is remote, in the chance of inheriting ability. Speaking roughly, the percentages are quartered at each successive remove, whether by descent or collaterally. Thus in the first degree of kinship the percentage is about 28; in the second, about 7; and in the third, $1\frac{1}{2}$.

The table also testifies to another fact, in which people do not commonly believe. It shows that when we regard the

TABLE III

PERCENTAGE OF EMINENT MEN IN EACH DEGREE OF
KINSHIP TO THE MOST GIFTED MEMBER OF DISTIN-
GUISHED FAMILIES

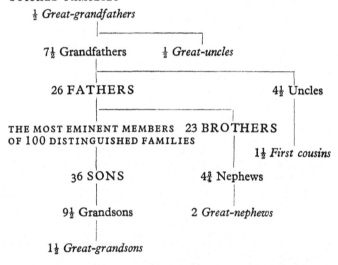

½ *Great-grandfathers*

7½ Grandfathers   ½ *Great-uncles*

26 FATHERS   4½ Uncles

THE MOST EMINENT MEMBERS   23 BROTHERS
OF 100 DISTINGUISHED FAMILIES
                                                    1½ *First cousins*

36 SONS   4¾ Nephews

9½ Grandsons   2 *Great-nephews*

1½ *Great-grandsons*

averages of many instances, the frequent sports of nature in
producing prodigies must be regarded as apparent, and not as
real. Ability, in the long run, does not suddenly start into
existence and disappear with equal abruptness, but rather, it
rises in a gradual and regular curve out of the ordinary level of
family life. The statistics show that there is a regular average
increase of ability in the generations that precede its culmination, and as regular a decrease in those that succeed it. In the
first case the marriages have been consentient to its production, in the latter they have been incapable of preserving it.

After three successive dilutions of the blood, the descendants
of the Judges appear incapable of rising to eminence. These
results are not surprising even when compared with the far
greater length of kinship through which features or diseases

may be transmitted. Ability must be based on a triple footing, every leg of which has to be firmly planted. In order that a man should inherit ability in the concrete, he must inherit three qualities that are separate and independent of one another: he must inherit capacity, zeal, and vigour; for unless these three, or, at the very least, two of them are combined, he cannot hope to make a figure in the world. The probability against inheriting a combination of three qualities not correlated together, is necessarily in a triplicate proportion greater than it is against inheriting any one of them.

There is a marked difference between the percentage of ability in the grandsons of the judge when his sons (the fathers of those grandsons) have been eminent than when they have not. Let us suppose that the son of a judge wishes to marry: what expectation has he that his own sons will become eminent men, supporters of his family, and not a burden to it, in their after life?

In the case where the son of the judge is himself eminent, I find, out of the 226 judges previous to the present reign, 22 whose sons have been distinguished men. I do not count instances in the present reign, because the grandsons of these judges are for the most part too young to have achieved distinction. 22 out of 226 gives 10 in 100 as the percentage of the judges that have had distinguished sons. (The reader will remark how near this result is to the $9\frac{1}{2}$ as entered in my table, showing the general truth of both estimates.) Of these 22 I count the following triplets. The Arkyns family as two. It is true that the grandfather was only Chief Justice of North Wales, and not an English judge, but the vigour of the blood is proved by the line of not only his son and two grandsons being English judges, but also by the grandson of one of them, through the female line, being an English judge also. Another line is that of the Pratts, viz. the Chief Justice and his son, the Lord Chancellor, Earl Camden, and his grandson, the son of the Earl, created the Marquis Camden; the latter was Chancellor of the University of Cambridge, and a man of note in many ways. Another case is in the Yorke line, for the son of the

Lord Chancellor, the Earl of Hardwicke, was Charles Yorke, himself a Lord Chancellor. His sons were able men: one became First Lord of the Admiralty, another was Bishop of Ely, a third was a military officer of distinction and created Baron Dover, a fourth was an admiral of distinction. I will not count all these, but will reckon them as three favourable instances, The total, thus far, is six; to which might be added in fairness something from that most remarkable Montagu family and its connexions, of which several judges, both before and after the accession of Charles I, were members. However, I wish to be well within bounds, and therefore will claim only six successes out of the 22 cases (I allow one son to each judge, as before), or 1 in 4. Even under these limitations it is only 4 to 1, on the average, against each child of an eminent son of a judge becoming a distinguished man.

Now for the second category, where the son is not eminent, but the grandson is. There are only seven of these cases to the (226 − 22 or) 204 judges that remain, and one or two of them are not of a very high order. They are the third Earl Shaftesbury, author of the *Characteristics*; Cowper, the poet; Lord Lechmere, the Attorney-General; Sir Wm. Mansfield, Commander-in-Chief in India; Sir Eardley Willmot, who filled various offices with credit and was created a baronet; and Lord Wyndham, Lord Chancellor of Ireland. Fielding, the novelist, was grandson of Judge Gould, by the female line. Hence it is 204 to 7, or 30 to 1, against the non-eminent son of a judge having an eminent child.

The figures in these two categories are clearly too few to justify us in relying on them, except so far as to show that the probability of a judge having an eminent grandson is largely increased if his sons are also eminent. It follows that the sons or daughters of distinguished men who are themselves gifted with decidedly high ability, as tested at the University or elsewhere, cannot do better than marry early in life. If they have a large family, the odds are in their favour that one at least of their children will be eminently successful in life, and will be a subject of pride to them and a help to the rest.

Let us for a moment consider the bearing of the facts just obtained, on the theory of an aristocracy where able men earn titles, and transmit them by descent through the line of their eldest male representatives. The practice may be justified on two distinct grounds. On the one hand, the future peer is reared in a home full of family traditions, that form his disposition. On the other hand, he is presumed to inherit the ability of the founder of the family. The former is a real justification for the law of primogeniture, as applied to titles and possessions; the latter, as we see from the table, is not. A man who has no able ancestor nearer in blood to him than a great-grandparent, is inappreciably better off in the chance of being himself gifted with ability, than if he had been taken out of the general mass of men. An old peerage is a valueless title to natural gifts, except so far as it may have been furbished up by a succession of wise inter-marriages. When, however, as is often the case, the direct line has become extinct and the title has passed to a distant relative, who had not been reared in the family traditions, the sentiment that is attached to its possession is utterly unreasonable. I cannot think of any claim to respect, put forward in modern days, that is so entirely an imposture, as that made by a peer on the ground of descent, who has neither been nobly educated, nor has any eminent kinsman, within three degrees.

I will conclude this chapter with a few facts I have derived from my various jottings, concerning the "natural history" of Judges. It appears that the parentage of the Judges in the last six reigns, viz. since the accession of George I, is as follows, reckoning in percentages: noble, honourable, or baronet (but not judges), 9; landed gentlemen, 35; judge, barrister, or attorney, 15; bishop or clergyman, 8; medical, 7; merchants and various, unclassed, 10; tradesmen, 7; unknown, 9. There is, therefore, no very marked class peculiarity in the origin of the Judges. They seem to be derived from much the same sources as the scholars of our Universities, with a decided but not excessive preponderance in favour of legal parents.

I also thought it worth while to note the order in which the Judges stood in their several families, to see whether ability affected the eldest more than the youngest, or if any important fact of the kind might appear. I find in my notes that I have recorded the order of the birth of 72 judges. The result of the percentages is, that the judge was an only son in 11 cases; eldest in 17; second in 38; third in 22; fourth in 9; fifth in 1; and of a yet later birth in 2 instances. It is clear that the eldest sons do not succeed as judges half as well as the cadets. I suppose that social influences are, on the whole, against their entering, or against their succeeding at the law.

APPENDIX TO JUDGES

There have been 286 Judges, according to the *Lives of the Judges*, by Foss, between the accession of Charles II and the year 1864. No less than 112 of them find a place in the following list. Among the Judges are included the Lord Chancellors, 30 in number, and of these eminent officers no less than 24, or 80 per cent. of the whole, will be found to have eminent relations.

Contractions employed in the List

The name of a Sovereign in parentheses, as (Charles II), shows the latest reign in which each judge held office

Ch. K.B. (or Q.B.)	= Chief Justice of the King's (or Queen's) Bench
Just. K.B. (or Q.B.)	= Justice of the King's (or Queen's) Bench
Ch. B.E.	= Chief Baron of the Exchequer
B.E.	= Baron of the Exchequer
Curs. B.E.	= Cursitor Baron of the Exchequer
Ch. C.P.	= Chief Justice of the Common Pleas
Just. C.P.	= Justice of the Common Pleas
M.R.	= Master of the Rolls

ABINGER, Lord. *See* SCARLETT.

ABNEY, Sir Thomas; Just. C.P. (Geo. II).

U.   Sir Thomas Abney, a famous Lord Mayor of London; one of the promoters of the Bank of England; protector of Dr. Isaac Watts. *See* Watts' Elegy on him.

[F.] Sir Edward Abney, LL.D. and M.P., a man of importance in his day.

ALDERSON, Sir Edward Hall; B.E. (Vict.).

F.   Recorder of Norwich, Ipswich, and Yarmouth.

U*s*. Mrs. Opie, the novelist.

ALIBONE, Sir Richard; Just. K.B. (James II).

G.   Eminent Protestant divine (F. turned Papist).

ATKYNS, Sir Edward; B.E. (Charles II).

[G.] Thomas, twice Reader in Lincoln's Inn.

F.   Sir Richard, Ch. Just. N. Wales.

S.   Sir Robert, Ch. Just. C.P. (Will. III).

S.   Sir Edward, B.E. (James II).

PS. Sir John Tracy, who assumed his mother's name of Atkyns, Curs. B.E. (Geo. III).

Thomas, Reader in Lincoln's Inn
|
Sir Richard, Ch. Just. N. Wales
|
Sir Edward, B.E. (Chas II).
|

Sir Robert, Ch. Just. C.P.   Sir Edward, B.E. (James II)
|
Daughter
|
Sir J. Tracy (Atkyns), Curs. B.E.

ATKYNS, Sir Robert; Ch.C.P. (Will. III).

G.   Sir Richard, Ch. Just. N. Wales.

F.   Sir Edward, B.E. (Charles II).

B.   Sir Edward, B.E. (James II).

p.   Sir John Tracy, who assumed the name of Atkyns, Curs. B.E.

ATKYNS, Sir Edward; B.E. (James II).
G.   Sir Richard, Ch. Just. N. Wales.
F.   Sir Edward, B.E. (Charles II).
B.   Sir Robert, Ch. C.P.
Bp.   Sir J. Tracy, assumed name of Atkyns, Curs. B.E.
ATKYNS, Sir John Tracy, (his mother was named Atkyns, and
      he adopted her name); Curs. B.E. (Geo. III).
g.   Sir Robert Atkyns, Ch. C.P.
gB.   Sir Edward Atkyns, B.E. (James II).
gF.   Sir Edward Atkyns, B.E. (Charles II).
BATHURST, Henry; 2d Earl of Bathurst; Ld. Chanc. (Geo.
      III).
F.   The first Earl, an accomplished wit.
n.   Sir Francis Buller, Just. K.B., the famous judge (Geo.
      III).
BEDINGFIELD, Sir Henry; Ch. C.P. (James II).
U.   Sir Thomas Bedingfield, Just. C.P. (Charles I).
BEST, Wm. Draper; created Ld. Wynford; Ch. C.P. (Geo.
      IV).
g.   General Sir William Draper, the well-known antagonist
      of "Junius."
BICKERSTETH, Henry; created Lord Langdale; M.R. (Vict.).
u.   Dr. Batty, the famous physician.
BIRCH, Sir John; Curs. B.E. (Geo. II).
[U.] Colonel Thomas Birch, well known under the Common-
      wealth.
BLACKBURN, Sir Colin; Just. Q.B. (Vict.).
B.   Professor of Mathematics at Glasgow.
g.   Rev. John Gillies, LL.D., historian, and successor to Dr.
      Robertson (the gr. uncle of Lord Brougham) as historio-
      grapher of Scotland.
BLACKSTONE, Sir William; Just. C.P. (Geo. III).
S.   His second son held all his University preferments.
N.   Henry, wrote "Reports" that were even more popular
      than his own.
BRAMSTON, Sir Francis; B.E. (Charles II).
F.   Sir John Bramston, Ch. K.B. under Charles I.

E

BROWNE, Samuel; Just. C.P. (Charles II).

uS.   Oliver St. John, Ch. Just. C.P. under the Protectorate.

BROUGHAM, Henry; cr. Ld. Brougham; Ld. Chanc. (Will. IV).

gB.   Robertson, the historian.

BULLER, Sir Francis; Just. C.P. (Geo. III).

U.   William Buller, Bishop of Exeter.

u.   Earl of Bathurst, Lord Chancellor (Geo. III).

N.   Rt. Hon. Charles Buller, statesman.

BURNET, Sir Thomas; Just. C.P. (Geo. II).

G.   Eminent Scotch lawyer, titled Lord Cramond.

F.   The celebrated Whig bishop, Bishop Burnet.

CAMDEN, Earl. *See* PRATT.

CAMPBELL, Lord; Lord Chancellor (Vict.).

[G.] Eminently successful scholar at St. Andrew's.

[F.] Had distinguished literary attainments; was pious and eloquent.

N.   George Campbell, member of Supreme Court of Calcutta; writer on Indian politics.

CHELMSFORD, Lord. *See* THESIGER.

CHURCHILL, Sir John; M.R. (James II).

GN.   John Churchill, the great Duke of Marlborough.

G*NS*. Duke of Berwick, great general.

CLARENDON, Earl. *See* HYDE.

CLARKE, Sir Charles; Ch. B.E. (Geo. II).

B.   Dean of Chester.

u.   Charles Trimnell, Bishop of Winchester.

CLIVE, Sir Edward; Just. C.P. (Geo. III).

U.   Sir George Clive, Curs. B.E. (Geo. II).

UP.   The great Lord Clive, Governor-General of India.

CLIVE, Sir George; Curs. B.E. (Geo. II).

N.   Sir Edward Clive, Just. C.P. (Geo. III).

N.S. The son of another nephew was the great Lord Clive.

COCKBURN, Sir Alexander James; Ch. Q.B. (Vict.).

[F.] Envoy and Minister Plenipotentiary to Columbia.

COLERIDGE, Sir John Taylor; Just. Q.B. (Vict.).

U. Samuel Taylor Coleridge, poet and metaphysician. *See under* POETS. (He was father of Hartley, Derwent, and Sara.)

US. Hartley Coleridge, poet.

US. Edward, Master at Eton.

US. Derwent Coleridge, Principal of St. Mark's College, Chelsea.

U*S*. Sara Coleridge, authoress. (Married her cousin, Henry Nelson Coleridge.)

US. Henry Nelson Coleridge (son of Col. Coleridge, brother of Samuel Taylor C.), author.

S. Sir John Duke Coleridge, Solicitor-General.

COOPER, Sir Anthony Ashley; created Earl of Shaftesbury; Lord Chancellor. (Charles II).

P. The 3d Earl, author of the *Characteristics.*

COPLEY, Sir John Singleton; cr. Ld. Lyndhurst; Ld. Chanc. (Vict.).

F. A painter, and an eminent one, judging from the prices that his pictures now fetch.

COTTENHAM, Lord. *See* PEPYS.

COWPER, Sir Wm.; created Earl Cowper; Ld. Chanc. (Geo. I).

B. Sir Spencer Cowper, Just. C.P. (Geo. II).

NS. The grandson of Sir Spencer was Cowper the poet. *See* POETS.

COWPER, Sir Spencer; Just. C.P. (Geo. II).

B. 1st Earl Cowper, Lord Chancellor (Geo. I).

P. William Cowper, the poet.

CRANWORTH, Lord. *See* ROLFE.

DAMPIER, Sir Henry; Just. K.B. (Geo. III).

F. Dean of Durham.

B. Bishop of Ely.

DE GREY, Sir Wm.; cr. Lord Walsingham; Ch. C.P. (Geo. III).

S. Thomas, 2d Baron; for twenty years Chairman of Committees in House of Lords.

DENISON, Sir Thomas; Just. K.B. (Geo. III).

4 NS. and [2 NS.] His brother was grandfather to a remarkable family of six brothers, namely, the present Speaker of the House of Commons, the Bishop of Salisbury, the Archdeacon of Taunton, the ex-Governor of South Australia, and two others, both of whom are scholars.

DENMAN, Sir Thomas; created Lord Denman; Ch. Q.B. (Vict.).

F.   Physician, a celebrated accoucheur.

S.   Hon. George Denman, Q.C., M.P., and the first classic of his year, 1842, at Cambridge.

uS.   Sir Benjamin Brodie, 1st Bart., the late eminent surgeon.

uP.   The present Sir Benjamin Brodie, 2d Bart., Professor of Chemistry at Oxford.

DOLBEN, Sir William; Just. K.B. (Will. III).

S.   Sir Gilbert Dolben, Just. C.P. in Ireland, created a Bart.

B.   John Dolben, Archbishop of York.

gB.   Archbishop John Williams, the Lord Keeper to James I.

ELDON, Lord. *See* SCOTT.

ELLENBOROUGH, Lord. *See* LAW.

ERLE, Sir William; Ch. C.P. (Vict.).

B.   Peter Erle, Commissioner of Charities.

ERSKINE, Thomas; cr. Lr. Erskine; Ld. Chand. (Geo. III).

B.   Henry Erskine, twice Lord Advocate of Scotland.

S.   Hon. Sir Thomas Erskine, Just. C.P. (Vict.).

ERSKINE, Hon. Sir Thomas; Just. C.P. (Vict.).

F.   Lord Erskine, Lord Chancellor (Geo. III).

U.   Henry Erskine, twice Lord Advocate of Scotland.

EYRE, Sir Robert; Ch. C.P. (Geo. II).

F.   Sir Samuel Eyre, Just. K.B. (Will. III).

EYRE, Sir Samuel; Just. K.B. (Will. III).

S.   Sir Robert Eyre, Ch. C.B. (Geo. II).
       [Sir Giles Eyre, Just. K.B. (Will. III), was only his 2d cousin.]

FINCH, Sir Heneage; cr. E. of Nottingham; Ld. Chanc. (Chas. II).

FINCH, Sir Heneage—*continued*

F.   Sir Heneage Finch, Recorder of London, Speaker of the House of Commons.

S.   Daniel, 2d Earl, and Principal Sec. of State to Will. III.

S.   Heneage Finch, Solicitor-general, and M.P. for University of Cambridge; created Earl Aylesford.

US. Thomas Twisden, Just. K.B. (Charles II).

GN. Lord Finch, Ch. C.P. and Lord Keeper (Charles I).

gN.(?) Dr. William Harvey (*see in* SCIENCE), discoverer of the circulation of the blood.

PS. Hon. Heneage Legge, B.E. *See*

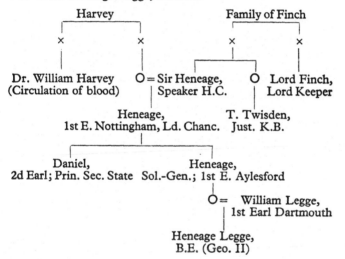

FORSTER, Sir Robert; Ch. K.B. (Charles II).

F.   Sir James Forster, Just. C.P. (Charles I).

GOULD, Sir Henry; Just. Q.B. (Anne).

P.   Sir Henry Gould, Just. C.P. (Geo. III).

p.   Henry Fielding, the novelist (*Tom Jones*).

GOULD, Sir Henry; Just. C.P. (Geo. III).

G.   Sir Henry Gould, Just. Q.B. (Anne.)

US. Henry Fielding, the novelist.

GUILFORD, Lord. *See* NORTH.

GURNEY, Sir John; B.E. (Vict.).

S.   Rt. Hon. Russell Gurney, M.P., Recorder of London.

HARCOURT, Sir Simon; cr. Lord Harcourt; Ld. Chanc. (Geo. I).

G.   Waller, the first Parliamentary general (and himself a relative of Waller the poet).

HARDWICKE, Earl of. *See* YORKE.

HEATH, Sir John; Just. C.P. (Geo. III).

S.   Dr. Benjamin Heath, Head Master of Eton.

HENLEY, Sir Robert; cr. E. of Northington; Ld. Chanc. (Geo. III).

F.   One of the most accomplished men of his day. M.P. for Weymouth.

HERBERT, Sir Edward; Lord Keeper (Charles II).

S.   Arthur, an admiral, created Lord Torrington.

S.   Sir Edward Herbert, Ch. K.B. and C.P. (James II).

US.   Lord Herbert of Cherbury, statesman and philosopher.

US.   George Herbert, poet and divine.

HERBERT, Sir Edward; Ch. K.B. and Ch. C.P. (James II).

D.   Sir Edward, Lord Keeper (Charles II).

B.   Arthur, an admiral, created Lord Torrington.

HEWITT, Sir James; created Lord Lifford; Just. K.B. (Geo. III).

S.   Joseph Hewitt, Just. K.B. in Ireland.

S.   Dean of Cloyne.

HOTHAM, Sir Beaumont; B.E. (Geo. III).

B.   An admiral, created Lord Hotham for naval achievements.

HYDE, Sir Edward; cr. Earl Clarendon; Ld. Chanc. (Chas. II).
The Hydes were a very able family both in law and state for many generations; but emerging, as they did, out of the regions of competition into that of favouritism, I cannot rightly appraise their merits. Moreover, the male line became extinct. The following are the near relations of the Lord Chancellor:—

U.   Sir Nicholas Hyde, Ch. K.B. (Charles I).

HYDE, Sir Edward—*continued*

U. Sir Lawrence Hyde, a great lawyer and Attorney-General to Consort of James I, who had eleven sons, most of whom distinguished themselves in their several vocations. Of these are:

US. Sir Robert Hyde, Ch. K.B. (Charles II).

US. Sir Frederick Hyde, a judge in S. Wales.

US. Alexander, Bishop of Salisbury.

[US.] Fellow of New College, and Judge of the Admiralty.

[US.] Dean of Windsor.

[US.] James, Principal of Magdalen Hall.

S. Henry, 2d Earl, Lord Privy Seal.

S. Lawrence, cr. Earl of Rochester, Lord Lieut. of Ireland, a person of great natural parts and honesty.

[*S.*] Anne, married to the Duke of York, afterwards James II. A woman of strong character, who insisted, in spite of menace, that publicity should be given to the marriage, let the consequences be what they might.

Family of Hyde

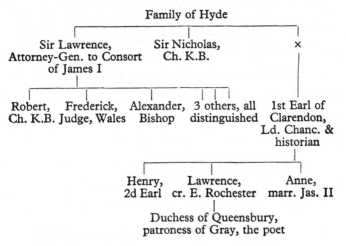

HYDE, Sir Robert; Ch. K.B. (Charles II).
F., 2 B., [3 B.], U., and U.S. *See above.*

JEFFREYS, Geo.; cr. Ld. Jeffreys of Wem; Ch. K.B., Ld.
    Chanc. (Jas. II).

G.   A judge in N. Wales.

US. Sir John Trevor, M.R. (Geo. I).

JERVIS, Sir John; Ch. C.P. (Vict.).

F.   Ch. Justice of Chester.

GN. J. Jervis, Admiral, 1st Earl St. Vincent. *See* PARKER.

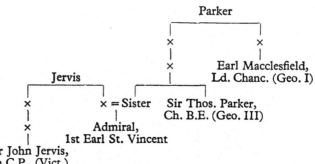

KEATING, Sir Henry Singer; Just C.P. (Vict.).

F.   Sir Henry Keating, K.C.B., distinguished in India,
    &c.

KING, Sir Peter; created Lord King; Ld. Chancellor (Geo.
    II).

u.   John Locke, the philosopher.

LANGDALE, Lord. *See* BICKERSTETH.

LAW, Sir Edward; cr. Ld. Ellenborough; Ch. K.B. (Geo.
    III).

F.   E. Law, Bishop of Carlisle, author.

S.   Edward, Governor-General of India, cr. Earl Ellen-
    borough.

S.   C. Ewan, Recorder of London and M.P. for Camb.
    University.

B.   G. H., Bishop of Bath and Wells.

B.   John, Bishop of Elphin, in Ireland.

    There are many other men of ability in this family.

LAWRENCE, Sir Soulden; Just. C.P. (Geo. III).

F.   President of the College of Physicians.

LECHMERE, Sir Nicholas; B.E. (Will. III).

P.   Nicholas Lechmere, Attorney-General, created Baron Lechmere.

u.   Sir Thomas Overbury, poet (poisoned).

LEE, Sir William; Ch. K.B. (Geo. II).

B.   George, Dean of the Arches and Judge of the Prerogative Court of Canterbury. Thus the two brothers were simultaneously, the one at the head of the highest court of Common Law, and the other of the highest court of Civil Law; a similar case to that of Lords Eldon and Stowell.

LEGGE, Hon. Heneage; B.E. (Geo. II).

F.   William, 1st Earl of Dartmouth, Secretary of State, &c.

G.   George, 1st Baron Dartmouth, Master of the Ordnance and Admiral of the Fleet.

g.   1st Lord Aylesford, Attorney-General and eminent lawyer.

gF. (Father of Lord Aylesford) was the 1st Earl of Nottingham, Lord Chancellor (*see* FINCH).

LIFFORD, Lord. *See* HEWITT.

LOVELL, Sir Salathiel; B.E. (Anne).

pS. Was Richard Lovell Edgeworth, author.

p*P*. Maria Edgeworth, novelist.

LYNDHURST, Lord. *See* COPLEY.

LYTTLETON, Sir Timothy; B.E. (Charles II).

GG. Sir Thomas Lyttleton, the eminent judge under Edward IV.

g.   Sir E. Walter, Ch. Justice of S. Wales.

u.   Sir John Walter, Ch. B.E. (Charles I).

F.   Sir Edward Lyttleton, Ch. Justice of N. Wales.

B.   Edward, Lord Lyttleton, Lord Keeper (Charles I).

*N*S. Sir Thomas Lyttleton, Speaker of the House of Commons, 1698. (His mother was daughter of the Lord Keeper.)

Sir Thos. Lyttleton, the eminent judge

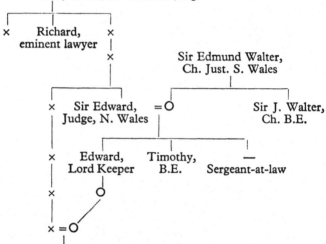

Sir Thos. Lyttleton, Speaker H. Commons

MACCLESFIELD, Lord. *See* PARKER.

MANNERS, Lord. *See* SUTTON.

MANSFIELD, Sir James; Ch. C.P. (Geo. III).

P.   General Sir William Mansfield, K.C.B., Commander-in-chief in India.

     [There are other gifted brothers.]

MILTON, Sir Christopher; Just. C.P. (James II).

B.   Milton the poet. *See under* POETS.

     [Milton's mother was a kinswoman (? what) of **Lord** President Bradshaw, the regicide.]

MONTAGU, Sir William; Ch. B.E. (James II).

F. Created Baron Montagu.

FB.   Sir Henry Montagu, 1st Earl of Manchester, Ch. K.B. (James I).

N.   Created Duke of Montagu; statesman.

g.   Sir John Jeffreys, Ch. B.E.

GF. Sir Edward Montagu, Ch. K.B. (Henry VIII).

                    (See pedigree pp. 140–1.)

MONTAGU, Sir J.; Ch. B.E. (Geo. I).

G.   Henry Montagu, 1st Earl of Manchester, Ch. K.B.

U.   Walter, Abbot of Pontoise; poet, courtier, councillor to Marie de Medicis.

U.   Edward, 2d Earl of Manchester, the successful Parliamentary General, Baron Kimbolton of Marston Moor.

GB.   1st Baron Montagu.

UP.   (Grandson of Baron Kimbolton.) The 4th Earl of Manchester, Principal Secretary of State, 1701, created 1st Duke of Manchester.

NARES, Sir George; Just. C.P. (Geo. III).

S.   Regius Professor of Modern History at Oxford.

B.   Dr. James Nares, musician.

NORTH, Francis; created Ld. Guilford; Ld. Chanc. (James II).

B.   Dudley North, Levantine merchant, eminent English financier.

B.   Rev. John North, D.D., scholar, Master of Trin. Coll. Camb.

B.   Roger North, the biographer; Attorney-General to the Queen.

b.   Mary, had a prodigious memory.

uS.   Charles Hatton, "the incomparable." (*See Lives of the Norths.*)

gB.   Sir Henry Montagu, 1st Earl of Manchester. *See* MONTAGU, Sir J.

gN.   Edward, 2d Earl of Manchester, the Baron Kimbolton of Marston Moor.

gN.   George Montagu, Abbot of Pontoise, courtier and minister of Catherine de Medicis.

gN.   Sir Edward Montagu, 1st Earl of Sandwich. (His uncle [u.] was Pepys, his *Diary*.)

[N.]   Dudleya North, Oriental scholar.

PS.   Frederick, 2d Earl Guilford, Premier. (The "Lord North" of George III's reign.)

NORTHINGTON, Lord. *See* HENLEY.

NOTTINGHAM, Earl of. *See* FINCH.

MONTAGU AND NORTH
(See also under LITERATURE *for* Sydney)

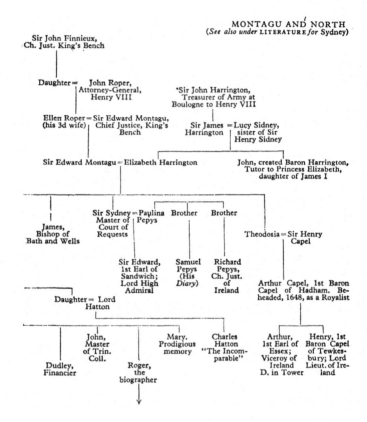

Sir John Finnieux,
Ch. Just. King's Bench

Daughter = John Roper,
Attorney-General,
Henry VIII

'Sir John Harrington,
Treasurer of Army at
Boulogne to Henry VIII

Ellen Roper = Sir Edward Montagu,
(his 3d wife) Chief Justice, King's
Bench

Sir James = Lucy Sidney,
Harrington   sister of Sir
Henry Sidney

Sir Edward Montagu = Elizabeth Harrington

John, created Baron Harrington,
Tutor to Princess Elizabeth,
daughter of James I

James,
Bishop of
Bath and Wells

Sir Sydney = Paulina   Brother   Brother
Master of   Pepys
Court of
Requests

Theodosia = Sir Henry
Capel

Sir Edward,
1st Earl of
Sandwich;
Lord High
Admiral

Samuel
Pepys
(His
Diary)

Richard
Pepys,
Ch. Just.
of
Ireland

Arthur Capel, 1st Baron
Capel of Hadham. Be-
headed, 1648, as a Royalist

Daughter = Lord
Hatton

John,
Master
of Trin.
Coll.

Mary.
Prodigious
memory

Charles
Hatton
"The Incom-
parable"

Arthur,
1st Earl of
Essex;
Viceroy of
Ireland
D. in Tower

Henry, 1st
Baron Capel
of Tewkes-
bury; Lord
Lieut. of Ire-
land

Dudley,
Financier

Roger,
the
biographer

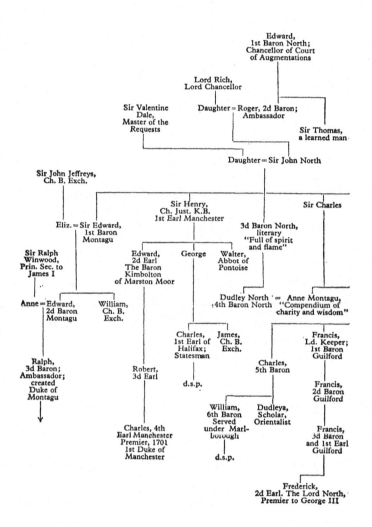

PARKER, Sir Thomas; cr. E. of Macclesfield; Ld. Chanc.
(Geo. I).

S.   2d Earl, President of the Royal Society, mathematician
       and astronomer.

UP.   Sir Thomas Parker, Ch. B.E.

PARKER, Sir Thomas; Ch. B.E. (Geo. III).

n.   John Jervis, admiral, 1st Earl St. Vincent. *See* JERVIS.

GN.   Sir T. Parker, 1st Earl of Macclesfield, Lord Chancellor.

PATTESON, Sir John; Just. K.B. (Vict.).

S.   Missionary Bishop to Pacific Islands.

PENGELLY, Sir Thomas; Ch. B.E. (Geo. II).

[G.]   (Reputed, but questionable.) Oliver Cromwell. (Foss's
       Judges.)

PEPYS, Sir Chas. Christopher; cr. E. of Cottenham; Ld.
Chanc. (Vict.).

[F.]   A Master in Chancery.

G.   Sir L. Pepys, physician to George III.

g.   Rt. Hon. W. Dowdeswell, Chancellor of the Exchequer.

B.   Bishop of Worcester.

POLLOCK, Sir Frederick; Ch. B.E. (Vict.).

B.   Sir David, Ch. Justice of Bombay.

B.   Sir George, general in Affghanistan.

S.   Frederick, Master in Chancery; translator of Dante.

[P.]   Frederick (also [p.] to the Right Hon. C. Herries, Chan-
       cellor of the Exchequer); second classic of his year,
       1867, at Cambridge.

POWIS, Sir Lyttleton; Just. K.B. (Geo. I).

B.   Sir Thomas Powis, Just. K.B. (Geo. I).

POWIS, Sir Thomas; Just. K.B. (Geo. I).

B.   Sir Lyttleton Powis, Just. K.B. (Geo. I).

PRATT, Sir John; Ch. K.B. (Geo. I).

S.   Sir Charles Pratt, 1st Earl Camden, Ld. Chanc. (Geo.
       III).

P.   J. J. Pratt, 2d Earl and created 1st Marquis Camden,
       Lord Lieut. of Ireland, Chancellor of University of
       Cambridge.

p.   George Hardinge (*see* next paragraph).

PRATT, Sir John—*continued*

ps. Field Marshal 1st Visct. Hardinge, Governor-General of India.

[ps.] (*See* next paragraph.)

PRATT, Sir Charles; cr. Earl Camden; Ld. Chanc. (Geo. III).

F. Sir John Pratt, Ch. K.B. (Geo. I).

S. J. J. Pratt, 2d Earl and created Marquis of Camden, Lord Lieutenant of Ireland, and Chancellor of the University of Cambridge.

n. George Hardinge, Attorney-General to the Queen, Chief Justice to the Brecon Circuit.

nS. Field Marshal 1st Viscount Hardinge, Governor-General of India. (His father was a literary man.)

[nS.] A naval Captain, to whom a monument in St. Paul's was voted by the nation.

RAYMOND, Sir Edward; cr. Ld. Raymond; Ch. K.B. (Geo. II).

F. Sir Thomas Raymond, a Judge in each of the three Courts. (Charles II).

RAYMOND, Sir Thomas; Just. K.B., &c. (Charles II).

S. Robert, Lord Raymond, Ch. K.B. (Geo. II).

REYNOLDS, Sir James (1); Ch. B.E. (Geo. II).

N. Sir James Reynolds (2), B.E. (Geo. II).

REYNOLDS, Sir James (2); B.E. (Geo. II).

U. Sir James Reynolds (1), Ch. B.E. (Geo. II).

ROLFE, Sir Robt. Monsey; cr. Ld. Cranworth; Ld. Chanc. (Vict.).

GN. Admiral Lord Nelson.

gF. Dr. Monsey, the celebrated and eccentric physician to Chelsea Hospital.

ROMILLY, Sir John; created Lord Romilly; M.R. (Vict.).

F. Sir Samuel Romilly, Solicitor-General and eminent jurist.

SCARLETT, Sir James; created Lord Abinger; Ch. B.E. (Vict.).

[B.] Sir William Scarlett, Ch. Justice of Jamaica.

S. Gen. Sir James Scarlett, chief in command of the cavalry in the Crimea; then Adjutant-General.

S. Sir Peter Campbell Scarlett, diplomatist.

SCOTT, Sir John; created Earl of Eldon; Ld. Chanc. (Geo. IV).

B.   Sir William Scott, created Lord Stowell, Judge of the High Court of Admiralty. (See remarks under Ch. Just. Sir W. LEE.)

SEWELL, Sir Thomas; M.R. (Geo. III).

p.   Matthew G. Lewis, novelist, commonly called "Monk" Lewis.

SHAFTESBURY, Earl of. *See* COOPER.

SOMERS, Sir J.; created Earl Somers; Lord Chanc. (Will. III).

NS.   Charles Yorke, Ld. Chanc. (Geo. III).

NS. and 2 NP. *See* YORKE.

gNP. Richard Gibbon, the historian.

SPELMAN, Sir Clement; Curs. B.E. (Charles II).

GF.   Just. K.B. (Henry VIII).

F.   Sir Henry, antiquarian author of celebrity.

[B.]   Sir John Spelman, also an antiquary. *Alfred the Great.*

SUTTON, Sir Thomas Manners; B.E.; subsequently Lord Chancellor of Ireland, and created Lord Manners (Geo. III).

B.   Charles Sutton, Archbishop of Canterbury.

N.   (Son of the Archbishop.) Charles Manners-Sutton, Speaker of the House of Commons, created Viscount Canterbury.

TALBOT, Hon. Chas.; cr. Lord Talbot; Ld. Chanc. (Geo. II).

F.   Bishop successively of three sees.

N.   Rev. William Talbot, an early and eminent advocate of Evangelism. (*See Venn's Life*, Preface, p. xii.)

THESIGER, Sir Frederick; cr. Ld. Chelmsford; Ld. Chanc. (Vict.).

S.   Adjutant-General of India.

[G., F., U.] All noteworthy, but hardly of sufficient eminence to be particularly described in this meagre outline of relationships.

THURLOW, Edward; cr. Lord Thurlow; Ld. Chanc. (Geo. III).

B.   Bishop of Durham.

[S.]   (Illegitimate.) Died at Cambridge, where, as is said, he was expected to attain the highest honours.

TREBY, Sir George; Ch. C.P. (Will. III).
S.   Rt. Hon. Robert Treby, Secretary at War.
TREVOR, Sir Thomas; created Lord Trevor; Ch. C.P. (Geo.
       I).
g.   J. Hampden, the patriot.
F.   Sir John Trevor, Secretary of State.
S.   Bishop of Durham.
U.   Sir John Trevor, Ch. B.E. (Charles I).
GB.   Sir Thomas Trevor, B.E. (Charles I).
TREVOR, Sir John; M.R. (Geo. I).
uS.   Lord Jeffreys, Lord Chancellor. (James II).
TRURO, Lord. *See* WILDE.
TURNER, Sir George James; Lord Justice (Vict.).
U.   Dawson Turner, botanist and antiquary.
U.   Dean of Norwich and Master of Pembroke Coll., Cam-
       bridge.
[S.]   Bishop of Grafton and Armidale, in Australia.
       (There are numerous other distinguished members of
       this family, including Dr. Hooker, the botanist, Gifford
       Palgrave, the Arabian traveller, and Francis Palgrave,
       author.)
TWISDEN, Sir Thomas; Just. K.B. (Charles II).
uS.   Earl of Nottingham (Finch), Lord Chancellor (Chas. II).
[B.]   Roger, antiquary and historian.
VAUGHAN, Sir John; Just. C.P. (Vict.).
B.   Henry Vaughan, assumed name of Halford and became
       the celebrated physician, Sir Henry Halford, 1st Bart.
B.   Rev. Edward (of Leicester), Calvinist theologian.
B.   Sir Charles R., Envoy Extraordinary to the United
       States.
[B.]   Peter, Dean of Chester.
N.   Rev. Charles Vaughan, D.D., joint first classic of his
       year, 1838, at Cambridge; Head Master of Harrow;
       refused two bishoprics.
N.   Professor Halford Vaughan, of Oxford.
p.   Vaughan Hawkins, first classic of his year, 1854, at Cam-
       bridge.

VERNEY, Hon. Sir John; M.R. (Geo. II).

g.   Sir R. Heath, Ch. K.B. (Charles I).

WALSINGHAM, Lord. *See* DE GREY.

WIGRAM, Sir James; V.C. (Vict.).

B.   Bishop of Rochester.

WILDE, Sir Thomas; created Lord Truro; Ld. Chanc. (Vict.).

B.   Ch. Justice, Cape of Good Hope.

N.   Sir James Wilde, B.E. (Vict.); now Lord Penzance.

WILDE, Sir James Plasted; B.E. (Vict.); since cr. Ld. Penzance.

U.   Lord Truro, Lord Chancellor (Vict.).

U.   Ch. Justice, Cape of Good Hope.

WILLES, Sir John; Ch. C.P. (Geo. III).

B.   Bishop of Bath and Wells.

S.   Sir Edward Willes, Just. K.B. (Geo. III).

WILLES, Sir Edward; Just. K.B. (Geo. III).

F.   Sir John Willes, Ch. C.P. (Geo. III).

U.   Bishop of Bath and Wells.

WILMOT, Sir John Eardley; Ch. C.P. (Geo. III).

P.   F.R.S. and F.A.S., Governor of Van Diemen's Land, and 1st Baronet.

PS.   Recorder of Warwickshire and Judge of the County Court of Bristol.

WOOD, Sir William Page; V.C. (Vict.) (Since created Lord Hatherley, Lord Chancellor, 1868.)

F.   Sir Matthew, M.P. for London for twenty-eight years and twice Lord Mayor.

[U.]   Benjamin Wood, M.P. for Southwark

[B.]   Western Wood, M.P. for London.

WYNDHAM, Sir Hugh; B.E., C.P. (Charles II).

B.   Sir William Wyndham, Just. K.B. (Charles II).

GN.   Sir Francis Wyndham, Just. C.P. (Eliz.).

NS.   Thomas Wyndham, Lord Chancellor of Ireland (Geo. I), created Baron Wyndham.

WYNDHAM, Sir Wadham; Just. K.B. (Charles II).

B.   Sir Hugh Wyndham, B.E., Just. C.P. (Charles II).

WYNDHAM, Sir Wadham—*continued*
P.   Thomas Wyndham, Lord Chancellor of Ireland (Geo. I), created Baron Wyndham.
GN. Sir Francis Wyndham, Just. C.P. (Eliz.).

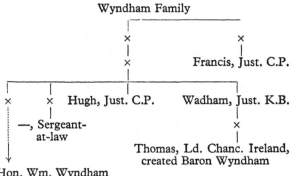

Wyndham Family

Rt. Hon. Wm. Wyndham

WYNFORD, Lord. *See* BEST.
YORKE, Philip; cr. Earl of Hardwicke; Ld. Chanc. (Geo. II).
S.   Hon. Charles (by niece of Lord Chancellor Somers), Lord Chancellor (Geo. III).
S.   Hon. James, Bishop of Ely.
P.   Philip, 3d Earl, Lord Lieutenant of Ireland.
P.   Rt. Hon. Charles Philip, F.R.S., First Lord of the Admiralty.
*P*S. Lord Goderich and Earl of Ripon, Premier.

(See pedigree p. 148.)

YORKE, Hon. Charles; Lord Chancellor (Geo. III).
F.   1st Earl of Hardwicke, Lord Chancellor (Geo. II).
S.   Philip, 3d Earl, Lord-Lieutenant of Ireland.
S.   Rt. Hon. Charles Philip, F.R.S., First Lord of the Admiralty.
B.   Hon. James, Bishop of Ely.
gb. 1st Earl Somers, Lord Chancellor (Will. III).
*N*S. Lord Goderich and Earl of Ripon, Premier.

Yorke Family

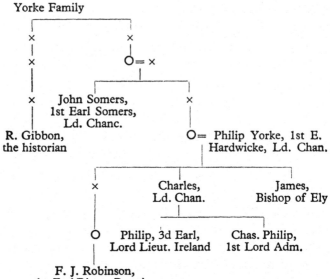

STATESMEN

I propose in this chapter to discuss the relationships of modern English Statesmen. It is my earnest desire, throughout this book, to steer safely between two dangers: on the one hand, of accepting mere official position or notoriety, as identical with a more discriminative reputation, and on the other, of an unconscious bias towards facts most favourable to my argument. In order to guard against the latter danger, I employ groups of names selected by others; and, to guard against the former, I adopt selections that command general confidence. It is especially important in dealing with statesmen, whose eminence, as such, is largely affected by the accident of social position, to be cautious in both these respects. It would not be a judicious plan to take for our select list the names of privy councillors, or even of Cabinet ministers; for though some of them are illustriously gifted, and many are eminently so, yet others belong to a decidedly lower natural grade. For instance, it seemed in late years to have become a mere incident to the position of a great territorial duke to have a seat in the Cabinet, as a minister of the Crown. No doubt some few of the dukes are highly gifted, but it may be affirmed, with equal assurance, that the abilities of the large majority are very far indeed from justifying such an appointment.

Again, the exceptional position of a Cabinet minister cannot possibly be a just criterion of a correspondingly exceptional share of natural gifts, because statesmanship is not an open profession. It was much more so in the days of pocket-boroughs, when young men of really high promise were eagerly looked for by territorial magnates, and brought into Parliament, and kept there to do gladiatorial battle for one or

other of the great contending parties of the State. With those
exceptions, parliamentary life was not, even then, an open
career, for only favoured youths were admitted to compete.
But, as is the case in every other profession, none, except those
who are extraordinarily and peculiarly gifted, are likely to
succeed in parliamentary life, unless engaged in it from their
early manhood onwards. Dudley North, of whom I spoke in
the chapter on Judges, was certainly a great success; so, in
recent times, was Lord George Bentinck; so in one way or
another, was the Duke of Wellington; and other cases could
easily be quoted of men beginning their active parliamentary
life in advanced manhood and nevertheless achieving success;
but, as a rule, to which there are very few exceptions, statesmen
consist of men who had obtained—it little matters how—the
privilege of entering Parliament in early life, and of being
kept there. Every Cabinet is necessarily selected from a limited
field. No doubt it always contains some few persons of very
high natural gifts, who would have found their way to the front
under any reasonably fair political *régime*, but it also invariably
contains others who would have fallen far behind in the struggle
for place and influence, if all England had been admitted on
equal terms to the struggle.

Two selections of men occurred to me as being, on the
whole, well worthy of confidence. One, that of the Premiers,
begun, for convenience' sake, with the reign of George III;
their number is 25, and the proportion of them who cannot
claim to be much more than "eminently" gifted, such as
Addington,—

"Pitt is to Addington as London to Paddington,"—

is very small. The other selection is Lord Brougham's *Statesmen of the Reign of George III*. It consists of no more than
53 men, selected as the foremost statesmen in that long reign.
Now of these, 11 are judges and, I may add, 7 of those judges
were described in the appendix to the last chapter, viz. Lords
Camden, Eldon, Erskine, Ellenborough, King, Mansfield, and
Thurlow. The remaining 4 are Chief Justices Burke and

Gibbs, Sir William Grant, and Lord Loughborough. Lord Brougham's list also contains the name of Lord Nelson, which will be more properly included among the Commanders; and that of Earl St. Vincent, which may remain in this chapter, for he was a very able administrator in peace as well as a naval commander. In addition to these, are the names of 9 Premiers, of whom one is the Duke of Wellington, whom I count here, and again among the Commanders, leaving a net balance, in the selection made by Lord Brougham, of 31 new names to discuss. The total of the two selections, omitting the judges, is 57.

The average natural ability of these men may very justly be stated as superior to class F. Canning, Fox, the two Pitts, Romilly, Sir Robert Walpole (whom Lord Brougham imports into his list), the Marquess Wellesley, and the Duke of Wellington, probably exceed G. It will be seen how extraordinary are the relationships of these families. The kinship of the two Pitts, father and son, is often spoken of as a rare, if not a sole, instance of high genius being hereditary; but the remarkable kinships of William Pitt were yet more widely diffused. He was not only son of a premier, but nephew of another, George Grenville, and cousin of a third, Lord Grenville. Besides this, he had the Temple blood. His pedigree, which is given in the appendix to this chapter, does scant justice to his breed. The Fox pedigree is also very remarkable in its connexion with the Lords Holland and the Napier family. But one of the most conspicuous is that of the Marquess Wellesley, a most illustrious statesman, both in India and at home, and his younger brother, the great Duke of Wellington. It is also curious, from the fact of the Marquess possessing very remarkable gifts as a scholar and critic. They distinguished him in early life and descended to his son, the late Principal of New Inn Hall, at Oxford, but they were not shared by his brother. Yet, although the great Duke had nothing of the scholar or art-critic in him, he had qualities akin to both. His writings are terse and nervous, and eminently effective. His furniture, equipages, and the like were characterised by unostentatious completeness and efficiency under a pleasing form.

I do not intend to go *seriatim* through the many names mentioned in my appendix. The reader must do that for himself, and he will find it well worth his while to do so; but I shall content myself here with throwing results into the same convenient statistical form that I have already employed for the Judges, and arguing on the same bases that the relationships of the Statesmen abundantly prove the hereditary character of their genius.

In addition to the English statesmen of whom I have been speaking, I thought it well to swell their scanty numbers by adding a small supplementary list, taken from various periods and other countries. I cannot precisely say how large was the area of selection from which this list was taken. I can only assure the reader that it contains a considerable proportion of the names, that seemed to me the most conspicuous among those that I found described at length, in ordinary small biographical dictionaries.

TABLE I

SUMMARY OF RELATIONSHIPS OF 35 ENGLISH
STATESMEN, GROUPED INTO 30 FAMILIES

One relation (or two in the family)

Bolingbroke (Visct. St. John)	g.	Horner	B.
Disraeli	F.	Perceval	n.
Francis, Sir P.	F.	Romilly, Sir S.	S.
Grattan	g.	Scott (Lord Stowell)	B.
		Wilberforce	S.

Two or three relations (or three or four in the family)

2. Bedford, Duke of, and gr.-gr.-
    grandson, Earl Russell   GF. G*f*. PP.
   Bentinck (Duke of Portland)   S. P.
   Canning   US. S.
   Jenkinson (Earl of Liverpool)   F. U. US.
   Jervis (Earl St. Vincent)   u. UP. UPS.

Two or three relations (or three or four in the family)—cont.

Lamb (Viscount Melbourne) 2 B. *b. p.*
Petty (Marquess of Lansdowne) *G*F. S.
Russell (*see* Bedford)
Stanley (Earl of Derby) F. uS. S.
Stewart (Marquess of London-
 derry) F. uS. B.

Four or more relations (or five or more in the family)

Dundas (Viscount Melville) G. F. B. N. S. P.
2. Fox and Lord Holland G. u. F. B. N. *N*S. 2*u*S.
3. Grenville, Lord; his father,
 George Grenville; also his
 cousin, William Pitt B. F. g. *u*S. U.
Grey, Earl F. B. 2S.
Holland, Lord (*see* Fox)
Peel F. g. 2B. 3S.
2. Pitt, viz. Earl Chatham and his
 son, Wm. Pitt (also, *see*
 Grenville) F. N. u. uS. *n.*
Robinson (Earl Ripon) G. F. gB. gF. S.
Sheridan F. *f.* g. G. S. *P. P*S.
Temple (Viscount Palmerston) V. GGB. GG. GGF.
Stuart (Marquess of Bute) *G*F. G. GU. GB. u. B. 2S.
Walpole (Earl of Orford) G. B. 2S. nG.
2. Wellesley, viz. the Marquess
 and his brother, the Duke of
 Wellington B. N. S. g*G*F.

SUPPLEMENTARY LIST OF 13 GREAT STATESMEN OF
VARIOUS PERIODS AND COUNTRIES GROUPED INTO
9 FAMILIES

2. Arteveldt, James, and son John S.
 Mirabeau F.
 More, Sir Thomas F.
2. De Witt, John, and brother
 Cornelius B.
 Adams S. P.
3. Cecil, Robt.; father, Lord
 Burleigh; and cousin, Lord
 Bacon F. *u*S.
 Colbert U. B. 2S. 2N.
 Guise, Duc de B. 2S. P. PS.
 Richelieu F. B. BP. BPS. nS.

TABLE II[1]

Degrees of Kinship					A	B	C	D
Name of the degree	Corresponding letters							
Father	13 F.	...	...	...	13	33	100	33·0
Brother	15 B.	...	...	...	15	39	150	26·0
Son	19 S.	...	...	...	19	49	100	49·0
Grandfather	6 G.	5 g.	...	...	11	28	200	14·0
Uncle	3 U.	4 u.	...	...	7	18	400	4·5
Nephew	6 N.	1 n.	...	...	7	18	400	4·5
Grandson	4 P.	0 p.	...	...	4	10	200	5·0
Great-grandfather	1 GF.	1 gF.	1 *GF*.	0 *g*F.	3	8	400	2·0
Great-uncle	1 GB.	1 gB.	0 *GB*.	0 *g*B.	2	5	800	0·6
First-cousin	2 US.	3 uS.	0 *US*.	3 *u*S.	8	21	800	2·6
Great-nephew	0 NS.	1 nS.	1 *NS*.	0 *n*S.	2	5	800	0·6
Great-grandson	0 PS.	0 pS.	0 *PS*.	0 *p*S.	0	0	400	0·0
All more remote	14	...	...	...	14	37	...	...

First, have the ablest statesmen the largest number of able
relatives? TABLE I answers this in the affirmative. There can
be no doubt, that its third section contains more illustrious
names than the first; and the more the reader will take the
pains of analysing and "weighing" the relationships, the more,
I am sure, will he find this truth to become apparent. Again,
the Statesmen, as a whole, are far more eminently gifted than
the Judges; accordingly it will be seen in TABLE II, by a
comparison of its column B with the corresponding column
in p. 102, that their relations are more rich in ability.

To proceed to the next test; we see, that the third section is
actually longer than either the first or the second, showing

[1] For explanation refer to the similar table in p. 102.

that ability is not distributed at haphazard, but, that it affects certain families.

Thirdly, the statesman's type of ability is largely transmitted or inherited. It would be tedious to count the instances in favour. Those to the contrary are Disraeli, Sir P. Francis (who was hardly a statesman, but rather a bitter controversialist), and Horner. In all the other 35 or 36 cases in my appendix, one or more statesmen will be found among their eminent relations. In other words, the combination of high intellectual gifts, tact in dealing with men, power of expression in debate, and ability to ensure exceedingly hard work, is hereditary.

TABLE II proves, just as distinctly as it did in the case of the Judges, that the nearer kinsmen of the eminent Statesman are far more rich in ability than the more remote. It will be seen, that the law of distribution, as gathered from these instances, is very similar to what we had previously found it to be. I shall not stop here to compare that law, in respect to the Statesmen and the Judges, for I propose to treat all the groups of eminent men, who form the subjects of my several chapters, in a precisely similar manner, and to collate the results, once for all, at the end of the book.

APPENDIX TO STATESMEN

STATESMEN OF THE REIGN OF GEORGE III

As selected by Lord Brougham in his well-known work bearing that title

The list consists of the following 53 persons, of whom 33, whose names are printed in *italics*, find a place in my dictionary of kinships. It often happens in this list that the same person is noticed under his title, as well as surname; as, "Dundas (Viscount Melville)"—"Melville, Lord (Dundas)."

Allen; *Bedford, 4th Duke*; *Bolingbroke*; Bushe, Ld. Ch. Just.; *Camden, Earl* (*Pratt*); *Canning*; Carroll; Castlereagh, Lord (Londonderry) *see* Stewart; *Chatham, Lord* (*Pitt*);

* Premier.

Curran; *Dundas (Visct. Melville)*; *Eldon, Lord (Scott)*;
Erskine, Lord; *Ellenborough, Lord (Law)*; *Fox*; *Francis, Sir
Philip*; Gibbs, Ld. Ch. Just.; Grant, Sir Wm.; *Grattan*;
**Grenville, George*; **Grenville, Lord*; *Holland, Lord*; *Horner*;
Jefferson; **Jenkinson (Earl Liverpool)*; *Jervis (Earl St. Vincent)*;
King, Lord; *Law (Lord Ellenborough)*; Lawrence, Dr.;
**Liverpool, Earl (Jenkinson)*; Loughborough, Lord (Wedder-
burn); Londonderry, Lord (Castlereagh: *see* Stewart);
Mansfield, Lord (Murray); *Melville, Lord (Dundas)*; *Murray
(Lord Mansfield)*; *Nelson, Lord*; **North, Lord*; *Perceval;
**Pitt (Earl of Chatham)*; *Pitt William; *Pratt (Earl Camden)*;
Ricardo; *Romilly*; *St. Vincent Earl (Jervis)*; *Scott (Lord
Eldon)*; *Scott (Lord Stowell)*; *Stowell, Lord (Scott)*; *Stewart
(Lord Castlereagh, Marquess of Londonderry)*; *Thurlow, Lord*;
Tierney; Tooke, Horne; *Walpole*; Wedderburn (Lord
Loughborough); *Wellesley, Marquess*; *Wilberforce*; Wilkes,
John; Windham.

PREMIERS SINCE ACCESSION OF GEORGE III

There have been 25 Premiers during this period, as shown in
the following list, of whom 17, whose names are printed in
italics, find a place in my dictionary of kinships.

Nine of these have already appeared under the title of
"Statesmen of George III." They are distinguished by a †.

It occasionally happens that the same individual is noticed
under his surname as well as his title; as "Chatham, Earl
(Pitt)"—"Pitt (Earl Chatham)."

Aberdeen, Earl. Addington (Sidmouth). †*Bedford, 4th
Duke. Bute, Marquess. Canning.* †*Chatham, Earl (Pitt). Derby,
Earl. Disraeli.* Gladstone. *Goderich.* Grafton, Duke. *Grenville,
George. Grenville, Lord. Grey, Earl. Lansdowne (Shelburne).*
†*Liverpool, Earl.* Melbourne, Visct. Newcastle, Duke. †*North,
Lord.* Palmerston, Lord. Peel, Sir Robert. †*Perceval.* Pitt (Earl
Chatham). †*Pitt, William.* Rockingham, Marquess. *Russell,*

---

* Premier.
† Included also in Brougham's list of Statesmen of Geo. III.

Earl. Shelburne, Earl (Lansdowne). Sidmouth, Lord (Addington). Wellington.

BEDFORD, John, 4th Duke.

GF. William, Lord Russell; patriot; executed 1683.

G*f*. Lady Rachel W. Russell, her husband's secretary. *Letters.*

PP. 1st Earl Russell: Reform leader as Lord John Russell; and three times Premier.

BENTINCK, William H. Cavendish; 3d Duke of Portland; Premier, 1783–4 and 1807–10.

S. Lord Wm. Henry Bentinck; Governor-General of India, who abolished Suttee, and established the liberty of the Indian press.

P. Lord George Bentinck, M.P.; became an eminent financier and a leading statesman in middle age, after a life previously devoted to racing interests.

BOLINGBROKE, Henry; created Viscount St. John; the celebrated Secretary of State to Queen Anne. (His name is appended to Brougham's list of Statesmen of Geo. III.)

g. Sir Oliver St. John, Ch. Just. C.P. under the Protectorate (and who himself was cousin to another judge, S. Brown (*see*), under Charles II).

BUTE, Earl. *See* STUART.

CAMDEN, Earl; Lord Chancellor. *See* under JUDGES.

F. and S.

CANNING, George; created Lord Canning; Premier, 1827. Not precocious as a child, but remarkable as a schoolboy. (*Microcosm*, æt. 15, and *Anti-Jacobin*.) Scholar, orator, and most able statesman. The Canning family had sensitive and irritable temperaments.

[F.] A man of considerable literary acquirements.

[*f*.] Had great beauty and accomplishments. She took to the stage after her husband's death with much success; they both had been separated from the rest of the Canning family.

CANNING, George—*continued*

US. Stratford Canning; created Lord Stratford de Redcliffe; ambassador at the Porte; the "great Elchi."

[US.] George Canning, F.R.S., F.S.A., created Lord Garvagh.

S. Charles; created Earl Canning; was Governor-General of India during the continuance and suppression of the Indian Mutiny.

CASTLEREAGH. *See* STEWART.

DISRAELI, Rt. Hon. Benjamin; Premier, 1868. Precocious; began life in an attorney's office; became, when quite young, a novel-writer of repute, and, after one noted failure, an eminent parliamentary debater and orator.

F. Isaac Disraeli; author of *Curiosities of Literature.*

DUNDAS, Henry; created Viscount Melville; friend and coadjutor of Wm. Pitt, and a leading member of his administration in various capacities.

F. Robert Dundas, of Arniston; Lord President of the Court of Session in Scotland.

G. Robert Dundas; Lord Arniston, eminent lawyer; Judge of Court of Session.

[GF.] Sir James Dundas, M.P. for Edinburgh, Senator of the College of Justice.

B. (A half-brother.) Robert Dundas; Lord President of the Court of Session, as his father had been before him.

N. (A half-nephew). Robert Dundas (son of above); Lord Chief Baron to the Court of Exchequer in Scotland.

S. Robert; 2d Viscount; Lord Privy Seal in Scotland.

P. Richard Saunders Dundas; twice Secretary to the Admiralty; succeeded Sir C. Napier in chief command of the Baltic fleet in the Russian War, 1855, and captured Sweaborg. (*Mem.* He was no relation to Sir James W. D. Dundas, who was in chief command of the Black Sea fleet during the same war.)

ELDON, Earl of; Lord Chancellor. *See* in JUDGES, under SCOTT.

ELLENBOROUGH, Lord; Chief Justice King's Bench. *See* in JUDGES.

ERSKINE, Lord; Lord Chancellor. *See* in JUDGES.

FOX, Rt. Hon. Charles James; statesman and orator; the great rival of Pitt. At Eton he was left much to himself, and was studious, but at the same time a dissipated dandy. He was there considered of extraordinary promise. Æt. 25, he had become a man of mark in the House of Commons, and also a prodigious gambler.

G.   Sir Stephen Fox; statesman; Paymaster of the Forces. Chelsea Hospital is mainly due to him; he projected it, and contributed £13,000 towards it.

u.   Charles; 3d Duke of Richmond; principal Secretary of State in 1766.

F.   Henry; created Lord Holland; Secretary at War.

B.   Stephen; 2d Lord Holland; statesman and social leader.

N.   Henry R., 3d Lord Holland; F.R.S., F.S.A., Recorder of Nottingham. (*See* Lord Brougham's panegyric of these men in his *Statesmen of George III*.)

His aunt, Lady Sarah, sister of the Duke of Richmond, married Colonel Napier, and was mother of the famous Napier family. Colonel Napier was himself cast in the true heroic mould. He had uncommon powers, mental and bodily; he had also scientific tastes. He was Superintendent of Woolwich Laboratory, and Comptroller of Army Accounts.

uS.   General Sir Charles James Napier, G.C.B.; Commander-in-Chief in India; Conqueror of Scinde.

uS.   General Sir William Napier; historian of the Peninsular War.

[3 uS.]   There were three other Napiers, brothers, who were considered remarkable men, namely, General Sir George, Governor of the Cape; Richard, Q.C.; and Henry, Captain, and author of *History of Florence*.

NS.   H. Bunbury, senior classic of his year (1833) at Cambridge.

FRANCIS, Sir Philip; reputed author of *Junius*; violent antagonist of Hastings in India.

F.   Rev. Philip; poet and dramatic writer; translator of *Horace* and other classics. Had a school where Gibbon was a pupil. He was also a political controversialist.

GODERICH, Viscount. *See* ROBINSON.

GRATTAN, Henry; orator and statesman.

[GB.]   Sir Richard Grattan, Lord Mayor of Dublin.

g.   Thomas Marley, Chief Justice of Ireland.

[F.]   James Grattan, Recorder of, and M.P. for, Dublin.

[S.]   Right Honourable James Grattan.

GRENVILLE, George, Premier, 1763.

    The very remarkable relationships of the Grenville family, and the results of the mixture of the Temple race with that of the 1st Earl of Chatham on the one hand, and of the Wyndham on the other, is best understood by the annexed table.

g.   Sir Richard Temple; a leading member of the House of Commons.

u.   General Sir Richard Temple; created Viscount Cobham, served under Marlborough.

B.   Richard, succeeded his mother the Countess, as 1st Earl Temple; statesman; Lord Privy Seal.

S.   William Wyndham Grenville; created Lord Grenville; Premier, 1806.

S.   George, 2d Earl Temple; created Marquis Buckingham; twice Viceroy of Ireland.

S.   Thomas, who bequeathed his library to the British Museum.

GRENVILLE, William Wyndham; created Lord Grenville; Premier, 1806; Chancellor of Oxford University.

B.   Marquess Buckingham, twice Viceroy of Ireland.

F.   George Grenville, Premier, 1763.

g.   Sir William Wyndham, Bart., Secretary at War and Chancellor of the Exchequer.

*u*S.   William Pitt, Premier.

U.   Richard Grenville, created Earl Temple; statesman.

Sir Richard Temple, a leading member of the House of Commons

Sir William Wyndham, Bart. Secretary at War, and Chancellor of the Exchequer

General Sir Richard Temple, created Viscount Cobham
d.s.p.

Hester Temple, 1st Countess Temple = Richard Grenville, M.P. for Andover

George Grenville, Premier = Elizabeth

William Pitt, 1st Earl of Chatham, Premier = Hester

Richard Grenville, 1st Earl Temple, Lord Privy Seal
d.s.p.

Rt. Hon. James Grenville

Henry, Ambassador to the Porte. His. dau. married Earl Stanhope

William Pitt, Premier

Daughter of Hon. Henry Grenville = Earl Stanhope, mechanician

Lady Hester Stanhope, eccentric, d. in Syria

George Grenville, 2d Earl Temple, 1st Marq. Buckingham, twice Viceroy of Ireland

William Wyndham Grenville, created Lord Grenville, Premier
d.s.p.

Thomas Grenville, Rt. Hon.: left Library to British Museum

Present Duke of Buckingham

5th Earl Stanhope, historian

F

GREY, Charles, 2d Earl; Premier, 1830–1834.

F.   General in America, and early part of French War; created Earl Grey for his services.

B.   Edward, Bishop of Hertford.

S.   Henry G., 3d Earl; statesman; writer on Colonial government, and on Reform.

S.   Sir Charles Grey, Private Secretary to the Queen.

HOLLAND, Lord. *See* FOX.

HORNER, Francis; statesman, financier. One of the founders of the *Edinburgh Review*; afterwards he rapidly rose to great note in Parliament. His career was ended by early death, æt. 39.

B.   Leonard Horner, geologist, for very many years a venerated member of the scientific world.

JENKINSON, Robert Banks; 2d Earl of Liverpool; Premier, 1812–27.

F.   Right Hon. Charles Jenkinson, created Earl Liverpool; Sec. of State; a confidential friend and adviser of Geo. III.

[U.]   John Jenkinson, colonel; Joint Secretary for Ireland.

[US.] John Banks Jenkinson, D.D., Bishop of St. David's.

JERVIS, John, admiral; created Earl St. Vincent; 1st Lord of the Admiralty.

u.   Right Hon. Sir Thomas Parker; Ch. B.E.

UP.   Thomas Jervis, M.P., Ch. Justice of Chester.

UPS.   Sir John Jervis, M.P., Attorney-General; Ch. C.P. (Vict.).

KING, Lord. *See* JUDGES.

LAMB, William, 2d Visct. Melbourne; Premier, 1834 and 1835–41.

B.   Frederick, diplomatist, ambassador to Vienna; created Lord Beauvale.

B.   George, M.P., Under-Sec. of State for Home Department.

b.   Lady Palmerston.

p.   Rt. Hon. Wm. F. Cowper, President of the Board of Works, &c.

LANSDOWNE, Marquis. *See* PETTY.

LIVERPOOL, Lord. *See* JENKINSON.

LONDONDERRY. *See* STEWART.

NELSON, Admiral; created Earl Nelson. *See* COMMANDERS.

NORTH, Lord; created Earl Guilford; Premier, 1770–82.

[G.F.] Francis, 1st Baron Guilford. Lord Keeper. (James II.) Whose three brothers and other eminent relations are described in JUDGES. (*See also* Genealogical Table.)

PALMERSTON. *See* TEMPLE.

PEEL, Sir Robert; Premier, 1834–5, 1841–5, 1945–6.

F.　Sir Robert Peel, M.P.; created a Bart. A very wealthy cotton manufacturer and of great mercantile ability, who founded the fortunes of the family. He was Vice-President of the Literary Society.

g.　Sir John Floyd, General, created a Bart. for services in India.

B.　Right Hon. General Peel, Secretary of State for War.

B.　Right Hon. Lawrence Peel, Chief Justice of Supreme Court of Calcutta.

There were also other brothers of more than average ability.

S.　Rt. Hon. Sir Robert, 2d Bart.; Chief Secretary for Ireland.

S.　Right Hon. Frederick, Under Secretary of State for War.

S.　Captain Sir William Peel, R.N., distinguished at Sebastopol and in India.

PERCEVAL, Spencer; Premier, 1810–12.

n.　2d Lord Redesdale, Chairman of Committees of House of Lords. (He was son of the Lord Chancellor of Ireland.)

n.　Right Hon. Spencer Walpole, Secretary of State for Home Department.

PETTY, William Petty; 2d Earl Shelburne; created Marquis Lansdowne; Premier, 1782–3. An ardent supporter of the Earl of Chatham; in early life he distinguished himself in the army, at Minden.

GF.　Sir William Petty, physician, politician, and author; Surveyor-General of Ireland; a man of singular versatility, and successful in everything, including money-making.

PETTY, William Petty—*continued*

S.   3d Marquis Lansdowne, statesman and man of letters. In youth, as Lord Henry Petty, he was one of the set who founded the *Edinburgh Review*. He then became prominent as a Whig, in Parliament, and was Secretary of State more than once. Was Chancellor of the Exchequer, æt. 26.

PITT, William; created Earl of Chatham; Premier, 1766. Originally in the army, which he left æt. 28; then the vigorous opponent of Walpole in Parliament, "the terrible cornet of Dragoons"; afterwards, æt. 49, he became one of the ablest of statesmen, most brilliant of orators, and the prime mover of the policy of England. Married a Grenville. (*See* GRENVILLE for genealogical tree.)

[G.]   Thomas Pitt, Governor of Fort George, who somehow or other amassed a large fortune in India.

S.   William Pitt, Premier.

p.   Lady Hester Stanhope.

PITT, William; 2d son of the 1st Earl of Chatham. Illustrious statesman; Premier, 1783–1801; and 1804–6. Precocious and of eminent talent; frequent ill-health in boyhood; æt. 14 an excellent scholar. Never boyish in his ways; became a healthy youth æt. 18. He was Chancellor of the Exchequer æt. 24, and Prime Minister æt. 25: which latter office he held for seventeen years consecutively. His constitution was early broken by gout; died æt. 47.

F.   Earl of Chatham, Premier.

N.   Lady Hester Stanhope.

u.   George Grenville, Premier.

uS.   Lord Grenville, Premier.

n.   Lady Hester Stanhope, who did the honours of his house, and occasionally acted as his secretary; she was highly accomplished, but most eccentric and more than half mad. After Pitt's death, she lived in Syria, dressed as a male native, and professed supernatural powers.

PORTLAND, Duke of. *See* BENTINCK.

RIPON, Earl of. *See* ROBINSON.

ROBINSON, Frederick John; 1st Viscount Goderich and Earl of Ripon; Premier, 1827–8.

G.   Thomas Robinson, created Baron Grantham, diplomatist; afterwards Secretary of State.

F.   Thomas Robinson, 2d Baron, also diplomatist, and afterwards Secretary of State for Foreign Affairs.

gB. Charles Yorke, Lord Chancellor. *See* JUDGES.

gF. Philip Yorke, 1st Lord Hardwicke, Ld. Chan. *See* JUDGES.

S.   George F. (inherited) Earl de Grey and Ripon, Secretary of State for War.

ROMILLY, Sir Samuel; eminent lawyer and statesman. His parents were French refugees. He was of a serious disposition in youth, and almost educated and supported himself. Entered the bar, and attracted notice by a pamphlet. He rose rapidly in his profession, and became Solicitor-General and M.P. Eminent reformer of criminal laws; committed suicide æt. 61.

S.   Right Hon. Sir John Romilly, created Lord Romilly; Attorney-General and Master of the Rolls. *See* JUDGES.

RUSSELL, 1st Earl; Premier. *See* BEDFORD.

SCOTT, William; cr. Lord Stowell, Judge of the Admiralty Court.

B.   Lord Eldon, Lord Chancellor. *See* JUDGES.
     Lord Stowell and Eldon were each of them twins, each having been born with a sister.

SHELBURNE, Earl of. *See* PETTY.

SHERIDAN, Richard Brinsley; orator, extraordinary wit, and dramatist. Was stupid as a boy of 7. When æt. 11 was idle and careless, but engaging, and showed gleams of superior intellect, as testified by Dr. Parr. On leaving school he wrote what he afterwards developed into the *Critic*. Wrote the *Rivals* æt. 24. Died worn out in body and spirits æt. 65.

He eloped in youth with Miss Linley, a popular singer of great personal charms and exquisite musical talents. Tom Sheridan was the son of that marriage. Miss Linley's father was a musical composer and manager of Drury Lane Theatre. The Linley family was "a nest of nightingales": all had genius, beauty, and voice. Mrs. Tickel was one of them. The name of Sheridan is peculiarly associated with a clearly marked order of brilliant and engaging but "ne'er-do-weel" qualities. Richard Brinsley's genius worked in flashes, and left results that were disproportionate to its remarkable power. His oratorical power and winning address made him a brilliant speaker and a star in society; but he was neither a sterling statesman nor a true friend. He was an excellent boon companion, but unhappy in his domestic relations. Reckless prodigality, gambling, and wild living, brought on debts and duns and a premature break of his constitution. These qualities are found in a greater or less degree among numerous members of the Sheridan family, as well as in those whose biographies have been published. It is exceedingly instructive to observe how strongly hereditary they have proved to be.

F.   Thomas Sheridan, author of the Dictionary. Taught oratory, connected himself with theatres, became, æt. 25, manager of Drury Lane. He was a whimsical but not an opinionated man.

f.   Frances Chamberlain, most accomplished and amiable. Her father would not allow her to learn writing; her brothers taught her secretly: æt. 15, her talent for literary composition showed itself. She wrote some comedies, one of which was as highly eulogised by Garrick, as her novel *Sydney Biddulph* was panegyrised by Fox and Lord North.

g.   Rev. Dr. Philip Chamberlain, an admired preacher, but a humorist and full of crotchets. (I know nothing of the character of his wife, Miss Lydia Whyte.)

G.   Rev. Dr. Thomas Sheridan, friend and correspondent of

Dean Swift. A social, punning, fiddling man, careless and indolent; high animal spirits. "His pen and his fiddle-stick were in continual motion."

S.   Tom Sheridan; a thorough scapegrace, and a Sheridan all over. (He had the Linley blood in him—*see* above); married and died young, leaving a large family, of whom one is—

P.   Caroline, Mrs. Norton; poetess and novelist.

PS. Lord Dufferin, late Secretary for Ireland, is the son of another daughter.

STANLEY, Edward Geoffrey; 14th Earl of Derby; Premier, 1952, 1859–9, 1866–8; scholar; translator of *Homer* into English verse, as well as orator and statesman.

F.   Naturalist; President of Linnæan and Zoological Societies; known by his endeavours to acclimatise animals.

uS. Rev. J. J. Hornby, Head Master of Eton; scholar and athlete.

S.   Edward, Lord Stanley, Secretary of State for Foreign Affairs.

STEWART, Robert; the famous Viscount Castlereagh, and 2d Marquess Londonderry. Great hopes were entertained of him when he entered Parliament, barely of age, but he disappointed them at first, for he was a very unequal speaker. However, he became leader of the House of Commons æt. 29. Committed suicide.

F.   Was M.P. for county Down, and raised through successive peerages to the Marquisate.

uS. Sir George Hamilton Seymour, G.C.B.; diplomatist, especially in Russia and Austria.

B.   (Half brother, grandson of Lord Chancellor Camden.) Charles William; created Earl Vane; Adjutant-General under Wellington in Spain æt. 30.

[p.] (And P. to Duke of Grafton, Premier 1767). Admiral Fitzroy; eminent navigator (*Voyage of the 'Beagle'*). Superintendent of the Meteorological Department of the Board of Trade.

STUART, John; 3d Earl of Bute; Premier, 1762–3.

u. 2d Duke of Argyll; created Duke of Greenwich; statesman and general. In command at Sheriffmuir:—

"Argyll, the State's whole thunder born to wield,
And shake alike the senate and the field."—POPE.

GF. Sir George Mackenzie, Lord Advocate; eminent lawyer.

G. Sir James Stuart, 1st Earl of Bute; Privy Councillor to Queen Anne.

GU. Robert Stuart, 1st Baronet; a Lord of Session, as Lord Tillicoultry.

GB. Dugald Stuart, also a Lord of Session.

B. Right Hon. James Stuart, who assumed the additional name of Mackenzie; Keeper of Privy Seal of Scotland.

S. General Sir Charles Stuart; reduced Minorca.

S. William, D.D.; Archbishop of Armagh.

P. Charles; ambassador to France; created Baron Stuart de Rothesay. His great-grandmother (*Gf.*) was Lady Mary Wortley Montagu; charming letter-writer; introducer of inoculation from the East.

TEMPLE, Henry J.; Lord Palmerston; octogenarian Premier, 1855–8, 1859–65. Was singularly slow in showing his great powers, though he was always considered an able man, and was generally successful in his undertakings. He had an excellent constitution, and high animal spirits, but was not ambitious in the ordinary sense of the word, and did not care to go out of his way to do work. He was fully 45 years old before his statesmanlike powers were clearly displayed.

His father is described as a model of conjugal affection; he wrote a most pathetic and natural epitaph on his wife. He was fond of literature and of pictures.

B. Sir William Temple; Minister Plenipotentiary to the Court of Naples; founder of the "Temple Collection" of Italian antiquities, and works of art in the British Museum.

GGB. Sir William Temple, Swift's patron.

TEMPLE, Henry J.—*continued*

GG. Sir John Temple, Attorney-General, and Speaker of the House of Commons in Ireland.

GGF. Sir John Temple, Master of the Rolls in Ireland; even he was not the first of this family that showed ability.

THURLOW, Lord; Lord Chancellor. *See under* JUDGES.

ST. VINCENT, Earl. *See* JERVIS.

WALPOLE, Sir Robert; created Earl of Orford; Premier 1721–42 (under Geo. I and II, but included in Brougham's volumes of the Statesmen of Geo. III).
In private life hearty, good-natured, and social. Had a happy art of making friends. Great powers of persuasion. For business of all kinds he had an extraordinary capacity, and did his work with the greatest ease and tranquillity.

G. Sir Edward Walpole, M.P.; distinguished member of the Parliament that restored Charles II.

B. Horatio; diplomatist of a high order; created Baron Walpole.

S. Sir Edward; Chief Secretary for Ireland.

S. Horace; famous in literature and art. Strawberry Hill. Excellent letter-writer: Byron speaks of his letters as incomparable. Gouty. Died æt. 80.

*n*p. Admiral Lord Nelson.
A grandson [G.] of Horatio was minister at Munich, and another was minister in Portugal. One of the sons of the former is Rt. Hon. Spencer Walpole, Secretary of State.

N. Mrs. Damer, sculptor, daughter of Field-Marshal Conway, cousin to Horace Walpole.

WELLESLEY, Richard; created Marquess of Wellesley; Governor-General of India; most eminent statesman and scholar.

B. Arthur; the great Duke of Wellington.

[B.] 1st Baron Cowley, diplomatist.

[F.] 1st Earl of Mornington; eminent musical tastes. He inherited the estates and the name, but not the blood, of the Wesleys, whose descendants were the famous

Dissenters, his father, Richard Colley, having obtained them from his aunt's *husband*, who was a Wesley.

gGF. The infamous judge, Sir John Trevor, M.R., the cousin and the rival of the abler, but hardly more infamous, Judge Jeffreys.

N. Henry Wellesley; created Earl Cowley; diplomatist; ambassador to France.

S. (Illegitimate.) Rev. Henry Wellesley, D.D.; Principal of New Inn Hall, Oxford; a scholar and man of extensive literary acquirements and remarkable taste in art.

WELLESLEY, Arthur; created Duke of Wellington; Premier.
See COMMANDERS.

B. Marquess Wellesley
F. Earl Mornington } as above.
N. Earl Cowley
N. Rev. Henry Wellesley

WILBERFORCE, William; philanthropist and statesman; of very weak constitution in infancy. Even æt. 7 showed a remarkable talent for elocution; had a singularly melodious voice, which has proved hereditary; sang well; was very quick; desultory at college. Entered Parliament æt. 21, and before æt. 25 had gained high reputation.

S. Samuel, Bishop of Oxford; prelate, orator, and administrator.

[S.] Robert, Archdeacon; Fellow of Oriel College, Oxford; subsequently became Roman Catholic.

[S.] Henry William; scholar, Oxford, 1830. Subsequently became Roman Catholic.

SUPPLEMENTARY LIST OF GREAT STATESMEN OF VARIOUS PERIODS AND COUNTRIES

ADAMS, John (1735–1826), the second President of the United States. Educated for the law, where he soon gained great reputation and practice; was an active politician æt. 30; took a prominent part in effecting the independence of his country.

ADAMS, John—*continued*

S. John Quincey Adams, sixth President of the United States; previously minister in Berlin, Russia, and Vienna.

P. Charles Francis Adams, the recent and well-known American minister in London; author of *Life of John Adams*.

ARTEVELDT, James Van (1345 ?); brewer of Ghent; popular leader in the revolt of Flanders; exercised sovereign power for nine years.

S. Philip Van Arteveldt. *See* below.

ARTEVELDT, Philip Van (1382 ?); leader of the popular party, long subsequently to his father's death. He was well educated and wealthy, and had kept aloof from politics till æt. 42, when he was dragged into them by the popular party, and hailed their captain by acclamation. He led the Flemish bravely against the French, but was finally defeated and slain.

F. James Van Arteveldt. *See* above.

BURLEIGH, Earl. *See* CECIL.

CECIL, William; created Lord Burleigh; statesman (Elizabeth); Lord Treasurer. "The ablest minister of an able reign." Was Secretary, or chief Minister, during almost the whole of Queen Elizabeth's long reign of forty-five years. He was distinguished at Cambridge for his power of work and for his very regular habits. Married for his second wife the daughter of Sir Anthony Cooke, director of the studies of Edward VI, and sister of Lady Bacon, the mother of the great Lord Bacon, and had by her—

S. Robert Cecil, who was created Earl of Salisbury the same day that his elder brother was created Earl of Exeter. He was of weakly constitution and deformed. Succeeded his father as Prime Minister under Elizabeth, and afterwards under James I; was unquestionably the ablest minister of his time, but cold-hearted and selfish. Lord Bacon was *u*S. to him.

[B.] 1st Earl of Exeter.

[F.] Master of the Robes to Henry VIII.

COLBERT, Jean Baptiste; French statesman and financier (Louis XIV); eminent for the encouragement he gave to public works and institutions, to commerce and manufacturers. He was fully appreciated in his early life by Mazarin, who recommended him as his successor. He became minister æt. 49, and used to work for sixteen hours a day. His family gave many distinguished servants to France.

U. Odart; a merchant who became a considerable financier.

B. Charles; statesman and diplomatist.

S. Jean Baptiste; statesman; intelligent and firm of purpose; commanded, when still a mere youth, the expedition against Genoa in 1684.

S. Jacques Nicholas, archbishop; member of the Academy.

N. Jean Baptiste (son of Charles); diplomatist.

N. Charles Joachim; prelate.

The family continued to show ability in the succeeding generation.

CROMWELL, Oliver; Lord Protector of the Commonwealth.

US. Hampden, the patriot, whom Lord Clarendon speaks of as having "a head to contrive, a tongue to persuade, and a heart to execute any mischief"—this word "mischief" meaning, of course, antagonism to the King.

Up. Edmund Waller, the poet, a man of very considerable abilities both in parliamentary eloquence and in poetry, but he was not over-stedfast in principle. He was n. to Hampden.

S. Henry; behaved with gallantry in the army, and acted with much distinction in Ireland as Lord Deputy.

He had one other son and four daughters, who married able men, but their descendants were not remarkable.

The Comwell breed has been of much less importance than might have been expected from his own genius and that of his collaterals, Hampden and Waller. Besides his son Henry, there is no important name in the numerous descendants of Oliver Cromwell. Henry's sons were insignificant people, so were those of Richard, and so also were those of Cromwell's daughters, notwithstanding their marriage with such eminent men as Ireton and Fleetwood. One of Oliver's sisters married Archbishop Tillotson, and had issue by him, but they proved nobodies.

GUISE, Francis Balafré, Duke of. The most illustrious among the generals and great political leaders of this powerful French family. He had high military talent. He greatly distinguished himself as a general æt. 34, and was then elevated to the dignity of Lieutenant-General of the kingdom.

B.   Charles, Cardinal of Lorraine.

S.   Henry (Duke of Guise, also called Belafré). He was less magnanimous and more factious than his father; was the adviser of the massacre of St. Bartholomew; and he caused Coligny to be murdered; was himself murdered by order of Henri III, æt. 38.

S.   Cardinal, arrested and murdered in prison, on the same day as his brother.

[S.]   Duc de Mayenne.

P.   Charles, who, together with his uncle, the Duc de Mayenne, was leader of the league against Henri IV.

PS.   Henry, conspired against Cardinal Richelieu.

Thus there were four generations of notable men in the Guise family.

MIRABEAU, H. G. Riquetti, Comte de; French statesman, "The Alcibiades of the French Revolution." A man of violent passions, ardent imagination, and great abilities. He had prodigious mental activity, and hungered for every kind of knowledge.

F.   Marquis de Mirabeau; author of *L'Ami des Hommes*, a leader of the school of the Economists; a philanthropist by profession, and a harsh despot in his own family.

[B and *b*.] There were remarkable characters among the brothers and sisters of Mirabeau, but I am unable to state facts by which their merits may be distinctly appraised. It is said that among many generations of the Mirabeaus

—or more properly speaking, of the Riquettis, for
Mirabeau was an assumed name—were to be found men
of great mental vigour and character. Thus St. Beuve
says—and I give the extract in full and without apology
on account of the interest ever attaching itself to Mirabeau's characteristics—

"Les Correspondances du père et de l'oncle du grand
tribun, la Notice sur son grand-père, et en général toutes
les pièces qui font le tissu de ces huit volumes, ont révélé
une race à part des caractères d'une originalité grandiose
et haute, d'où notre Mirabeau n'a eu qu'à descendre
pour se répandre ensuite, pour se précipiter comme il l'a
fait et se distribuer à tous, tellement qu'on peut dire
qu'il n'a été que l'enfant perdu, l'enfant prodigue et
sublime de sa race."

He combined his paternal qualities with those of his
mother:—

"Ce n'était suivant la définition de son père qu'un mâle
monstreux au physique et au moral.

"Il tenait de sa mère la largeur du visage, les instincts,
les appétits prodigues et sensuels, mais probablement
aussi ce certain fond *gaillard* et gaulois, cette faculté
de se familiariser et de s'humaniser que les Riquetti
n'avaient pas, et qui deviendra un des moyens de sa
puissance.

"Une nature riche, ample, copieuse, généreuse, souvent
grossière et vicée, souvent fine aussi, noble, même
élégante, et, en somme, pas du tout monstreuse, mais
des plus humaines."

MORE, Sir Thomas; Lord Chancellor (Henry VIII); eminent
statesman and writer; singularly amiable, unaffectedly
pious, and resolute to death. When æt. 13, the Dean of
St. Paul's used to say of him, "There was but one wit in
England, and that was young More."

F.   Sir John More, Just. K.B.

[S. and 3 *s.*] Besides his three accomplished daughters,
Margaret Roper, Elizabeth Dauncy, and Cecilia Heron,

Sir Thomas More had one son called John. Too much has been said of the want of capacity of this son. His father commended the purity of his Latin more than that of his daughters, and Grynæus (*see under* DIVINES) dedicated to him an edition of Plato, while Erasmus inscribed to him the works of Aristotle. He had enough strength of character to deny the king's supremacy, and on that account he lay for some time in the Tower under sentence of death. (*Life of More*, by Rev. Joseph Hunter, 1828, Preface, p. xxxvi.)

RICHELIEU, Armand J. du Plessis, Cardinal Duc de. The great minister of France under Louis XIV. He was educated for arms, but devoted himself to study, and entered the Church at a very early age—earlier than was legal—and became Doctor. Æt. 39 he was chief minister, and thenceforward he absolutely reigned for eighteen years. He was not a lovable man. He pursued but one end—the establishment of a strong despotism. Died æt. 57.

F. François du Plessis, seigneur de Richelieu; signalised himself as a soldier and a diplomatist. Was promoted to be "grand prévôt de France," and was highly rewarded by Henri IV.

[B.] Henri; became "maréchal de camp," and was killed in a duel just when he was about to be promoted to the government of Angers.

B. Alphonse L.; Cardinal of Lyons. Became a monk of the Chartreuse, and practised great austerity. He behaved nobly in Lyons at the time of the plague.

BP. (Grandson of Henri). Louis F. Armand, Duc de Richelieu. He was Marshal of France, and personified the eighteenth century; being frivolous, fond of intrigue, immoral without remorse, imperturbably good-humoured, and courageous. He was a seven months' child, and lived to æt. 92. His children were—

BPS. The "trop célèbre" Duc de Fronsac.

BP*S*. The witty and beautiful Countess of Egmont.

RICHELIEU, Armand J. du Plessis—*continued*

BPP. (Son of the Duc de Fronsac.) Armand E., Duc de Richelieu; Prime Minister of France under Louis XVIII. Died in 1822.

nS. Comte de Gramont, wit and courtier. *See under* LITERARY MEN.

WITT, De, John. The younger brother of two of the ablest and more honourable of Dutch statesmen. They were inseparable in their careers, but different in character; each, however, being among the finest specimens of his peculiar type. John played the more prominent part, on account of his genial, versatile, and aspiring character. He rose through various offices, until, æt. 27, he became Grand Pensionary, virtually the chief magistrate, of Holland. He was savagely murdered, æt. 47.

B. Cornelius De Witt. *See* below.

[F.] A party leader of some importance.

WITT, De, Cornelius; had more solid, though less showy parts, than his brother, but was in reality the more efficient supporter of that power which his brother John exercised. He, also, was savagely murdered, æt. 49.

B. John De Witt. *See* above.

[F.] *See* above.

ENGLISH PEERAGES,

THEIR INFLUENCE UPON RACE

It is frequently, and justly, remarked, that the families of great men are apt to die out; and it is argued from that fact, that men of ability are unprolific. If this were the case, every attempt to produce a highly-gifted race of men would eventually be defeated. Gifted individuals might be reared, but they would be unable to maintain their breed. I propose in a future chapter, after I have discussed the several groups of eminent men, to examine the degree in which transcendent genius may be correlated with sterility, but it will be convenient that I should now say something about the causes of failure of issue of Judges and Statesmen, and come to some conclusion whether or no a breed of men gifted with the average ability of those eminent men, could or could not maintain itself during an indefinite number of consecutive generations. I will even go a little further a-field, and treat of the extinct peerages generally.

First, as to the Judges: there is a peculiarity in their domestic relations that interferes with a large average of legitimate families. Lord Campbell states in a foot-note to his life of Lord Chancellor Thurlow, in his *Lives of the Chancellors*, that when he (Lord Campbell) was first acquainted with the English Bar, one half of the judges had married their mistresses. He says it was then the understanding that when a barrister was elevated to the Bench, he should either marry his mistress, or put her away.

According to this extraordinary statement, it would appear that much more than one half of the judges that sat on the Bench in the beginning of this century, had no legitimate offspring before the advanced period of their lives at which they were appointed judges. One half of them could not, because it was at that stage in their career that they married their mistresses; and there were others who, having then put away their mistresses, were, for the first time, able to marry. Nevertheless, I have shown that the number of the legitimate children of the Judges is considerable, and that even under that limitation, they are, on the whole, by no means an unfertile race. Bearing in mind what I have just stated, it must follow that they are extremely prolific. Nay, there are occasional instances of enormous families, in all periods of their history. But do not the families die out? I will examine into the descendants of those judges whose names are to be found in the appendix to the chapter upon them, who gained peerages, and who last sat on the Bench previous to the close of the reign of George IV. There are thirty-one of them; nineteen of the peerages remain and twelve are extinct. Under what conditions did these twelve become extinct? Were any of those conditions peculiar to the twelve, and not shared by the remaining nineteen?

In order to obtain an answer to these inquiries, I examined into the number of children and grandchildren of all the thirty-one peers, and into the particulars of their alliances, and tabulated them; when, to my astonishment, I found a very simple, adequate, and novel explanation, of the common cause of extinction of peerages, stare me in the face. It appeared, in the first instance, that a considerable proportion of the new peers and of their sons married heiresses. Their motives for doing so are intelligible enough, and not to be condemned. They have a title, and perhaps a sufficient fortune, to transmit to their eldest son, but they want an increase of possessions for the endowment of their younger sons and their daughters. On the other hand, an heiress has a fortune, but wants a title. Thus the peer and heiress are urged to the same issue of marriage by different impulses. But my statistical lists showed, with unmistakable emphasis, that these marriages are peculiarly unprolific. We might, indeed, have expected that an heiress, who is the sole issue of a marriage, would not be so fertile as a woman who has many brothers and sisters. Comparative infertility must be hereditary in the same way as other physical attributes, and I am assured it is so in the case of the domestic animals. Consequently, the issue of a peer's marriage with an heiress frequently fails, and his title is brought to an end. I will give the following list of every case in the first or second generation of the Law Lords, taken from the English Judges within the limits I have already specified, where there has been a marriage with an heiress or a co-heiress, and I will describe the result in each instance. Then I will summarise the facts.

Influence of Heiress-marriages on the Families of those English Judges who obtained Peerages, and who last sat on the Bench between the beginning of the reign of Charles II and the end of the reign of George IV.

(The figures within parentheses give the date of their peerages)

COLPEPPER, 1st Lord (1664). Married twice, and had issue by both marriages; in all, five sons and four daughters. The eldest son married an heiress, and died without issue. The second son married a co-heiress, and had only one daughter. The third married, but had no children, and the other two never married at all, so the title became extinct.

COOPER, 1st Earl of Shaftesbury (1672). His mother was a sole heiress. He married three times, and had only one son. However, the son was prolific, and the direct male line continues.

COWPER, 1st Earl (1718). First wife was an heiress; he had no surviving issue by her. His second wife had two sons and two daughters. His eldest son married a co-heiress for his first wife, and had only one son and one daughter. The direct male line continues.

FINCH, 1st Earl of Nottingham (1681). Had fourteen children. The eldest married a co-heiress for his first wife, and had one daughter by her.

HARCOURT, 1st Lord (1712). Had three sons and two daughters. Two of the sons died young. The eldest married an heiress, whose mother was an heiress also. He had by her two sons and one daughter. Both of the sons married, and both died issueless, so the title became extinct.

HENLEY, 1st Earl of Northington (1764). His mother was a co-heiress. He married, and had one son and five daughters. The son died unmarried, and so the title became extinct.

HYDE, 1st Earl of Clarendon (1661). Married a lady who was eventually sole heiress, and had four sons and two daughters by her. The third son died unmarried, and the fourth was drowned at sea, consequently there remained only two available sons to carry on the family. Of these, the eldest, who became the 2d Earl, married a lady who died, leaving an only son. He then married for his second wife, an heiress, who had no issue at all. This only son had but one male child, who died in youth, and was succeeded in the title by the descendants of the 1st Earl's second son. He (the son of an heiress) had only one son and four daughters, and this son, who was 4th Earl of Clarendon, had only one son and two daughters. The son died young, so the title became extinct.

JEFFREYS, 1st Lord (of Wem—1685). Had one son and two daughters. The son married an heiress, and had only one daughter, so the title became extinct.

KENYON, 1st Lord (1788). Had three sons. Although one of them married a co-heiress, there were numerous descendants in the next generation.

NORTH, 1st Lord Guilford (1683). Married a co-heiress. He had only one grandson, who, however, lived and had children.

PARKER, 1st Earl of Macclesfield (1721). This family has narrowly escaped extinction, threatened continually by its numerous errors of alliance. The 1st Earl married a co-heiress, and had only one son and one daughter. The son married a co-heiress, and had two sons; of these, the second married a co-heiress, and had no issue at all. The eldest son (grandson of the 1st Earl) was therefore the only male that remained in the race. He had two sons and one daughter.

Now, of these two, the only male heirs in the third generation, one married a co-heiress, and had only one daughter. The remaining one fortunately married twice, for by the first marriage he had only daughters. A son by the second marriage is the present peer, and is the father, by two marriages—in neither case with an heiress—of eleven sons and four daughters.

PRATT, 1st Earl of Camden (1786). This family affords a similar instance to the last one, of impending destruction to the race. The 1st Earl married an heiress, and had only one son and four daughters. The son married an heiress, and had only one son and three daughters. The son married a co-heiress, but fortunately had three sons and eight daughters.

RAYMOND, 1st Lord (1731). He had one son, who married a co-heiress, and left no issue at all, so the title became extinct.

SCOTT, Lord Stowell. *See* further on, under my list of STATESMEN.

TALBOT, 1st Lord (1733). This family narrowly escaped extinction. The 1st Lord married an heiress, and had three sons. The eldest son married an heiress, and had only one daughter. The second son married a co-heiress, and had no issue by her. However, she died, and he married again, and left four sons. The third son of the first Earl had male issue.

TREVOR, 1st Lord (1711). Married first a co-heiress, and had two sons and three daughters. Both of the sons married, but they had only one daughter each. Lord Trevor married again, and had three sons, of whom one died young, and the other two, though they married, left no issue at all.

WEDDERBURN, 1st Lord Loughborough and Earl of Rosslyn (1801). Married an heiress for his first wife, and had no issue at all. He married again, somewhat late in life, and had no issue. So the direct male line is extinct.

YORKE, 1st Earl of Hardwicke (1754). Is numerously represented, though two of his line of descent have failed, in one of which there was a marriage with a co-heiress.

The result of all these facts is exceedingly striking. It is:

1st. That out of the thirty-one peerages, there were no less than seventeen in which the hereditary influence of an heiress or co-heiress affected the first or second generation. That this influence was sensibly an agent in producing sterility in sixteen out of these seventeen peerages, and the influence was sometimes shown in two, three, or more cases in one peerage.

2d. That the direct male line of no less than eight peerages, viz. Colpepper, Harcourt, Northington, Clarendon, Jeffreys, Raymond, Trevor, and Rosslyn, were actually extinguished through the influence of the heiresses, and that six others, viz. Shaftesbury, Cowper, Guilford, Parker, Camden, and Talbot, had very narrow escapes from extinction, owing to the same cause. I literally have only one case, that of Lord Kenyon, where the race-destroying influence of heiress-blood was not felt.

3d. Out of the twelve peerages that have failed in the direct male line, no less than eight failures are accounted for by heiress-marriages.

Now, what of the four that remain? Lords Somers and Thurlow both died unmarried. Lord Alvanley had only two sons, of whom one died unmarried. There is only his case and that of the Earl of Mansfield, out of the ten who married and whose titles have since become extinct, where the extinction may not be accounted for by heiress-marriages. No one can therefore maintain, with any show of reason, that there are grounds for imputing exceptional sterility to the race of judges. The facts, when carefully analysed, point very strongly in the opposite direction.

I will now treat the Statesmen of George III and the Premiers since the accession of George III down to recent times, in the same way as I have treated the Judges; including, however, only those whose pedigrees I can easily find, namely, such as were peers or nearly related to peers. There are twenty-two of these names. I find that fourteen have left no male descendants, and that seven of those fourteen peers or their sons have married heiresses—namely, Canning, Castlereagh,

Lord Grenville, George Grenville, Lord Holland, Lord Stowell, and Walpole (the first Earl of Orford). On the other hand, I find only three cases of peers marrying heiresses without failure of issue,—namely, Addington (Lord Sidmouth), the Marquis of Bute, and the Duke of Grafton.

The seven whose male line became extinct from other causes are Bolingbroke, Earl Chatham, Lord Liverpool, Earl St. Vincent, Earl Nelson, William Pitt (unmarried), and the Marquess of Wellesley (who left illegitimate issue). The remaining five required to complete the twenty-two cases are the Duke of Bedford, Dundas (Viscount Melville), Perceval, Romilly, and Wilberforce. None of these were allied or descended from heiress-blood, and they have all left descendants.

I append to this summary the history of the heiress-marriages, to correspond with what has already been given in respect to the Judges.

BUTE, Marquess of. Married a co-heiress, but had a large family.

CANNING, George. Married an heiress, and had three sons and one daughter. The eldest died young; the second was drowned in youth; and the third, who was the late Earl Canning, married a co-heiress, and had no issue: so the line is extinct.

CASTLEREAGH, Viscount. Married a co-heiress, and had neither son nor daughter; so the line became extinct.

GRAFTON, Duke of. Married an heiress, and had two sons and one daughter. By a second wife he had a larger family.

GRENVILLE, George. Had three sons and four daughters. The eldest son married an heiress, and had no male grand-children; the second was apparently unmarried; the third was Lord Grenville (Premier): he married, but was issueless; so the line is extinct.

HOLLAND, Lord. Had one son and one daughter. The son married an heiress, and had only one son and one daughter. That son died issueless; so the male line is extinct.

ROCKINGHAM, 2d Marquis. Married an heiress, and had no issue; so the title became extinct.

SIDMOUTH, Viscount (Addington). Was son of an heiress, and he had only one son and four daughters. The son had numerous descendants.

STOWELL, Lord. Married a co-heiress. He had only one son, who died unmarried, and one daughter; so the male line is extinct.

WALPOLE, 1st Earl of Orford. Had three sons and two daughters. The eldest son married an heiress, and had only one son, who died unmarried. The second and third sons died unmarried; so the male line is extinct.

The important result disclosed by these facts, that inter-marriage with heiresses is a notable agent in the extinction of families, is confirmed by more extended inquiries. I devoted some days to ransacking Burke's volumes on the extant and on the extinct peerages. I first tried the marriages made by the second peers of each extant title. It seemed reasonable to expect that the eldest son of the first peer, the founder of the title, would marry heiresses pretty frequently; and so they do, and with terrible destruction to their race. I examined one-seventh part of the peerage. Leaving out co-heiresses—for I shall weary the reader if I refine overmuch—the following were the results:

NO. OF CASES

1 Abingdon, 2d Earl; wife and mother both heiresses. No issue.
2 Aldborough, 2d Earl; married two heiresses. No issue.
1 Annesley, 2d Earl; wife and mother both heiresses, 3 sons and 2 daughters.
1 Arran, 2d Earl; wife and mother both heiresses. 4 sons and 3 daughters.
1   (His son, the 3d Earl, married an heiress, and had no issue.)
1 Ashburnham, 2d Baron; wife and mother both heiresses. No issue.
1   (His brother succeeded as 3d Earl, and married an heiress; by her no issue.)
1 Aylesford, 2d Earl; wife heiress, mother co-heiress. 1 son and 3 daughters.

1 Barrington, 2d Viscount; wife and mother both heiresses. No issue.
2 Beaufort, 2d Duke, marr. two heiresses. By one no issue; by the other, 2 sons.
1 Bedford, 2d Duke; married heiress. 2 sons and 2 daughters.
1 Camden, 2d Earl; wife and mother both heiresses. 1 son and
—   3 daughters.
14

Making a grand total of fourteen cases out of seventy peers, resulting in eight instances of absolute sterility, and in two instances of only one son.

I tried the question from another side, by taking the marriages of the last peers and comparing the numbers of the children when the mother was an heiress with those when she was not. I took precautions to exclude from the latter all cases where the mother was a co-heiress, or the father an only son. Also, since heiresses are not so very common, I sometimes went back two or three generations for an instance of an heiress-marriage. In this way I took fifty cases of each. I give them below, having first doubled the actual results, in order to turn them into percentages:—

Number of sons to each marriage	100 Marriages of each description	
	Number of cases in which the mother was an heiress	Number of cases in which the mother was not an heiress
0	22	2[1]
1	16	10
2	22	14
3	22	34
4	10	20
5	6	8
6	2	8
7	0	4
above	0	0
	100	100

[1] I fear I must have overlooked one or two sterile marriages; otherwise I cannot account for the smallness of this number.

I find that among the wives of peers—

100 who are heiresses have   208 sons and 206 daughters.
100 who are not heiresses have 336 sons and 284 daughters.

The table shows how exceedingly precarious must be the line of a descent from an heiress, especially when younger sons are not apt to marry. One-fifth of the heiresses have no male children at all; a full third have not more than one child; three-fifths have not more than two. It has been the salvation of many families that the husband outlived the heiress whom he first married, and was able to leave issue by a second wife.

Every advancement in dignity is a fresh inducement to the introduction of another heiress into the family. Consequently, dukes have a greater impregnation of heiress-blood than earls, and dukedoms might be expected to be more frequently extinguished than earldoms, and earldoms to be more apt to go than baronies. Experience shows this to be most decidedly the case. Sir Bernard Burke, in his preface to the *Extinct Peerages*, states that all the English dukedoms created from the commencement of the order down to the commencement of the reign of Charles II are gone, excepting three that are merged in royalty, and that only eleven earldoms remain out of the many created by the Normans, Plantagenets, and Tudors.

This concludes my statistics about the heiresses. I do not care to go farther, because one ought to know something more about their several histories before attempting to arrive at very precise results in respect to their fertility. An heiress is not always the sole child of a marriage contracted early in life and enduring for many years. She may be the surviving child of a larger family, or the child of a late marriage, or the parents may have early left her an orphan. We ought also to consider the family of the husband, whether he be a sole child, or one of a large family. These matters would afford a very instructive field of inquiry to those who cared to labour in it, but it falls outside my line of work. The reason I have gone so far is simply to show that, although many men of eminent ability (I do not speak of illustrious or prodigious genius) have not left descendants behind them, it is not because they are sterile, but because they are apt to marry sterile women, in order to obtain wealth to support the peerage with which their merits have been rewarded. I look upon the peerage as a disastrous institution, owing to its destructive effects on our valuable races. The most highly-gifted men are ennobled; their elder sons are tempted to marry heiresses, and their younger ones not to marry at all, for these have not enough fortune to support both a family and an aristocratical position. So the side-shoots of the genealogical tree are hacked off, and the leading shoot is blighted, and the breed is lost for ever.

It is with much satisfaction that I have traced and, I hope, finally disposed of the cause why families are apt to become extinct in proportion to their dignity—chiefly so, on account of my desire to show that able races are not necessarily sterile, and secondarily because it may put an end to the wild and ludicrous hypotheses that are frequently started to account for their extinction.

COMMANDERS

In times of prolonged war, when the reputation of a great commander can alone be obtained, the profession of arms affords a career that offers its full share of opportunities to men of military genius. Promotion is quick, the demand for able men is continuous, and very young officers have frequent opportunities of showing their powers. Hence it follows that the list of great commanders, notwithstanding it is short, contains several of the most gifted men recorded in history. They showed enormous superiority over their contemporaries by excelling in many particulars. They were foremost in their day, among statesmen and generals, and their energy was prodigious. Many, when they were mere striplings, were distinguished for political capacity. In their early manhood, they bore the whole weight and responsibility of government; they animated armies and nations with their spirit; they became the champions of great coalitions, and coerced millions of other men by the superior power of their own intellect and will.

I will run through a few of these names in the order in which they will appear in the appendix to this chapter, to show what giants in ability their acts prove them to have been, and how great and original was the position they occupied at ages when most youths are kept in the background of general society, and hardly suffered to express opinions, much less to act, contrary to the prevailing sentiments of the day.

Alexander the Great began his career of conquest at the age of twenty, having previously spent four years at home in the exercise of more or less sovereign power, with a real statesman-like capacity. His life's work was over æt. 32. Bonaparte, the Emperor Napoleon I, was general of the Italian army æt. 26, and thenceforward carried everything before him, whether in the field or in the State, in rapid succession. He was made emperor æt. 35, and had lost Waterloo æt. 46. Cæsar, though he was prevented by political hindrances from obtaining high office and from commanding in the field till æt. 42, was a man of the greatest political promise as a youth; nay, even as a boy. Charlemagne began his wars æt. 30. Charles XII of Sweden began his, æt. 18; and the ability showed by him at that early period of life was of the highest order. Prince Eugene commanded the imperial army in Austria æt. 25. Gustavus Adolphus was as precocious in war and statesmanship as his descendant Charles XII. Hannibal and his family were remark- ﹀ able for their youthful superiority. Many of them had obtained the highest commands, and had become the terror of the Romans, before they were what we call "of age." The Nassau family are equally noteworthy. When William the Silent was a mere boy, he was the trusted confidant, even adviser, of the Emperor Charles V. His son, the great general Maurice of Nassau, was only eighteen when in chief command of the Low Countries, then risen in arms against the Spaniards. His grandson, Turenne, the gifted French general, and his great-grandson, our William III, were both of them illustrious in early life. Marlborough was from 46 to 50 years of age during the period of his greatest success, but he was treated much earlier as a man of high mark. Scipio Africanus Major was only 24 when in chief command in Spain against the Carthaginians. Wellington broke the Mahratta power æt. 35, and had won Waterloo æt. 46.

But though the profession of arms in time of prolonged war affords ample opportunities to men of high military genius, it is otherwise in peace, or in short wars. The army, in every country, is more directly under the influence of the sovereign than any other institution. Guided by the instinct of self-preservation, the patronage of the army is always the last privilege that sovereigns are disposed to yield to democratic demands. Hence it is, that armies invariably suffer from those evils that are inseparable from courtly patronage. Rank and political services are apt to be weighed against military ability, and incapable officers to occupy high places during periods of peace. They may even be able to continue to fill their posts during short wars without creating a public scandal; nay, sometimes to carry away honours that ought in justice to have been bestowed on their more capable subordinates in rank.

It is therefore very necessary, in accepting the reputation of a commander as a test of his gifts, to confine ourselves, as I propose to do, to those commanders only whose reputation has been tested by prolonged wars, or whose ascendency over other men has been freely acknowledged.

There is a singular and curious condition of success in the army and navy, quite independent of ability, that deserves a few words. In order that a young man may fight his way to the top of his profession, he must survive many battles. But it so happens that men of equal ability are *not* equally likely to escape shot free. Before explaining why, let me remark that the danger of being shot in battle is considerable. No less than seven of the thirty-two commanders mentioned in my appendix, or between one-quarter and one-fifth of them, perished in that way; they are Charles XII, Gustavus Adolphus, Sir Henry Lawrence, Sir John Moore, Tromp, and Turenne. (I may add, while talking of these things, though it does not bear on my argument, that four others were murdered, viz. Cæsar, Coligny, Philip II of Macedon, and William the Silent; and that two committed suicide, viz. Lord Clive and Hannibal. In short, 40 per cent. of the whole number died by violent deaths.)

There is a principle of natural selection in an enemy's bullets which bears more heavily against large than against small men. Large men are more likely to be hit. I calculate that the chance of a man being accidentally shot is as the square root of the product of his height multiplied into his weight;[1] that where a man of 16 stone in weight, and

---

[1] The chance of a man being struck by accidental shots is in proportion to his sectional area—that is, to his shadow on a neighbouring wall cast by a distant light; or to his height multiplied into

6 feet 2½ inches high, will escape from chance shots for two years, a man of 8 stone in weight and 5 feet 6 inches high, would escape for three. But the total proportion of the risk run by the large man, is, I believe, considerably greater. He is conspicuous from his size, and is therefore more likely to be recognised and made the object of a special aim. It is also in human nature, that the shooter should pick out the largest man, just as he would pick out the largest bird in a covey, or antelope in a herd. Again, of two men who are aimed at, the bigger is the more likely to be hit, as affording a larger target. This chance is a trifle less than the ratio of his increased sectional area, for it is subject to the law discussed in p. 69, though we are unable to calculate the decrease, from our ignorance of the average distance of the enemy and the closeness of his fire. At long distances, when the shooting was wild, the decrease would be insensible; at comparatively close ranges it would be unimportant, for even the sums of A and B, p. 75, are only about one-fifth more than 2 A. (In the last column of the table 77 + 48 = 125 is only 21, or about one-fifth more than 2 × 48 = 96.) As a matter of fact, commanders are very frequently the objects of special aim. I remember, when Soult visited England, that a story appeared in the newspapers, of some English veteran having declared that the hero must have lived a charmed life, for he had "covered" him with his rifle (I think my memory does not deceive me) upwards of thirty times, and yet had never the fortune to hit him. Nelson was killed by one of many shots aimed directly at him, by a rifleman in the maintop of the French vessel with which his own was closely engaged.

---

his average breadth. However, it is equally easy and more convenient to calculate from the better known data of his height and weight. One man differs from another in being more or less tall, and more or less thick-set. It is unnecessary to consider depth (of chest, for example) as well as width, for the two go together. Let h = a man's height, w = his weight, b = his average breadth taken in any direction we please, but it must be in the same direction for all. Then his weight, w, varies as hb^2, and his sectional area varies as hb, or as $\sqrt{h} \times hb^2$, or as $\sqrt{hw}$.

The total relative chances against being shot in battle, of two men of the respective heights and weights I have described, are as 3 to 2 in favour of the smaller man in respect to accidental shots, and in a decidedly more favourable proportion in respect to direct aim; the latter chance being compounded of the two following,—first, a better hope of not being aimed at, and secondly, a hope very little less than 3 to 2, of not being hit when made the object of an aim.

This is really an important consideration. Had Nelson been a large man, instead of a mere feather-weight, the probability is that he would not have survived so long. Let us for a moment consider the extraordinary dangers he survived. Leaving out of consideration the early part of his active service, which was only occasionally hazardous, as also the long interval of peace that followed it, we find him, æt. 35, engaged in active warfare with the French, when, through his energy at Bastia and Calvi, his name became dreaded throughout the Mediterranean. Æt. 37, he obtained great renown from his share in the battle of St. Vincent. He was afterwards under severe fire at Cadiz, also at Teneriffe where he lost an arm by a cannon-shot. He then received a pension of £1,000 a year. The memorial which he was required to present on this occasion, stated that he had been in action one hundred and twenty times, and speaks of other severe wounds besides the loss of his arm and eye. Æt. 40, he gained the victory of the Nile, where the contest was most bloody. He thereupon was created Baron Nelson with a pension of £3,000 a year, and received the thanks of Parliament; he was also made Duke of Brontë by the King of Naples, and he became idolised in England. Æt. 43, he was engaged in the severe battle of Copenhagen, and æt. 47 was shot at Trafalgar. Thus his active career extended through twelve years, during the earlier part of which he was much more frequently under fire than afterwards. Had he only lived through two-thirds, or even three-fourths, of his battles, he could not have commanded at the Nile, Copenhagen, or Trafalgar. His reputation under those circumstances would have been limited to that of a dashing captain or a young and promising admiral. Wellington was a small man; if he had been shot in the Peninsula, his reputation, though it would have undoubtedly been very great, would have lost the lustre of Waterloo. In short, to have survived is an essential condition to becoming a famed commander; yet persons equally endowed with military gifts—such as the requisite form of high intellectual and moral ability and of constitutional vigour—are by no means equally qualified to escape shot free. The enemy's bullets are least dangerous to the smallest men, and therefore small men are more likely to achieve high fame as commanders than their equally gifted contemporaries whose physical frames are larger.

I now give tables on precisely the same principle as those in previous chapters.

TABLE I

SUMMARY OF RELATIONSHIPS OF 32 COMMANDERS GROUPED INTO 27 (or ? 24[1]) FAMILIES

One relation (or two in family)

Berwick, Duke (*see* Marlborough)		Lawrence, Sir H.	B.
		Pyrrhus (*see* Alexander)	
Doria	N., &c.	Titus	F.
Hyder Ali	S.	Tromp	S.

Two or three relations (or three or four in family)

2. Charlemagne & Chas. Martel	F. G. GF.
Charles Martel (*see* Charlemagne)	
Clive	GB. GN.
Coligny (*but see* Maurice)	F. u. pP.
Cromwell	S. *u*S. *u*P.
Eugene	gB. g*N*.

[1] Coligny, Maurice, Turenne, and William I are impossible either to separate or to reckon as one family. If they were considered as only one family, the number of groups would be reduced from 27 to 24.

Two or three relations (or three or four in family)—cont.

2. Marlborough and Duke of
    Berwick   n. UP.
    Moore, Sir John   F. B.
    Nelson   *u*P. *g*u.
    Runjeet Singh   G. F.
    Saxe, Marshal   F. u. p*s*.
    Wellington   B. 2N.

Four or more relations (or five or more in family)

3. Alexander, Philip, and
    Pyrrhus   F. *f*. B. N. gBP.
    Bonaparte   *f*. B. *b*. S. 2N.
    Cæsar   *s*. *f*. *n*. *n*S.
    Charles XII (*see* Gustavus
    Adolphus)
2. Gustavus Adolphus and
    Charles XII   *s*. GF. G*b*. NP.
    Hannibal   F. 3B.
(? 4). Maurice of Nassau, Wil-
    liam the Silent, Coligny,
    and Turenne   F. g. n. NS.
    Napier   GGF. F. *u*S. 2B. n. US., &c.
    Napoleon (*see* Bonaparte)
    Philip and Pyrrhus (*see*
    Alexander)
    Raleigh   3B. 2uS.
    Scipio   F. G. 2S. 2P. GN.
    Turenne (*but see* Maurice) F., &c.
    William I (*but see* Maurice) 2S. P. PS.

Precisely similar conclusions are to be drawn from these
tables, as from those I have already given; but they make my
case much stronger than before.

I argue that the more able the man, the more numerous
ought his able kinsmen to be. That, in short, the names in the
third section of TABLE I should, on the whole, be those of men
of greater weight, than are included in the first section. There
cannot be a shadow of doubt that this is the fact. But the table
shows more. Its third section is proportionally longer than it
was in the Statesmen, and it was longer in these than in the
Judges. Now, the average natural gifts of the different groups

TABLE II[1]

Name of the degree	Corresponding letters				A	B	C	D
	Degrees of Kinship							
Father	12 F.	...	...	...	12	47	100	47·0
Brother	13 B.	...	...	...	13	50	150	33·3
Son	8 S.	...	...	...	8	31	100	32·0
Grandfather	3 G.	1 g.	...	...	4	16	200	8·0
Uncle	0 U.	2 u.	...	...	2	8	400	2·0
Nephew	6 N.	3 n.	...	...	9	35	400	9·0
Grandson	3 P.	0 p.	...	...	3	12	200	6·0
Great-grandfather	2 GF.	0 gF.	0 GF.	0 gF.	2	8	400	2·0
Great-uncle	1 GB.	1 gB.	0 GB.	0 gB.	2	8	800	1·0
First-cousin	1 US.	2 uS.	1 US.	1 uS.	5	20	800	2·5
Great-nephew	1 NS.	0 nS.	0 NS.	1 nS.	2	8	800	1·0
Great-grandson	0 PS.	0 pS.	0 PS.	0 pS.	0	0	400	0·0
All more remote	11	...	...	...	...	44	...	...

are apportioned in precisely the same order. The Commanders are more able than the Statesmen, and the Statesmen more able than the Judges. Consequently, comparing the three groups together, we find the abler men to have, on the average, the larger number of able kinsmen. Similarly, the proportion borne by those Commanders who have any eminent relations at all, to those who have not, is much greater than it is in Statesmen; and in these, much greater than in the Judges.

Their peculiar type of ability is largely transmitted. My limited list of Commanders contains several notable families of generals. That of William the Silent is a most illustrious

[1] For explanation, see similar table, p. 102.

family, and I must say, that in at least two out of his four wives—namely, the daughter of the Elector of Saxony and that of the great Coligny—he could not have married more discreetly. To have had Maurice of Nassau for a son, Turenne for a grandson, and our William III for a great-grandson, is a marvellous instance of hereditary gifts. Another most illustrious family is that of Charlemagne. First, Pepin de Heristhal, virtual sovereign of France; then his son, Charles Martel, who drove back the Saracenic invasion that had overspread the half of France; then his grandson, Pepin le Bref, the founder of the Carlovingian dynasty; and lastly, his great-grandson, Charlemagne, founder of the Germanic Empire. The three that come last, if not the whole of the four, were of the very highest rank as leaders of men.

Another yet more illustrious family is that of Alexander, including Philip of Macedon, the Ptolemys, and his second cousin, Pyrrhus. I acknowledge the latter to be a far-off relation, but Pyrrhus so nearly resembled Alexander in character, that I am entitled to claim his gifts as hereditary. Another family is that of Hannibal, his father and his brothers; again, there is that of the Scipios; also the interesting near relationship between Marlborough and the Duke of Berwick. Raleigh's kinships are exceedingly appropriate to my argument, as affording excellent instances of hereditary special aptitudes. I have spoken in the last chapter about Wellington and the Marquess of Wellesley, so I need not repeat myself here. Of Commanders of high but not equally illustrious stamp, I should mention the family of Napier, of Lawrence, and the singular naval race of Hyde Parker. There were five brothers Grant, all highly distinguished in Wellington's campaigns. I may as well mention, that though I know too little about the great Asiatic warriors, Genghis Khan and Timurlane, to insert them in my appendix, yet they are doubly though very distantly inter-related.

The distribution of ability among the different degrees of kinship, will be seen to follow much the same order that it did in the Statesmen and in the Judges.

APPENDIX TO COMMANDERS

LIST OF COMMANDERS THAT HAVE BEEN EXAMINED

*Those printed in Italics are included in my Dictionary of Kinships.
They are 32 in number; the remaining 27 are by no means wholly
destitute of gifted relations.*

Alexander; Baber; Belisarius; *Berwick, Duke of*; Blake;
Blucher; *Bonaparte*; *Cæsar*; *Charlemagne*; *Charles Martel*;
Charles XII; *Clive*; *Coligny*; Condé; *Cromwell*; Cyrus the
elder; Dandolo; *Doria*; Dundonald, Lord; *Eugene, Prince*;
Frederick the Great; Genghis Khan; *Gustavus Adolphus*;
Hannibal; Henri IV; *Hyder Ali*; *Lawrence, Sir H.*; Mahomet
Ali; Marius; Massena; *Maurice of Nassau*; *Marlborough*;
Miltiades; *Moore, Sir J.*; Moreau; *Napier, Sir Charles*;
Napoleon, see *Bonaparte*; *Nelson*; Peter the Great; Pericles;
Philip of Macedon; Pompey; *Pyrrhus*; *Raleigh*; *Runjeet Singh*;
Saladin; *Saxe, Marshal*; Schomberg; *Scipio Africanus*; Soult;
Themistocles; Timurlane; *Titus*; Trajan; *Tromp Marten*;
Turenne; Wallenstein; *Wellington*; *William I of Orange*; Wolfe.

ALEXANDER the Great. Is commonly reputed to be the commander of the greatest genius that the world has produced. When only æt. 16 he showed extraordinary
judgment in public affairs, having governed Macedonia
during the absence of his father. He succeeded to the
throne, and began his great career of conquest æt. 20,
and died æt. 32. Living as he did in a time when the
marriage tie was loose, there necessarily exists some doubt
as to his relationships. However, his reputed relationships are of a very high order. He inherited much of the
natural disposition of both of his parents; the cool forethought and practical wisdom of his father, and the ardent
enthusiasm and ungovernable passions of his mother.
He had four wives, but only one son, a posthumous child,
who was murdered æt. 12.

F.　Philip II of Macedonia, an illustrious general and statesman, who created and organised an army that was held

together by a system of discipline previously unknown, and kept the whole of Greece in check. Æt. 24 he had shown his cool forethought and practical skill in delivering himself from embarrassing political difficulties. He had a robust frame, a noble and commanding presence, a ready eloquence, and dexterity in the management of men and things. Cicero praises him for having been "always great." He keenly enjoyed the animal pleasures of life. He was murdered æt. 47.

f.   Olympias, ardent in her enthusiasms, ungovernable in her passions, ever scheming and intriguing. She suffered death like a heroine.

B.   (Half-brother.) Ptolemy Soter I. He became the first king of Egypt after Alexander's death, and was the son of Philip II by Arsinoe. Alexander rated him very highly. He was very brave, and had all the qualities of an able and judicious general. He was also given to literature, and he patronised learned men. He had twelve descendants, who became kings of Egypt, who were all called Ptolemy, and who nearly all resembled one another in features, in statesmanlike ability, in love of letters, and in their voluptuous dispositions. This race of Ptolemys is at first sight exceedingly interesting, on account of the extraordinary number of their close intermarriages. They were matched in and in like prize cattle; but these near marriages were unprolific—the inheritance mostly passed through other wives. Indicating the Ptolemys by numbers, according to the order of their succession, II married his niece, and afterwards his sister; IV his sister; VI and VII were brothers, and they both consecutively married the same sister—VII also subsequently married his niece; VIII married two of his own sisters consecutively; XII and XIII were brothers, and both consecutively married their sister, the famous Cleopatra. Thus there are no less than nine cases of close intermarriages distributed among the thirteen Ptolemys. However, when we put them, as below, into the form of a genealogical tree, we shall clearly see that the main line of descent was untouched by these intermarriages, except in the two cases of III and of VIII. The personal beauty and vigour of Cleopatra, the last of the race, cannot therefore be justly quoted in disproof of the evil effects of close breeding. On the contrary, the result of Ptolemaic experience was distinctly to show that intermarriages are followed by sterility.

GENEALOGICAL TREE OF THE PTOLEMYS

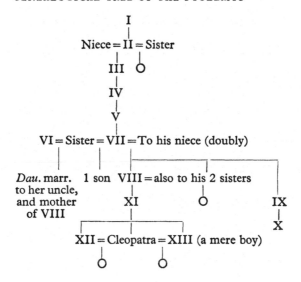

SURNAMES OF THE PTOLEMYS

I. Soter	VIII. Soter II
II. Philadelphus	IX. Alexander
III. Euergetes	X. Alexander II
IV. Philopator	XI. Auletes
V. Epiphanes	XII. Dionysus
VI. Philometor	XIII. Murdered when a boy
VII. Euergetes II (Physcon)	

ALEXANDER the Great—*continued*

N.   (Half-nephew). Ptolemy Philadelphus, a man of feeble
and sickly constitution, but of great ability and energy.
He cleared Egypt of marauding bands. He was the first
to tame African elephants, the elephants previously used
in Egypt having been invariably imported from India.
He founded the city Ptolemais, on the borders of
Ethiopia, expressly to receive the captured African
elephants, for the purpose of training them. He recom-
menced the old Egyptian enterprise of the Isthmus of
Suez canal, sent voyages of discovery down the Red Sea,
founded the Alexandrian library and caused the Septuagint
translation of the Bible to be made. With all this intelligence and energy, he had, as we have before said, a feeble
and sickly constitution, and the life he led was that of a
refined voluptuary.

[NS.] Ptolemy Euergetes. Was by no means his father's equal
in virtue and ability; but he was scarcely less celebrated
for his patronage of literature and science.

gBP. Pyrrhus, king of Epirus, the famous general. (I am not
sure of the second of these letters, whether B. or *b*.) He
was one of the greatest commanders that ever lived, and
might have become the most powerful monarch of his
day if he had had perseverance. The links that connected
him in blood with Alexander appear to have mostly been
of a remarkable character, but hardly deserving of special
record here. The character of Pyrrhus resembled that of
Alexander, whom he also took as his model from an early
age, being fired with the ambition of imitating his
exploits.

BERWICK, James Fitzjames, Duke of. One of the most distinguished commanders of the reign of Louis XIV. He was
the illegitimate son of James II by Arabella Churchill,
and became commander-in-chief of his father's Irish
army. He accompanied James II into exile, and entered
the French service, where he obtained great distinction,
especially in the war of the Spanish succession. He was

then made lieutenant-general of the French armies, and created a Spanish grandee.

u.   John Churchill, the great Duke of Marlborough. *See.*

BONAPARTE, Napoleon I. His extraordinary powers did not show themselves in boyhood. He was a taciturn lad. The annual report of the Inspector-General of Schools, made when Bonaparte was æt. 15, describes him as "Distinguished in mathematical studies, tolerably versed in history and geography, much behind in his Latin and belles-lettres and other accomplishments, of regular habits, studious and well-behaved, and enjoying excellent health" (Bourienne). He first distinguished himself, æt. 24, at the siege of Toulon. Became general of the army of Italy, when it was in a disorganised condition, æt. 26; and thenceforward began his almost uninterrupted career of victory. He was emperor, æt. 35; was vanquished at Waterloo, æt. 46; and died at St. Helena six years after. Among the more remarkable qualities of this extraordinary man were a prodigious memory and intellectual restlessness. His vigour was enormous.

There are so many considerable persons in the Bonaparte family, while at the same time some of these have been so helped and others so restrained by political circumstances, that it is very difficult to indicate which should be and which should not be selected as instances of hereditary genius. I will give a genealogical tree of the family (p. 202), and shall assume the ratio of hereditary influence to be—

f., B., *b.*, S., and 2 N.

Lucien, Eliza, and Louis were very gifted persons, and others of the brothers and sisters of Napoleon I were certainly above the average. There are members of the family yet alive, including the Cardinal at Rome, who may have high political parts to play.

GENEALOGY OF THE BONAPARTE FAMILY

Carlo Bonaparte, a Corsican judge

‖

Letitia Ramolini, known as "Madame la Mere." Was a heroine by nature, and one of the most beautiful young women of her day. She followed her husband in all his journeys through the then dangerously disturbed island. She was firm and undaunted. Afterwards she became "a pale but earnest woman, who, after speaking of anything that interested her deeply, sat with compressed lips and wide-open eyes, an image of firmness of purpose combined with depth of feeling" (Duchesse d'Abrantes). Napoleon esteemed her highly.

1. Joseph, King of Naples and then of Spain; *m.* Julia Clary
   } Daughters

2. Napoleon I; *m.* twice
   1. King of Rome, but now styled Napoleon II; a consumptive youth, *d. æt.* 20.
   2. Count Walewski (illegitimate); eminent diplomatist; French ambassador in England

3. Lucien, Prince de Canino; *m.* twice
   1. Charles Lucien
   2. Prince Louis; philologist

4. Eliza, Princess Piombino and Lucca; "the Italian Semiramis";
   } Napoleon Eliza

5. Louis, King of Holland; *m.* Hortense Beauharnais
   1. Napoleon Ch.
   2. Charles Napoleon
   3. Louis, Napoleon III

6. Marie Pauline; *m.* 1. Genl. Leclerc 2. Prince Camillo Borghese
   } No children

7. Jerome, King of Westphalia; President of State Council under Napoleon III; *m.* Princess of Wurtemburg
   1. Princess Mathilde; *m.* Prince Demidoff
   2. Prince Napoleon; *m.* Clothilde, dau. of King of Italy

8. Caroline; *m.* Murat, King of Naples
   } Lucien Napoleon Murat

CÆSAR, Julius; Dictator of Rome. Was not only a general of the highest order and a statesman, but also an orator and man of letters. He gave the greatest promise, even when a boy, and was remarkable in his youth for his judgment, literary ability, and oratorical powers. Owing to the disturbed state of Roman politics, he did not become Consul till æt. 41, nor begin his military career till æt. 42. Thenceforward he had unbroken success for fourteen years. He was assassinated æt. 56. He must be considered as a peculiarly profligate man, even when his character is measured by the low standard of the time in which he lived. He had no brothers, only two sisters. He was married four times, and had one illegitimate son, by Cleopatra, called Cæsarion, whom Augustus caused to be executed while still a boy, for political reasons; also one daughter, as follows—

s. Julia, married to Pompey, and greatly beloved by him (though the marriage was merely made up for political reasons) and by the whole nation. She was singularly endowed with ability, virtue, and beauty. Died prematurely, four years after her marriage, from the shock of a serious alarm, when she was advanced in pregnancy.

f. Aurelia: seems to have been no ordinary woman; she carefully watched over the education of her children, and Cæsar always treated her with the greatest affection and respect.

n. Atia, the mother of Augustus, who carefully tended his education, and who is classed along with Cornelia, the mother of the Gracchi, and Aurelia, the mother of Cæsar.

*n*S. Augustus Cæsar, 1st Emperor of Rome. The public opinion of his own time considered him to be an excellent prince and statesman. He was adopted by Cæsar, who rated him very highly, and devoted much time out of his busy life to his education. He had great caution and moderation. Was very successful as a general in early life, after the death of Julius Cæsar. Married three wives, but left only one daughter.

CÆSAR, Julius—*continued*

U.   Sex. Julius Cæsar; Consul, B.C. 91.

?.   Mark Antony. His mother belonged to the family of
     Julius Cæsar, but in what degree she was connected with
     it is unknown.

     (Caius Marius, the general, married the aunt (*u.*) of
     Julius Cæsar, but had no children by her: Marius the
     younger, who had much of the character and ability of
     Caius, being only an adopted son.)

CHARLEMAGNE, founder of the Germanic Empire and a great
     general. Began his wars æt. 30; died æt. 72. Was an
     eminent legislator and great patron of learning. Had very
     many children, including Louis le Débonnaire, both
     legitimate and illegitimate.

GF. Pepin le Gros (de Heristhal), general of distinction. He
     put an end to the Merovingian dynasty, and was virtual
     sovereign of France.

G.   Charles Martel. *See below.*

F.   Pepin le Bref, the first of the Carlovingian kings of
     France.

CHARLES MARTEL. Ancestor of the Carlovingian race of kings
     of France. Victor over the Saracens in the great and
     decisive battle between Tours and Poictiers.

F.   Pelin le Gros. *See paragraph above.*

S.   Pepin, the first of the Carlovingian kings of France.

P.   Charlemagne. *See above.*

CHARLES XII of Sweden. *See under* GUSTAVUS ADOLPHUS.

CLIVE, 1st Lord; Governor-General of India. "A heaven-
     born general, who, without experience, surpassed all the
     officers of his time" (Lord Chatham). Victorious at Plassy
     æt. 32. Committed suicide æt. 49.

GB. Sir G. Clive, Judge, Curs. B. Exch. (Geo. II).

GN. Sir E. Clive, Judge, Just. C.P. (Geo. III).

COLIGNY, Gaspard de; French admiral, general, and states-
     man. Famous Huguenot leader. Perished at the Massacre
     of St. Bartholomew.

COLIGNY, Gaspard de—*continued*

F. Gaspard de Coligny, Marshal of France; distinguished in the Italian wars of Charles VIII, Louis XI, and Francis I.

u. Duc de Montmorency, Marshal and Constable of France. The most illustrious member of a great French family. He was illiterate, but, owing to his natural ability and large experience, became a most able counsellor and statesman.

pP. William III of England. *See pedigree under* MAURICE.

CROMWELL, Oliver; Lord Protector of the Commonwealth.

US. Hampden the patriot, whom Lord Clarendon speaks of as having "a head to contrive, a tongue to persuade, and a heart to execute any mischief"—this word "mischief" meaning, of course, antagonism to the King.

Up. Edmund Waller, the poet, a man of very considerable abilities both in parliamentary eloquence and in poetry, but he was not over-steadfast in principle. He was n. to Hampden.

S. Henry; behaved with gallantry in the army, and acted with much distinction in Ireland as Lord Deputy.
He had one other son, and four daughters, who married able men, but their descendants were not remarkable.

DORIA, Andrea; naval commander and illustrious statesman. He drove the French from Genoa, and was entitled by the Genoese Senate "The father and saviour of their country." Famous for his victories over the corsairs of the Mediterranean. He was æt. 85 at his last battle. He was of a younger branch of the great Doria family, very many of whom are highly distinguished in Italian history. He had no children. Died æt 94.

N. Fillipino Doria, who succeeded him as admiral, and obtained an important victory over the French.

EUGENE, Prince; Austrian general and statesmen. Colleague of Marlborough; victor over the Turks. He was intended for the Church, but showed a decided preference for arms. He had eminent bravery and ability, and great physical strength. His qualities and birth ensured him such rapid promotion that he commanded the Austrian imperial army in Piedmont æt. 25. Napoleon ranked him in generalship along with Turenne and Frederick the Great.

gB. Cardinal Mazarin, the great minister during the minority of Louis XIV.

gN. Hortense Mancini, the accomplished and beautiful Duchess of Mazarin, and married to the Duc de la Meilleraie. She was greatly admired in England, where she died 1699.

GUSTAVUS ADOLPHUS. Not only a very eminent general and statesman, but also a patron of science and literature. He succeeded to the throne æt. 17, and immediately afterwards distinguished himself in war. He became the head of the German Protestant cause. He was shot in battle, at Lutzen, æt. 38.

s. Christina, Queen of Sweden; his only child. She was a woman of high ability, but of masculine habits, and very eccentric. She was a great admirer of Alexander the Great. She attracted to her court many eminent European philosophers and scholars, including Grotius, Descartes, and Vossius. She became Roman Catholic, and abdicated the crown in a fit of caprice, but endeavoured, unsuccessfully, after some years, to resume it.

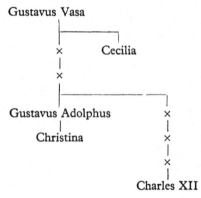

There was much ability and eccentricity in the Swedish royal family, scattered over several generations. Thus Gustavus Vasa, his daughter Cecilia, and, in a much lower generation, Charles XII, were all of them very remarkable and, in many respects, very similar characters. The connexion between them is easily seen in the table above. I will now describe them in order.

GF. Gustavus Vasa, though proscribed and an outcast, yet, æt. 31, succeeded in uniting the Swedes to expel the Danes, and became the founder of the Swedish dynasty.

G*b*. Cecilia, his daughter, who was "a very prototype of the wayward and eccentric Christina; had an intense longing to travel, and imitate the far-famed example of the Queen of Sheba." She went to England with her husband, where she got frightfully into debt. She died æt. 87, after leading a rambling and dissolute life. (Introduction to *England as seen by Foreigners*, by W. B. Rye, 1865.)

NP. Charles XII. Showed great self-will and remarkable fondness for military exercises from his earliest youth. He had a great desire to emulate Alexander. Succeeded to the throne æt. 15; began his wars, æt. 18, with Russia, Denmark, and Poland, defeating them all in turn. He had great courage and constitutional power; was obstinate, rash, and cruel (his father, Charles XI, was also obstinate, harsh, and despotic). He was killed in battle æt. 37.

HANNIBAL, the great Carthaginian general. He was entrusted with high command æt. 18, and had become illustrious æt. 26. He led his Carthaginian army, with its troops of elephants, from Spain across France and the Alps. Descending into Italy, he forced his way against the Roman power, and at that immense distance from his base of operations utterly defeated them at Cannæ. He was afterwards defeated by them under Scipio in Africa. He poisoned himself to avoid Roman vengeance, æt. 64.

F. Hamilcar Barca, "the Great"; commanded in Spain while still a mere youth. Nothing is known of his ancestry.

HANNIBAL—*continued*

B.   Hasdrubal, a worthy rival of the fame of his father and brother. He crossed the Alps subsequently to Hannibal, and was at last defeated by the Romans and killed.

B.   Mago, a good general, who co-operated with his brothers.

B.   (Half-brother, son of Hannibal's mother.) Hasdrubal, general in Spain.

HYDER ALI. The ablest and most formidable enemy of the British power in India. He began life as a soldier of fortune; he rose to be prime minister, and then Sultan of Mysore, æt. 44.

S.   Tippoo Saib. Less able than his father, but more ferocious, and an equally determined enemy of England; killed in battle at Seringapatam.

LAWRENCE, Sir Henry; Governor of Oude; a man of high military and administrative genius; the principal support of the British rule at the outbreak of the Indian Mutiny; he defended Lucknow, and was killed there. He was greatly beloved and eminently esteemed.

[F.] An officer of some distinction in India.

B.   John, created Lord Lawrence, Governor-General of India; excellent administrator; was one of the principal saviours of the British rule at the time of the Indian Mutiny.

MAURICE OF NASSAU. One of the greatest captains of his age; governed the Low Countries, æt. 18, after his father's death, with great courage and talent; defeated and drove away the Spaniards in 1597, æt. 30.

(See pedigree p. 209)

F.   William the 1st of Nassau, "the Silent." "The guiding-star of a great nation" (Motley). When æt. 15 he was the intimate and almost confidential friend of Charles V. He became the fierce antagonist of Philip in defence of Protestantism, and finally, after vanquishing the Spaniards, created the Union of Utrecht, the basis of the Dutch Republic. He was assassinated æt. 51. He married

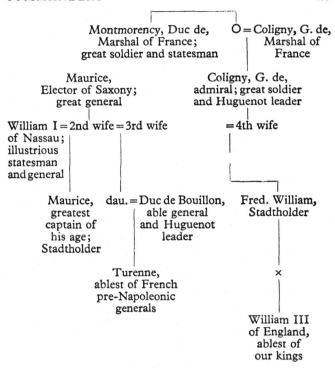

four times; was father of Maurice of Nassau, grandfather of Turenne, and great-grandfather of our William III.

g. Maurice, Elector of Saxony; great military genius.

n. (half-brother's son.) Turenne, the great French general. *See.*

NS. William III, Stadtholder, and King of England. He was an able general in Holland æt. 22, and then, partly by virtue of his marriage, became King of England, and was the ablest monarch we ever possessed. He was cold and taciturn, but singularly clear-sighted, steadfast, and courageous. He was a seven months' child. Died æt. 52, from an accident when riding.

MARLBOROUGH, John Churchill, Duke of. The ablest general and most consummate statesman of his time. He invariably distinguished himself in his early campaigns. He attracted the notice of Turenne æt. 22, who prophesied that his "handsome Englishman" would one day prove himself a master of the art of war. He was singularly cool in danger, and had more head than heart, for he was selfish and calculating. He had one son, who died very young, and four daughters.

n.   James Fitzjames, Duke of Berwick. *See* BERWICK. "A commander of renown, only less illustrious than his maternal uncle."

UP.   Sir J. Churchill, Judge M.R. (James II).

MOORE, Sir John. One of the most distinguished British officers of modern times; commanded the reserve of the British army in Egypt, æt. 40; was killed in battle at Corunna, æt. 48. He was a man of chivalrous courage.

F.   Dr. John Moore, a well-known miscellaneous writer, *Zeluco*, &c. A man of high morals, shrewd in his remarks, and of a caustic humour.

B.   Admiral Sir Graham Moore, G.C.B., &c.

[S.]   Captain John Moore, R.N.; distinguished himself in command of the *Highflyer* in the Crimean War, and was private secretary to the Duke of Somerset when First Lord of the Admiralty.

NAPIER, Sir Charles; general; conqueror of Scinde. The most eminent member of a very eminent military family.

GGF.   Napier of Merchistoun, inventor of logarithms.

F.   Colonel Napier; was himself cast in the true heroic mould. He had uncommon powers of mind and body; had scientific tastes and ability; was Superintendent of Woolwich Laboratory and Comptroller of Army Accounts.

*u*S.   Right Hon. Charles James Fox, statesman and orator. *See* Fox for his numerous gifted relatives.

B.   General Sir William Napier, historian of the Peninsular War.

NAPIER, Sir Charles—*continued*

B.   General Sir George Napier, Governor of the Cape; was
       offered in 1849 the command of the Piedmontese army,
       which he declined.

[2B.] There were two other brothers, Richard, Q.C., and Henry,
       Captain, R.N., who might fairly be also adduced as
       examples of inherited genius.

US.   Admiral Sir Charles Napier; distinguished for gallantry
       in his youth in the French War, afterwards in Portugal,
       then at the Siege of Acre. When broken in health, he
       was made Commander-in-Chief of the Baltic Fleet in the
       Russian War.
       Lord Napier, the diplomatist, is another able relative.
       Mem. Lord Napier of Magdala is not a relative of this
       family.

NAPOLEON I. *See* BONAPARTE.

NELSON, Lord; admiral. The greatest naval hero of England.
       He had neither a strong frame nor a hardy constitution
       when a boy. He had won all his victories, and was killed,
       æt. 47. His remarkable relationships are distant, but
       worthy of record; they are—

[g.]   Maurice Suckling, D.D., Prebendary of Westminster.

uP.   Lord Cranworth, Lord Chancellor.

gu.   (Mother's mother's uncle.) Sir Robert Walpole. *See.*

PHILIP OF MACEDONIA. *See under* ALEXANDER.

S.   Alexander the Great ⎫
S.   Ptolemy I of Egypt   ⎬ *See under* ALEXANDER.
P.   Ptolemy Philadelphus ⎭

PYRRHUS.

GBp.   Alexander the Great was his second cousin through
       Alexander's mother, but I am not informed of the other
       links. *See under* ALEXANDER.

RALEIGH, Sir Walter; adventurous explorer and coloniser,
       also statesman, courtier, and writer, as well as an
       eminent commander by land and by sea.

B.   (half-brother.) Sir Humphrey Gilbert, renowned navi-
       gator; proposer of the North-west passage to China.

It was he who took possession of Newfoundland. He was lost at sea.

2B. John and Adrian Gilbert. "Sir Humphrey's fame has eclipsed that of his brothers John and Adrian, but all three helped notably to make England what it is, and all were fellow-workers in the colonisation of North America" (Edwards' *Life of Raleigh*).

uS. Henry Champernoun, leader of the band of English volunteers to the Huguenot camp.

uS. Gawen Champernoun, engaged with Raleigh in later service in the civil wars of France.

RUNJEET SINGH, founder of the Sikh empire. His father died when he was still a boy; and his mother, who was young and handsome, did all she could to corrupt him, that he might be unfit to rule when he grew to manhood: nevertheless he entered, æt. 17, on a career of ambition, and by æt. 29 he had acquired large dominion. This energetic man ruled for forty years in undisputed mastery over numerous turbulent provinces, although his health was so broken by excesses and low indulgence, æt. 50, that he could not stand without support. He retained authority till his death in 1839, æt. 59.

G. Churruth Singh, from a low condition and a vagrant life, became master of Sookur Chukea, in the Punjaub.

F. Maha Singh extended his father's rule, and though he died æt. 30, had carried on war with his neighbours for fourteen years, and, it is said, had commanded at one time 60,000 horsemen.

SAXE, Marshal; famous general under Louis XV. He was of large size and extraordinary physical strength; was distinguished in bodily exercises from childhood. Æt. 12 he ran away to join the army. In character he was exceedingly *Don Juanesque*. He was a well-practised commander, who loved his profession, but his abilities were not of the very highest order.

F. Augustus II, King of Poland (the Marshal being one of his numerous progeny of illegitimate sons). Augustus was elected king out of many competitors, and though beaten by Charles XII was, nevertheless, a man of mark. He was luxurious and licentious.

u. Count Köningsmarck was brother to Marshal Saxe's beautiful but frail mother. He intrigued with the wife of George I of England, and was assassinated. Was a handsome dashing man, always in gay adventures.

ps. Madame Dudevant (Georges Sand), the French novelist. Her grandmother was a natural daughter of Marshal Saxe.

SCIPIO, P. Cornelius; Africanus Major; conqueror of Hannibal, and scholar. The greatest man of his age; perhaps the greatest of Rome, with the exception of Julius Cæsar. He was only 24 years old when appointed to the supreme command of the Roman armies in Spain.

The Scipio family produced many great men, and to that family Rome was largely indebted for obtaining the empire of the world.

F. P. Cornelius Scipio; a great general, but defeated by Hannibal, and finally defeated and killed by the Carthaginian forces under Hasdrubal and Mago.

G. L. Cornelius Scipio; drove the Carthaginians out of Corsica and Sardinia.

S. P. Corn. Sc. Africanus; prevented by weak health from taking part in public affairs, but Cicero remarks that with the greatness of his father's mind he possessed a larger amount of learning.

His brother, L. Corn. S. Afr., is called "a degenerate son of his illustrious sire."

s. Cornelia, who married Tiber. Sempr. Gracchus, was almost idolised by the people. She inherited from her father a love of literature, and united in her person the severe virtues of the old Roman matron with the superior knowledge, refinement, and civilisation which then began to prevail in the higher classes of Rome. Her letters were extant in the time of Cicero, and were considered models of composition.

SCIPIO, P. Cornelius—*continued*

2P.   Tiberius and Caius Gracchus, bold defenders of popular rights; famous for their eloquence and their virtues. Both were assassinated.

GN.   Scipio Nasica, the jurist.

    Mem. P. Corn. Sc. Æmilianus, Africanus Minor, was not of Scipio blood, but was cousin by the mother's side of P. Corn. Sc. Africanus (*see above*), who adopted him as his son. He was a most accomplished scholar and distinguished orator.

TITUS, Flav. Vesp.; Emperor of Rome. Able and virtuous; distinguished in war; exceedingly beloved. In his youth he was somewhat dissipated, but after he became emperor he showed himself eminently moderate and just.

F.   Vespasian. Rose through successive ranks to be Emperor of Rome, entirely through his own great merits as a general and as a statesman.

TROMP, Marten; famous Dutch admiral, who rose through his own merits to the supreme command at a momentous epoch. Though he was captured in youth, and his professional advancement thereby checked for some years, he had become a noted admiral and a dreaded opponent of the English æt. 40. Killed in battle æt. 56.

S.   Cornelius van Tromp, celebrated Dutch admiral, who obtained that rank, on active service, æt. 33. His professional eminence was beyond all question, though scarcely equal to that of his father.

TURENNE, Henri, Viscount de; the greatest of French generals before the time of Napoleon. All his acts bear the impress of a truly great mind. He was clear and comprehensive in his views, energetic in action, and above the narrow feelings of a mere religious partisan. He was eminently pure in domestic life. He had weak health till æt. 11. As a boy he was fond of books, and pored over the lives of eminent warriors. He learned slowly and with difficulty, rebelled against restraint, and showed dogged perseverance. He was very fond of athletic exercises, and improved his health by practising them. His first opportunity of distinction was æt. 23, on which occasion he was made "maréchal du camp," then the next step in rank to Maréchal de France. He was killed by a cannon-shot æt. 64.

F. Henri, Duc de Bouillon, one of the ablest soldiers bred in the school of Henry IV. His high rank, love of letters, attachment to the Calvinistic faith, and abilities as a statesman, raised him to the leadership of the Huguenot party after the death of that prince.

g. William I of Orange, "the Silent." *See under* MAURICE.

u. (mother's half-brother.) Maurice of Nassau. *See.*

uP. William III of England.

WELLINGTON, the Duke of; greatest of modern English generals, a firm statesman, and a terse writer. He broke the Mahratta power in India æt. 35; then became Secretary for Ireland. Æt. 39 was appointed to command the British army in Spain, and he had won Waterloo and completed his military career æt. 46.

B. Marquess Wellesley (*see under* STATESMEN), Governor-General of India, statesman and scholar.

[B.] Baron Cowley, diplomatist.

[F.] Earl of Mornington, of musical ability.

N. Earl Cowley, diplomatist, English ambassador to France.

N. Rev. Henry Wellesley, D.D., scholar and man of remarkable taste, Principal of New Inn Hall, Oxford.

WILLIAM I of Orange, "the Silent." *See under* MAURICE.

S. Maurice of Nassau. *See.*

S. Frederick William, Stadtholder in the most flourishing days of the Republic.

p. Turenne (*see*), the great French general.

SP. William III of England.

LITERARY MEN

Those who are familiar with the appearance of great libraries, and have endeavoured to calculate the number of famed authors, whose works they include, cannot fail to be astonished at their multitude. The years go by: in every year, every nation produces literary works of sterling value, and stores of books have accumulated for centuries. Among the authors, who are the most eminent? This is a question I feel incompetent to answer. It would not be difficult to obtain lists of the most notable literary characters of particular periods, but I have found none that afford a compact and trustworthy selection of the great writers of all times. Mere popular fame in after ages is an exceedingly uncertain test of merit, because authors become obsolete. Their contributions to thought and language are copied and re-copied by others, and at length they become so incorporated into the current literature and expressions of the day, that nobody cares to trace them back to their original sources, any more than they interest themselves in tracing the gold converted into sovereigns, to the nuggets from which it was derived or to the gold-diggers who discovered the nuggets.

Again: a man of fair ability who employs himself in literature turns out a great deal of good work. There is always a chance that some of it may attain a reputation very far superior to its real merits, because the author may have something to narrate which the world wants to hear; or he may have had particular experiences which qualify him to write works of fiction, or otherwise to throw out views, singularly apposite to the wants of the time but of no importance in after years. Here, also, fame misleads.

Under these circumstances, I thought it best not to occupy myself over-much with older times; otherwise, I should have been obliged to quote largely in justification of my lists of literary worthies: but rather to select authors of modern date, or those whose reputation has been freshly preserved in England. I have therefore simply gone through dictionaries, extracted the names of literary men whom I found the most prominent, and have described those who had decidedly eminent relations in my appendix. I have, therefore, left out several, whom others might with reason judge worthy to have appeared. My list is a very incongruous collection; for it includes novelists, historians, scholars, and philosophers. There are only two peculiarities common to all these men; the one is a desire of expressing themselves, and the other a love of ideas, rather than of material possessions. Mr. Disraeli, who is himself a good instance of hereditary literary power, in a speech at the anniversary of the Royal Literary Fund, May 6, 1868, described the nature of authors. His phrase epitomises what has been graphically delineated in his own novels, and, I may add, in those of Sir Edward Bulwer Lytton, now Lord Lytton (who, with his brother Sir Henry Bulwer, and in his son "Owen Meredith," is a still more remarkable example of hereditary literary gifts than Mr. Disraeli). He said: "The author is, as we must ever remember, a peculiar organisation. He is a being with a predisposition which with him is irresistible—a bent which he cannot in any way avoid; whether it drags him to the abstruse researches of erudition, or induces him to mount, into the fervid and turbulent atmosphere of imagination." The majority of the men described in the appendix to this chapter justify the description by Mr. Disraeli. Again, that the powers of many of them were of the highest order, no one can doubt. Several were prodigies in boyhood, as Grotius, Lessing, and Niebuhr; many others were distinguished in youth; Charlotte Brontë published *Jane Eyre* æt. 22; Chateaubriand was of note at an equally early age; Fénelon made an impression when only 15; Sir Philip Sidney was of high mark before he was 21, and had acquired his great fame, and won the heart of the nation in a few more years, for he was killed in battle when only 32. I may add, that there are occasional cases of great literary men having been the reverse of gifted in youth. Boileau is the only instance in my appendix. He was a dunce at school, and dull till he was 30. But, among other literary men of whom I have notes, Goldsmith was accounted a dull child, and he was anything but distinguished at Dublin University. He began to write well æt. 32. Rousseau was thought a dunce at school when he ran away æt. 16.

It is a striking confirmation of what I endeavoured to prove in an early chapter—that the highest order of reputation is independent of external aids—to note how irregularly many of the men and women have been educated whose names appear in my appendix—such as Boileau, the Brontë family, Chateaubriand, Fielding, the two Gramonts, Irving, Carsten Niebuhr, Porson (in one sense), Roscoe, Le Sage, J. C. Scaliger, Sévigné, and Swift.

I now give my usual table, but I do not specify with confidence the numbers of eminent literary people contained in the thirty-three families it includes. They have many literary relations of considerable merit, but I feel myself unable, for the reasons stated at the beginning of this chapter, to sort out those that are "eminent" from among them. The families of Taylor, both those of Norwich and those of Ongar, have been inserted as being of great hereditary interest, but only a few of their members (*see* AUSTEN) are summed up in the following table.

TABLE I

SUMMARY OF RELATIONSHIPS OF 52 LITERARY PERSONS, GROUPED INTO 33 FAMILIES

One relation (or two in the family)

	Addison	F.	Edgeworth	F.
	Aikin	b.	Lamb	b.
2.	Arnold	S.	2. Mill	S.
2.	Bossuet	N.	2. Niebuhr	F.
2.	Champollion	B.	Roscoe	S.
	Chateaubriand	b.	2. Scaliger	F.

Two or three relations (or three or four in the family)

	Austen, Mrs.	*s*. N.		Lessing	2 B. N.
	Bentham	B. N.	2.	Palgrave	2 S.
	Boileau	2 S.		Sage, Le	2 S.
	Brontë	B. 2*b*.	3.	Seneca	F. B. N.
3.	Fénelon	N. 2 NS.		Sévigné	S. 2 US.
2.	Gramont	gB. B. P.	2.	Swift	GN. UP. UPS.
	Helvetius	F. G.		Trollope	2 S.

Four or more relations (or five or more in the family)

	Alison	B. F. u. g. gB. gF. gG.
	Fielding	g. uS. B. *b*.
2.	Grotius	G. F. U. B. S.
	Hallam	F. *f*. 2 S. *s*.
	Macaulay	G. F. 2 U. US. n.
	Porson	F. *f*. B. *b*.
2.	Schlegel	F. 2 U. B.
2.	Staël	G. F. U. *f*. US. UP.
2.	Stephen	F. B. 2 S.
4.	Stephens	F. g. *f*. B. U*s*. p.
	Sidney	F. g. u. u*S*. *b*. n. P. PS., &c.
	[Taylors of Norwich]	
	[Taylors of Ongar]	

It would be both a tedious and an unnecessary task, if I applied the same tests to this table with the same minuteness that they were applied to those inserted in previous chapters. Its contents are closely similar in their general character, and therefore all that can be derived from an analysis of the others may, with equal justice, be derived from this. The proportion of eminent grandsons is small, but the total number is insufficient to enable us to draw conclusions from that fact, especially as the number of eminent sons is not small in the same ratio. There are other major peculiarities which will appear more distinctly when all the corresponding tables are collated and discussed towards the end of the book. In the meantime, we may rest satisfied that an analysis of kinsfolk shows literary genius to be fully as hereditary as any other kind of ability we have hitherto discussed.

TABLE II[1]

Degrees of Kinship					A	B	C	D
Name of the degree	Corresponding letters							
Father	16 F.	...	...	...	16	48	100	48
Brother	14 B.	...	...	...	14	42	150	28
Son	17 S.	...	...	...	17	51	100	51
Grandfather	4 G.	4 g.	...	...	8	24	200	12
Uncle	6 U.	2 u.	...	...	8	24	400	6
Nephew	6 N.	2 n.	...	...	8	24	400	6
Grandson	2 P.	1 p.	...	...	3	9	200	4·5
Great-grandfather	0 GF.	1 gF.	0 GF.	0 gF.	1	3	400	1
Great-uncle	0 GB.	2 gB.	0 GB.	0 gB.	2	6	800	1
First-cousin	4 US.	2 uS.	0 US.	0 uS.	6	18	800	2·5
Great-nephew	2 NS.	0 nS.	0 NS.	0 nS.	2	6	800	1
Great-grandson	1 PS.	0 pS.	0 PS.	0 pS.	1	3	400	1
All more remote	5	...	...	...	5	15	...	0

[1] See p. 102 for explanation.

APPENDIX TO LITERARY MEN

The merits of literary men are so differently rated by their contemporaries and by posterity, that I gave up in despair the project of selecting a small list of first-class authors. I have, therefore, confined myself to the names of able writers that came most prominently in my way, and have occasionally inserted men who were not quite of the first class, but who were interesting in other respects. It is remarkable to find how little is known of the near kinsmen of many of the greatest literary men, especially of those who lived in ancient times; and I have reason to think that our ignorance is in many cases due to mere historical neglect rather than to the fact of their abilities or achievements being unworthy of record. The general result of my inquiries is such as to convince me, that more than one-half of the great literary men have had kinsmen of high ability.

The total number of names included in my list of kinships is thirty-seven. I will here add the names of those into whose lives I inquired, who do not appear to have had "eminent" relations; they are nineteen in number, as follow:—

Cervantes; De Foe (his son wrote, but was ridiculed by Pope); Fichte; La Fontaine; Genlis, Mme.; Gibbon (however, *see* Lord Chancellor Hardwicke for a distant kinship); Goldsmith; Jeffrey; Samuel Johnson (but his father was not an ordinary man); Montaigne; Montesquieu; Rabelais; Richardson, the novelist; Rousseau; Scott, Sir W.; Sydney Smith; Smollett; Sterne; and Voltaire.

ADDISON, Joseph: author of the *Spectator*, &c. He was well known to the great patrons of literature, æt. 25. Was a most elegant writer. Secretary of State under George I.

F. Launcelot Addison; a divine of considerable learning and observation; Dean of Lichfield; author.

AIKIN, John, M.D.; eminent physician and popular author of the last century. (*Evenings at Home.*)

b. Mrs. Barbauld, charming writer of children's tales.

[S.] Arthur Aikin, inherited much of his father's literary talent, but was chiefly interested in science. Editor of the *Annual Review*.

[s.] Lucy Aikin, also authoress.

ALISON, Sir Archibald: author of *History of Europe*; created a Baronet for his literary merits.

B. Dr. William Pulteney Alison, Professor of Medicine in Edinburgh, and first Physician to the Queen in Scotland.

F. Rev. Archibald, author of *Essays on the Nature and Principles of Taste*.

ALISON, Sir Archibald—*continued*
u.   Dr. James Gregory, Professor of Medicine in Edinburgh.
g.   Dr. John Gregory, Professor of Philosophy and of Medicine in Aberdeen, afterwards of Medicine in Edinburgh.
gB. and gF., also Professors of Medicine.
gG.   James Gregory, inventor of the reflecting telescope. *See* GREGORY, *under* SCIENCE.

ARNOLD, Thomas, D.D.; Head Master of Rugby; scholar, historian, divine, and administrator; founder of the modern system of public school education. Was stiff and formal as a child; hated early rising; became highly distinguished at Oxford, and was singularly beloved by those who knew him.
S.   Matthew Arnold, poet, and Professor of Poetry at Oxford. [Also other sons of more than average ability.]

BENTHAM, Jeremy; political and juridical writer; founder of a school of philosophy.
B.   General Sir Samuel Bentham, an officer of distinction in the Russian service, who had a remarkable mechanical genius.
N.   George, eminent modern botanist. President of the Linnæan Society.

BOILEAU, Nicholas (surnamed Despréaux); French poet, satirist, and critic. Was educated for the law, which he hated; showed no early signs of ability, but was dull until æt. 30. As a boy he was thought a confirmed dunce.
S.   Gilles, an eminent literary man, writer of satires of great merit; had a lively wit. His health was bad; *d.* young, æt. 38.
S.   Jacques, a Doctor of the Sorbonne, of great learning and ability. Author of various publications, all on singular subjects.

BOSSUET, Jacques Bénigne; one of the most famous of Papal controversialists against Protestantism; was a laborious student. He was a priest, and therefore had no family.
N.   Bishop of Troyes; editor of his uncle's works.

BRONTE, Charlotte (her *nom de plume* was Currer Bell); novelist. She was the most conspicuous member of a family remarkable for their intellectual gifts, restless mental activity, and wretched constitutions. Charlotte Brontë and her five brothers and sisters were all consumptive, and died young. *Jane Eyre* was published when Charlotte was æt. 22.

[F.] Rev. Patrick Brontë. Had been precocious and was ambitious, though a clergyman of scanty means, in a rude, out-of-the-way village.

[U. and *U.* several.] Rev. Patrick Brontë had nine brothers and sisters, all remarkable for their strength and beauty.

[*f.*] Was refined, pious, pure, and modest.

[*u.*] Was precise, old-looking, and dressed utterly out of fashion.

B. Patrick, who went altogether astray, and became a grief to the family, was perhaps the greatest natural genius among them all.

b. Emily Jane (Ellis Bell), *Wuthering Heights* and *Agnes Grey.*

b. Anne (Acton Bell), *Tenant of Wildfield Hall.*

[2*b.*] Maria and Jane; were almost as highly endowed with intellectual gifts as their sisters.

CHAMPOLLION, Jean François; interpreter of hieroglyphic writing, and author on Egyptian antiquities. He was one of the party of *savans* in Napoleon's expedition.

B. Jean Jacques, historian and antiquary. Author of several works. Librarian to the present Emperor of the French.

CHATEAUBRIAND, Fr. Aug. Vicomte de; a distinguished French writer and a politician, but half mad; his education was desultory, for he was first intended for the Navy, then for the Church, and then for the Army. He wholly abandoned himself to study and retirement, æt. 20; afterwards he sought adventures in the unsettled parts of America. He served in several ministerial posts under Louis XVIII. He sank into despondency in advanced life. Most of his ten brothers and sisters died in youth;

several of them resembled him in genius and disposition; one of them, viz.—

b. Lucile, had the genius, the constitution, and the eccentricity of J. J. Rousseau.

EDGEWORTH, Maria; a favourite authoress and moralist, whose writings exhibit "a singular union of sober sense and inexhaustible invention." She was æt. 31 when she began to write; *d.* æt. 83.

F. Richard Lovell Edgeworth (*see* LOVELL the Judge), writer on various subjects, in much of which he was aided by his daughter; a wonderfully active man in body and mind; interested in everything, and irrepressible. Married four wives. There was forty years' difference of age between the eldest and youngest of his numerous children. Maria was daughter of the first wife.

ETIENNE. *See* STEPHENS.

FÉNELON, François; Archbishop of Cambrai, in France; author of *Télémaque*; remarkable for his graceful, simple, and charming style of composition; a man of singular serenity and Christian morality. He was very eloquent in the pulpit. He preached his first sermon æt. 15, which had a great success. (Being a priest, he had no family.)

?. Bertrand de Salagnac, Marquis de la Mothe, diplomatist, Ambassador to England in the time of Elizabeth, and a distinguished officer, was his ancestor (but *quære* in what degree: he died seventy years before François was born).

N. Gabriel Jacques Fénelon, Marquis de la Mothe, Ambassador of France to Holland; wrote *Mémoires Diplomatiques*.

NS. François Louis, littérateur.

NS. Abbé de Fénelon, head of a charitable establishment for Savoyards in Paris; greatly beloved. Was guillotined in the French Revolution.

FIELDING, Henry; novelist, author of *Tom Jones*. Byron calls him the "prose Homer of human nature." His education was desultory, owing to the narrow means of his father, then a Lieutenant, but afterwards General. Began playwriting æt. 21, was very dissipated, and reckless in money matters. Entered the Temple and studied law with ardour; wrote two valuable pamphlets on crime and pauperism, and was made a Middlesex Justice.

g. Sir Henry Gould, Justice Queen's Bench (Q. Anne).

uS. Sir Henry Gould, Justice Common Pleas (Geo. III).

[G.] John Fielding, Chaplain to William III.

B. (Half brother.) Sir John Fielden, excellent magistrate, though blind. He wrote on police administration.

b. Sarah, a women of considerable learning, and an authoress.

GRAMONT, Anthony, Duke of; marshal of France; soldier and diplomatist; author of famous *Memoirs*, but not quite so charming to read as those of his brother.

*g*B. Cardinal Richelieu. *See*

B. Gramont, Philibert, Comte de; wit and courtier; *d.* æt. 86. His memoirs, written by a friend, containing all his youthful escapades, were commenced for his amusement when he was æt. 80.

[S.] Armand, French general.

P. Duc de Gramont and Duc de Guiche, marshal of France.

GROTIUS, Hugo (de Groot); an illustrious and profound Dutch writer, statesman, and authority on international law; showed extraordinary abilities as a child; was educated carefully, and at æt. 14 his learning attracted considerable notice. He was a man of great mark, and lived an eventful life; was sentenced to perpetual imprisonment for his Arminian religious opinions, but escaped first to France, then to Sweden. He became ambassador from Sweden to France, in which capacity he did his duties in a trying time, with great credit. Ultimately he was received with high honours in Holland. He belonged to an eminently gifted and learned family. He married a woman of rare merit.

G. Hugues de Groot, great scholar.

F. John, Curator of the University of Leyden; a learned man.

U. Corneille, professor both of philosophy and of law.

H

GROTIUS, Hugo—*continued*

B.   William, who collected and edited Hugo's poems; was himself a learned man and an author.

S.   Peter, able diplomatist and scholar.

HALLAM, Henry; one of the most distinguished of modern writers, and most just of critics; author of the *Constitutional History of England* and of the *Literature of Europe*; was one of the earliest contributors to the *Edinburgh Review*. The epitaph on his own tomb is so condensed and just, and those written by himself on his children who died before him are so accurate as well as touching, that I insert them here. His own epitaph in St. Paul's Cathedral is as follows:—

"HENRY HALLAM, the historian of the Middle Ages, of the Constitution of his country, and of the Literature of Europe. This monument is raised by many friends, who, regarding the soundness of his learning, the simple eloquence of his style, his manly and capacious intellect, the fearless honesty of his judgments, and the moral dignity of his life, desire to perpetuate his memory within these sacred walls, as of one who has best illustrated the English language, the English character, and the English name."

He had a vigorous constitution; his massive head was well carried by a robust frame; he was precocious as a child; could read well at 4 years old, and wrote sonnets at 9 or 10; *d. æt.* 82. Married a sister of Sir Charles Elton, Bart.; he was author of poems and translations.

F.   John Hallam, D.D., Dean of Bristol, Canon of Windsor; declined the Bishopric of Chester; educated at Eton; the son and the only child that lived beyond childhood, of John Hallam, surgeon, twice Mayor of Boston.

f.   Daughter of Richard Roberts, M.D., was a very superior person, somewhat over-anxious; she resembled her son in features; had only two children that lived.

u.   Dr. Roberts, Provost of Eton.

[*b.*] Elizabeth; had great intellectual taste.

HALLAM, Henry—*continued*

S.   Arthur Henry, *d.* æt. 23; the subject of Tennyson's *In Memoriam*. His epitaph at Clevedon is as follows:—
"And now, in this obscure and solitary church, repose the mortal remains of one too early lost for public fame, but already distinguished among his contemporaries for the brightness of his genius, the depth of his understanding, the nobleness of his disposition, the fervour of his piety, and the purity of his life. Vale dulcissime, desideratissime. Requiescas in pace usque ad tubam."

s.   Eleanor Hallam, *d.* æt. 21. "Her afflicted parents, bending under this second bereavement, record here that loveliness of temper and that heavenly-minded piety which are lost to them, but are gone to their own reward." She had great abilities.

S.   Henry Fitzmaurice Hallam, *d.* æt. 26. "In whose clear and vivid understanding, sweetness of disposition, and purity of life, an image of his elder brother was before the eyes of those who had most loved him. Distinguished, like him, by early reputation, and by the affection of many friends, he was, like him also, cut off by a short illness in a foreign land."

HELVETIUS, Claude Adrian (Schweitzer) (1715–1771). The celebrated and persecuted author of a materialistic philosophy. He was universally accomplished; handsome, graceful, robust, and full of genius. By æt. 23 he had obtained a farmer-generalship in France. Became a refugee in England and elsewhere. He married a charming lady—Mdlle. de Ligueville, whom, it is said, both Franklin and Turgot desired to marry in her widowhood. He had two daughters.

F.   John Claude Adrian, physician of great eminence in Paris; Inspector-General of Hospitals; was liberal and benevolent.

G.   Jean Adrian, Dutch physician, who died in Paris; was Inspector-General of Hospitals. It was he who first showed the importance of ipecacuanha as a medicine.

IRVING, Washington; American author, novelist, and historian; was minister to Spain; had weak health; was educated by his elder brothers; had desultory habits; his means were ample.

[2B.] His brothers were men of considerable literary attainments; one of them conducted the *New York Chronicle.*

LAMB, Charles (*Essays of Elia*); a quaint and genial humorist; dearly beloved.

b.   A sister, who, in a fit of insanity, murdered her mother, and whom Charles Lamb watched with the utmost solicitude. She ultimately recovered her reason, and was then described by those who knew her, as of a strong intellect and of a heart the counterpart of her brother's in humanity. She was authoress of many pieces that are published in her brother's works.

LESSING, Gotthold Ephraim; a universal writer, who added immensely to the stores of German literature. He was a devourer of books from his earliest childhood. His health broke rapidly æt. 50.

B.   Karl Gotthelf ⎫
B.   Johann Gottlieb ⎬ were all distinguished as literary men.
N.   Karl Friedrich ⎭

MACAULAY, Thomas Babington; created Lord Macaulay; historian, poet, essayist, and conversationalist; a man of transcendent power of memory.

G.   Rev. John Macaulay, Scotch minister at Inverary; most eloquent preacher; mentioned in Dr. Johnson's Tour.

F.   Zachary, slave abolitionist; very able; a lucid and rapid writer, but singularly wanting in facility of oratorical expression.

U.   Colin Macaulay, general. Was the right-hand man of the Duke of Wellington, in his Indian campaigns. He governed for many years a large part of the Madras Presidency, and, in spite of his active life, was a first-rate scholar both in ancient and modern literature. He was constantly mentioned in contemporary literature as a wonder for his erudition and abilities.

MACAULAY, Thomas Babington—*continued*

U. Aulay Macaulay, brilliant conversationalist; wrote much of value, that remains unfinished and unprinted; tutor to Caroline of Brunswick; *d.* in prime of life.

[US.] (Son of Aulay.) John Heyrick, Head Master of Repton, a good scholar.

US. Kenneth Macaulay, M.P. for Cambridge, was the son of the above. There were also other brothers who had ability.

n. George Trevelyan, M.P., Junior Lord of the Treasury (son of Sir Charles Trevelyan, statesman), was second classic of his year (1861) at Cambridge; author of *Cawnpore*, &c.

MILL, James; historian of British India.

S. John Stuart Mill, the eminent modern philosopher and political writer.

NIEBUHR, Barthold George; historical critic (*Roman History*); afterwards a financial statesman. All his time was devoted to study. He had a fair education. Æt. 7 he was considered a prodigy of application; but his constitution was weak and nervous, and further injured by a marsh fever. Macaulay (Preface, *Lays of Ancient Rome*) says, Niebuhr would have been the first writer of his age if his talent in communicating truths had been more in proportion to his talent in discovering them. He was Prussian Ambassador at Rome.

F. Carsten Niebuhr, a celebrated traveller and writer on Arabia. His father had been a farmer. Both parents died when he was a child, and he had to work as a labourer, and was almost uneducated, till æt. 21. Thenceforward he zealously educated himself. Died æt. 82.

[S.] Marcus, a high official in the Prussian civil service.

PALGRAVE, Sir Francis; historian and antiquary, especially of the Anglo-Saxon period. Married a Dawson-Turner (*see* HOOKER in SCIENCE).

S. Francis; literature and art (*Golden Treasury*).

S. Giffard; orientalist and traveller in Arabia.

PORSON, Richard; eminent Greek scholar and critic. From childhood, his mother used to say, whatever Richard did, was done in a superior manner. He spun better yarn than his brothers or sisters, and yet he had always a book lying open before him while he was spinning. Before he could write, he had taught himself, from an old book, as far as the cube root in arithmetic. As he grew up his memory became stupendous. He had unwearied application, great acuteness, strong sound sense, a lively perception both of the beautiful and the ludicrous, and a most pure and inflexible sense of truth. He had great bodily strength; was often known to walk from Cambridge to London, a distance of fifty-two miles, to attend his club in the evening, not being able to afford the coach fare. Got drunk occasionally, as was not an infrequent custom in his day, but he ended by doing so habitually.

F.   A weaver and parish clerk, a man of excellent sense and great natural powers of arithmetic.

f.   A housemaid at the clergyman's, who read his books on the sly. He found her one day at Shakespeare, and discovered, to his amazement, that she had a sound knowledge of the book, and of very much else, so he helped her as he best could. She had a remarkable memory.

B.   Thomas. In the opinion of Dr. Davy, the then Master of Caius College, Cambridge, who was intimately acquainted with both brothers, he was fully the equal of Richard in scholastic ability. He kept a classical school, but died æt. 24.

b.   Had the wonderful Porson memory. She married and had children, but they were of no mark whatever.

[B.]   Henry; a good arithmetician, who had no inclination for literature. Died æt. 33.

ROSCOE, William; historian and poet (*Life of Lorenzo de Medici*); son of a market gardener, educated at a common school; placed with a bookseller, then at an attorney's office, where he taught himself. Began to be known æt.

30. Became a banker; founded the Royal Institution at Liverpool; was M.P. for that place. Died æt. 78.

S.   Henry; wrote his father's life. *Lives of Eminent Lawyers.*

[S.]   Robert; was a lawyer; wrote the epic *Alfred.*

[S.]   Thomas; wrote several poems and tales, and illustrated works of travel.

LE SAGE; novelist (*Gil Blas*); was an only son, and early an orphan. He became a handsome and engaging youth; he married at 26, and worked hard. His first success was the *Diable Boiteux* æt. 39. He was 67 when the last volume of *Gil Blas* appeared. He began to be deaf at 40, and at last his deafness became complete. He had three sons, as follow:—

S.   René-André (Montménil) was an abbé, but broke away from the Church and joined the stage, to his father's great grief. He was an excellent comedian. The father saw him act, and forgave him. He died young and suddenly.

S.   A canon. He was a jolly fellow, with whom Le Sage spent his last days. He enjoyed life, and loved theatricals, and would have made an excellent comedian.

[S.]   Became a bad actor, and died in obscurity.

SCALIGER, Julius Cæsar; scholar and natural philosopher (1484–1558, æt. 64); was of doubtful parentage. He served in the army till æt. 29, then studied theology, which he abandoned for medicine, and then began to learn Greek. He commenced his studies so late in life, that none of his works were published till æt. 47. He was one of the most extraordinary men of his age. He had a most tenacious memory and sound understanding, but was excessively irritable and vain, and made enemies. Scholars of subsequent ages have vied in panegyrising him, but his fame as a scholar and critic, though very great in his own days, was far eclipsed by that of his son Joseph.

S.   Joseph Justus Scaliger. *See below.*

SCALIGER, Joseph Justus; scholar and critic (1540–1609, æt. 69). Was well educated, and he read intensely on his own account. He was one of that constellation of great scholars who ornamented the University of Leyden at the end of the sixteenth century. He was wholly absorbed in study. He never married. Was irritable and vain, like his father. As a critic he is considered to have been pre-eminent, and there are very few scholars who can be compared with him.

F.   Julius Cæsar Scaliger. *See above.*

SCHLEGEL, August Wilhelm von; celebrated German scholar, critic, and poet, a translator of Shakespeare, and of Indian literature. At an early age he showed remarkable aptitude for languages. His fault, if any, was that of aiming too much at universality. He attached himself to Madame de Staël, and entirely abandoned himself to her intellectual influence. Died æt. 78. He and his brother have been called the "literary Dioscures" of their day. His grandfather was Councillor of the Court of Appeal of Meissen. He educated his children—the father and the uncles—carefully.

F.   Jean Adolphe; preacher of repute, also writer of poems.

U.   Jean Elie; poet, dramatist, and critic. "He is without exception the best dramatic author that Germany produced during the first half of the eighteenth century." Died æt. 31, overworked.

U.   Jean Henri; Danish Historiographer Royal. Resided in Copenhagen.

B.   Friedrich Carl Wilhelm von Schlegel. *See below.*

SCHLEGEL, Friedrich Carl Wilhelm von; historian, philosopher, and philologist. Was not precocious as a child, but became strongly drawn to literature when a youth. He lectured on the philosophy of history and language, edited, wrote poems, and at last became a diplomatic official under Metternich, who was his constant patron. Died æt. 57.

F. U. U. As above.

B.   August Wilhelm von Schlegel. *See above.*

SENECA, Lucius Annæus; Roman philosopher; educated for rhetoric, but his taste rebelled against it, and he devoted himself to philosophy. His noble sentiments and grand stoicism have greatly influenced even the Christian world, for Seneca was formerly much read and admired. He amassed an immense fortune, no one knows how, but it is suspected by equivocal means. He was the tutor of Nero, and naturally has not acquired much credit by his pupil, who put him to death æt. 63.

F.   Marcus Annæus Seneca; rhetorician and author. He was a man of prodigious memory; he could repeat two thousand words in the order he heard them. Married a Spanish lady.

B.   Marcus Novatus, who took the name Junius Gallio, and became proconsul of Achaia. It was before his tribunal that St. Paul was brought, on the accusation of introducing innovations in religious matters. Eusebius describes him as a distinguished rhetorician, and his brother calls him the most tolerant of men.

N.   Lucanus Marcus Annæus (Lucan), the poet. His *Pharsalia* is the only one of his works that has reached us. His father, the brother of Seneca, married the daughter of Lucanus, an eminent orator, from whom the son took his name.

SÉVIGNÉ, Marquise de (born Marie de Rabutin Chantal); authoress of charming letters. She was unsurpassed, perhaps unequalled, as a letter-writer. Her father was killed in battle when she was an infant, her mother died when she was æt. 6. She was an only child. Married, not happily, to a profligate man, who was killed in a duel on account of another lady. She wrote well before her widowhood, but not much; then she retired from the world to educate her children, and reappeared æt. 27, when she shone in society. Society improved, and did not spoil her. Her daughter married the Lieutenant-Governor of Provence, and it was to her that the famous letters were written. She had a joyous nature, beauty, grace, and wit; nothing concealed; all open as day. Even while living, her letters were celebrated in the Court and in society; they were handed about and read with infinite pleasure.

S. Marquis de Sévigné; a man of much ability and courage, who ended a restless and somewhat dissipated life in the practice of devotion, under the direction of ecclesiastics. He had not sufficient perseverance to succeed in anything.

US. Bussy-Rambutin; a very excellent soldier, adventurous, rash, and somewhat dissipated. Would certainly have been made Marshal of France but for his ill-natured, caustic personalities, which led to his exile, and loss of all hope of advancement. He was an excellent letter-writer. He was really a man of great literary power, who improved the French language.

There was a great deal more of sporadic talent in the family of Madame de Sévigné, but it never elsewhere achieved a full success.

SIDNEY, Sir Philip; scholar, soldier, and courtier. "A gentleman finished and complete, in whom mildness was associated with courage, erudition modified by refinement, and courtliness dignified by truth." Was grave as a boy. He left Cambridge æt. 18 with a high reputation, and at once became a courtier, and a very successful one, owing to his accomplishments and figure. His *Arcadia* is a work of rare genius, though cast in an unfortunate mould. It had an immense reputation in its day. He was killed in battle æt. 32, and was mourned in England by a general mourning,—the first, it is believed, of the kind in this country. (See also the genealogical tree under MONTAGU, in JUDGES, pp. 140, 141.)

F. Sir Henry Sidney, a man of great parts, much considered by both Mary and Elizabeth; was three times Lord Deputy of Ireland, and governed wisely.

[G.] Sir William Sidney, a soldier and knight of some renown in the time of Henry VIII.

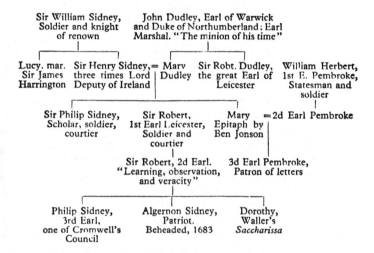

g.   John Dudley, Earl of Warwick and Duke of Northumberland, "the minion of his time;" Earl-Marshal of England, and the most powerful of subjects; attainted and beheaded 1553.

u.   Sir Robert Dudley, the great Earl of Leicester, the favourite of Queen Elizabeth.

uS. Sir Robert (son of the great Earl of Leicester, but not enjoying the title), was "a complete gentleman in all suitable employments, an exact seaman, an excellent architect, mathematician, physician, chemist, and what not. . . . A handsome personable man, . . . noted for . . . tilting, and for his being the first of all that taught a dog to sit, in order to catch partridges." (Anthony Wood, as quoted in Burke's *Extinct Peerages*.)

b.   Mary, Countess of Pembroke; was of congenial tastes and qualities with her brother, who dedicated his *Arcadia*

to her. Was the subject of Ben Jonson's well-known
epitaph:

> "Underneath this sable hearse
> Lies the subject of all verse,
> Sidney's sister, Pembroke's mother.
> Death, ere thou has slain another
> Wise and fair and good as she,
> Time shall throw a dart at thee."

n.   3d Earl of Pembroke, Chancellor of Oxford; a scholar, poet, and patron of learned men.

[B.]   Sir Robert Sidney, created Earl of Leicester. (There almost seems a fatality attached to this title, judging from the number of times it has been re-created; no less than six different families have held it and become extinct.) He was a soldier of some renown.

N.   Sir Robert Sidney, 2d Earl of Leicester; a man of great learning, observation, and veracity.

NS.   Algernon Sidney, the patriot, beheaded 1683. He had great natural ability, but was too rough and boisterous to bear contradiction. He studied the history of government in all its branches, and had an intimate knowledge of men and their tempers. Was of extraordinary courage and obstinacy.

[Ns.]   Dorothy, Waller's *Saccharissa*.

Up.   Sir Henry Montagu, 1st Earl of Manchester, Ch. Just. King's Bench. See MONTAGU (in JUDGES) for this most remarkable family, whose high qualities appear to have been mainly derived through an infusion of the Sydney blood, inasmuch as of the vast number of the other descendants of the first Ch. Just. Montagu in Henry VIII's reign, no line was distinguished except this that had mixed its blood with that of the Sidneys.

3 UpS.   Baron Kimbolton; Walter Montagu, Abbot of Pontoise; and the 1st Earl Sandwich, the great admiral.

8 UpP.   1st Duke of Montagu; William Montagu, Ch. Baron Exchequer; Charles Montagu, 1st E. of Halifax; Francis

North, 1st Lord Guilford, Lord Chancellor; and his three brothers; Charles Hatton, "the incomparable." Still more could be said, but I refer the reader to the Montagu genealogy.

STAEL, Anne Germaine de; one of the most distinguished writers of her age. She was an only child. When quite young, she interested herself vastly in the philosophy and politics talked at her father's table. Then she overworked herself, æt. 15, partly urged on in her studies by her mother. After a serious illness she became quite altered, and was no longer a pedantic child, but full of *abandon* and charm. She married twice, and had three children.

G. Charles Frederick Necker, a German legal and political writer, who settled in Geneva, where a chair of law was instituted for him.

F. Jacques Necker, the celebrated French statesman and finance minister of Louis XVI. Had a strong natural bias for literature; æt. 18, showed remarkable aptitude for business; was intensely fond of his daughter, and she of him.

U. Louis Necker, Professor of Mathematics at Geneva. He began by banking in Paris, and had much success in his speculations both there and afterwards at Marseilles, but the troubled state of France determined him to return to Geneva.

f. Susanna Curchod; Gibbon had wished to marry her. She was a precocious child, singularly well read, a distinguished wit, but pedantic. She was a rigorous Calvinist. It is a wonder she did not stifle her daughter's wit.

US. Jacques Necker, son of Louis, Professor of Botany at Geneva; married a daughter of De Saussure the geologist.

UP. Louis Albert, son of Jacques and grandson of De Saussure, Professor of Geology and Mineralogy in Geneva. (See a long memoir of him, by Dr. James David Forbes, in an Address to the Royal Society of Edinburgh, 1863.)

STEPHEN, Right Hon. Sir James; historian (*Essays in Ecclesiastical Biography*); Under Secretary of State for the Colonies.

F.   James Stephen, Master in Chancery; a leading slave abolitionist.

B.   Henry John Stephen, eminent legal writer (*Stephen on Pleading*).

[B.] Sir George, barrister, successful novelist (*Adventures of an Attorney in search of Practice*).

S.   FitzJames Stephen, Q.C., author of *Criminal Law*; large contributor to periodical literature.

S.   Leslie Stephen, also a well-known contributor to periodical literature; mountaineer, president of the Alpine Club.

STEPHENS, Robert (or ETIENNE), was the first eminent member of a family of the most illustrious scholars and printers that has ever appeared. It must be recollected that in the early days of printing, all printers were scholars. Robert was an extraordinary scholar, exceedingly precocious, considered by his contemporaries greater than any other scholar. He printed the Bible in many forms, was persecuted, and driven to Geneva. Married Petronella (*see below*).

B.   Charles, a sound classic, but chiefly attached to physical science, medicine, and natural history.

S.   Henry. *See pedigree on page 239.*

S.   Robert (2); was worthy of his father in his activity and in the accuracy of his editions.

N.   Nicole, no less celebrated for her beauty than for her talents and accomplishments.

STEPHENS, Henry (or ETIENNE), the greatest of the whole family. He was exceedingly precocious. He invested a large part of his fortune in costly preparations for his Greek Lexicon, which one of his *employés*, Scapula, pirated from him in the form of an abridgment. Through this piece of roguery Stephens became greatly embarrassed, and died poor, but Scapula made a fortune.

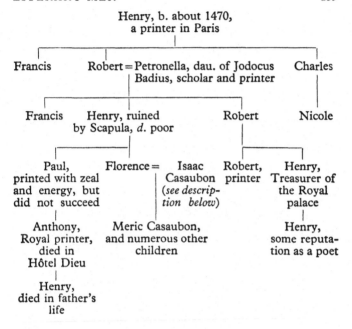

Henry, b. about 1470,
a printer in Paris
│
┌──────────────┬────────────────────────────────────┬──────────────┐
Francis   Robert = Petronella, dau. of Jodocus   Charles
│ Badius, scholar and printer
┌──────────┬─────────────────────────┬──────────────┐
Francis   Henry, ruined   Robert   Nicole
by Scapula, *d.* poor
┌──────────────┬─────────────────────┬──────────────┐
Paul,   Florence = Isaac   Robert,   Henry,
printed with zeal   Casaubon   printer   Treasurer of
and energy, but   (*see descrip-*   the Royal
did not succeed   *tion below*)   palace
│   │   │
Anthony,   Meric Casaubon,   Henry,
Royal printer,   and numerous other   some reputa-
died in   children   tion as a poet
Hôtel Dieu
│
Henry,
died in father's
life

F.   Robert. *See above.*
g.   Jodocus Badius, celebrated scholar and printer.
f.   Petronella, a woman of great talents and literary accom-
     plishments.
B.   Robert (2). *See above.*
Us. Nicole. *See above.*
     Isaac Casaubon, whose name appears in the above list,
     was a learned Swiss divine and critic; professor of Greek
     at Geneva æt. 23, and subsequently at Paris. He passed
     the last years of his life in England, where he was greatly
     esteemed, and was made Prebend of Westminster and
     was highly pensioned by James I.
p.   Meric Casaubon, his son, was equally eminent, but seems
     to have shrunk from public service. He was in vain
     solicited by Cromwell to write the history of the war,

and by Christina, Queen of Sweden, to superintend the universities in her kingdom.

SWIFT, Jonathan, D.D.; Dean of St. Patrick's; satirist, politician. Was tall, muscular, and well-made; had attacks of giddiness all his life. Educated by help of his uncles, at Trinity College, Dublin, where he was idle. Then he became secretary to Sir Wm. Temple, who had married a relation of his mother, and began to work seriously æt. 21. Lost his mind at 69, *d.* æt. 78 of water on the brain.

Several of the Swift family, in some distant degrees, have had abilities. Thus—

GN. Dryden the poet.

UP. Deane Swift, biographer of Dean Swift.

UPS. Theophilus Swift, son of above; political writer.

TAYLORS of Norwich. This family—Mrs. Austen being the most eminent among its deceased members—contains a large number of well-known names. The Martineau section also includes a large amount of diffused ability, much more than would be supposed from the scanty records in the annexed diagram. Many of its members have attained distinction in the law, in the arts, and in the army. The Nonconformist element runs strong in the blood of the Martineaus and Taylors.

(1)   (*See pedigree on next page.*) The five sons were—
John and Philip Taylor, both of them men of science.
Richard, editor of the *Diversions of Purley* and of the *Philosophical Magazine.*
Edward, Gresham Professor of Music.
Arthur, F.S.A., author of *The Glory of Regality.*

(2)   The three grandsons are—
Edgar Taylor, an accomplished writer on legal subjects, and translator of Grimm's *Popular Tales.*
Emily, a pleasing poetess.
Richard, geologist, author of *Statistics of Coal.*

(3)   Colonel Meadows Taylor, writer on Indian affairs.

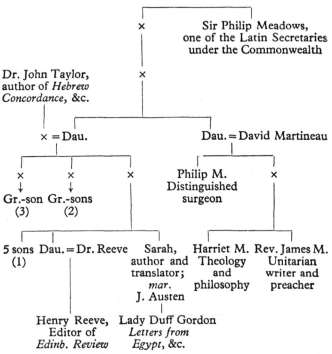

TAYLORS of Ongar. This family is remarkable from the universality with which its members have been pervaded with a restless literary talent, evangelical disposition, and an artistic taste. The type seems to be a very decided one, and to be accompanied with constitutional vigour; thus Mrs. Gilbert died a short time since at the advanced age of 84. None of its members have attained the highest rank among authors, but several are considerably above the average. The accompanying genealogical tree, taken from *The Family Pen*, by the Rev. I. Taylor, explains their relationships.

I should add that Mr. Tom Taylor, dramatic author, &c., is not a relation of either of these families.

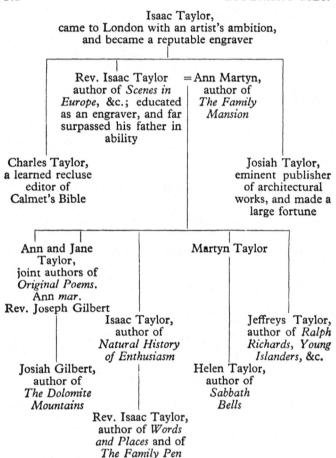

Isaac Taylor,
came to London with an artist's ambition,
and became a reputable engraver

Rev. Isaac Taylor   = Ann Martyn,
author of *Scenes in*   author of
Europe, &c.; educated   *The Family*
as an engraver, and far   *Mansion*
surpassed his father in
ability

Charles Taylor,   Josiah Taylor,
a learned recluse   eminent publisher
editor of   of architectural
Calmet's Bible   works, and made a
large fortune

Ann and Jane   Martyn Taylor
Taylor,
joint authors of
Original Poems.
Ann *mar*.
Rev. Joseph Gilbert

Isaac Taylor,   Jeffreys Taylor,
author of   author of *Ralph*
Natural History   *Richards, Young*
of Enthusiasm*   *Islanders*, &c.

Josiah Gilbert,   Helen Taylor,
author of   author of
The Dolomite   *Sabbath*
Mountains   *Bells*

Rev. Isaac Taylor,
author of *Words
and Places* and of
The Family Pen

TROLLOPE, Mrs. Frances; novelist of considerable power.
[F.]   Rev.—Milton, an able man.
S.   Anthony Trollope, eminent novelist.
S.   Thomas Adolphus Trollope, miscellaneous writer.

MEN OF SCIENCE

My choice of Men of Science, like that of the men of literature, may seem capricious. They were both governed to some extent by similar considerations, and therefore the preface to my last chapter is in a great degree applicable to this. There is yet another special difficulty in the selection of a satisfactory first-class of scientific men.

The fact of a person's name being associated with some one striking scientific discovery helps enormously, but often unduly, to prolong his reputation to after ages. It is notorious that the same discovery is frequently made simultaneously and quite independently, by different persons. Thus, to speak of only a few cases in late years, the discoveries of photography, of electric telegraphy, and of the planet Neptune through theoretical calculations, have all their rival claimants. It would seem, that discoveries are usually made when the time is ripe for them—that is to say, when the ideas from which they naturally flow are fermenting in the minds of many men. When apples are ripe, a trifling event suffices to decide, which of them shall first drop off its stalk; so a small accident will often determine the scientific man who shall first make and publish a new discovery. There are many persons who have contributed vast numbers of original memoirs, all of them of some, many of great, but none of extraordinary importance. These men have the capacity of making a striking discovery though they had not the luck to do so. Their work is valuable, and remains, but the worker is forgotten. Nay, some eminently scientific men have shown their original powers by little more than a continuous flow of helpful suggestions and criticisms which were individually of too little importance to be remembered in the history of Science, but which, in their aggregate, formed a notable aid towards its progress. In the scanty history of the once well-known "Lunar Society" of the Midland Counties—of which Watt, Boulton, and Darwin were the chief notabilities—there is frequent allusion to a man of whom nothing more than the name now remains, but who had apparently very great influence on the thoughts of his contemporaries—I mean Dr. Small. Or, to take a more recent case, I suppose that Dr. Whewell would be generally ranked in the class G of natural ability. His intellectual energy was prodigious, his writing unceasing, and his conversational powers extraordinary. Also, few will doubt that, although the range of his labours was exceedingly wide and scattered, Science in one form or another was his chief pursuit. His influence on the progress of Science during the earlier years of his life was, I believe, considerable, but it is impossible to specify the particulars of that influence, or so to justify our opinion that posterity will be likely to pay regard to it. Biographers will seek in vain for important discoveries in Science, with which Dr. Whewell's name may hereafter be identified.

Owing to these considerations, the area of my choice is greatly narrowed. I can only include those scientific men who have achieved an enduring reputation, or who are otherwise well known to the present generation. I have proceeded in my selection just as I did in the case of the literary men— namely, I have taken the most prominent names from ordinary biographical dictionaries.

I now annex my usual tables.

TABLE I

SUMMARY OF RELATIONSHIPS OF 65 SCIENTIFIC MEN, GROUPED INTO 43 FAMILIES

One relation (or two in family)

Ampère	S.		2. Hooker	S.
Buckland	S.		Humboldt	B.
Cavendish	gB.		Linnæus	S.
2. Cuvier	B.		Pliny	n.
Davy	B.		Porta	B.
Galilei	F.		2. Stephenson	S.
Harvey	Up.		Watt	S.

Two or three relations (or three or four in family)

Aristotle	F. P. UP.		Haller	g. S.
Buffon	*f*. S.	2.	Herschel	*b*. S.
2. Celsius	S. P.	2.	Hunter	B. n. *n*.
Condorcet	U. 2?		Huyghens	F. B.
2. Darwin	2S. P.		Leibnitz	g. F. u.
2. De Candolle	F. S.		Napier	F. S.
Euler	3S.	3.	Newton and	
Forbes	*f*. B.		Huttons	2*u*Pp.
Franklin	2PS.		Oersted	B. N.
Geoffroy	B. S.	2	Saussure	F S.

Four or more relations (or five or more in family)

	Arago	3B. 2S.
	Bacon	F. *f*. g. *u*S. 2B. N.
4.	Bernoulli	B. 3N. 3NS. 2?
	Boyle	F. *f*. g. 2US. UP. 4B. 2NS. 2NP.
2.	Brodie	*u*S. *u*P. S.
3.	Cassini	G. F. S. P.
	D'Alembert	*f*. u. 2*u*S.
4.	Gmelin	F. U. US. S.
	Gregory	g. *f*. gB. B. 3N. NS. *N*S. S. 2P. PS. 2Pp.
3.	Jussieu	3U. S.

TABLE I confirms all that has been already deduced from the corresponding tables in other groups, but the figures in TABLE II are exceptional. We find a remarkable diminution in the numbers of F. and G., while S. and P. hold their own. We also find that, although the female influence, on the whole, is but little different from previous groups, inasmuch as in the first degree—

1 G. + 5 U. + 8 N. + 6 P. = 20 kinsmen through males
5 g. + 2 u. + 2 n. + 0p. = 9 kinsmen through females

and in the second degree—

0 GF. + 0 GB. + 3 US. + 6 NS. + 3 PS. = 12 kinsmen through males

0 *g*F. + 0 *g*B. + 4 *u*S. + 0 *n*S. + 0 *p*S. = 4 kinsmen through females

Totals, 32 through males; 13 through females

TABLE II[1]

Degrees of Kinship					A	B	C	D
Name of the degree	Corresponding letter							
1 degree Father	11 F.	...	...	...	11	26	100	26
Brother	20 B.	...	...	...	20	47	150	31
Son	26 S.	...	...	...	26	60	100	60
2 degrees Grandfather	1 G.	5 g.	...	...	6	14	200	7
Uncle	5 U.	2 u.	...	...	7	16	400	4
Nephew	8 N.	2 n.	...	...	10	23	400	6
Grandson	6 P.	0 p.	...	...	6	14	200	7
3 degrees Great-grandfather	0 GF.	0 gF.	0 GF.	0 gF.	0	0	400	0
Great-uncle	0 GB.	2 gB.	0 GB.	0 gB.	2	5	800	0·6
First-cousin	3 US.	0 uS.	0 US.	4 uS.	7	16	800	2·0
Great-nephew	6 NS.	0 nS.	1 NS.	0 nS.	7	16	800	2·0
Great-grandson	3 PS.	0 pS.	0 PS.	0 pS.	3	7	400	2·7
All more remote	...	...	...	...	10	23	...	0·0

yet, when we examine the lists of kinsmen more closely, we shall arrive at different conclusions, and we shall find the maternal influence to be unusually strong. There are 5 g. to 1 G.; and in fully eight cases out of the forty-three, the mother was the abler of the two parents. These are the mothers of Bacon (remember also his four maternal aunts), of Buffon, Condorcet, Cuivier, D'Alembert, Forbes, Gregory, and Watt. Both Brodie and Jussieu had remarkable grandmothers. The eminent relations of Newton were connected with him by female links.

It therefore appears to be very important to success in science, that a man should have an able mother. I believe the reason to be, that a child so circumstanced has the good fortune to be delivered from the ordinary narrowing, partisan influences of home education. Our race is essentially slavish;

[1] See, for explanation, the footnote to the similar table on page 102.

it is the nature of all of us to believe blindly in what we love, rather than in that which we think most wise. We are inclined to look upon an honest, unshrinking pursuit of truth as something irreverent. We are indignant when others pry into our idols, and criticise them with impunity, just as a savage flies to arms when a missionary picks his fetish to pieces. Women are far more strongly influenced by these feelings than men: they are blinder partisans and more servile followers of custom. Happy are they whose mothers did not intensify their naturally slavish dispositions in childhood, by the frequent use of phrases such as, "Do not ask questions about this or that, for it is wrong to doubt;" but who showed them, by practice and teaching, that inquiry may be absolutely free without being irreverent, that reverence for truth is the parent of free inquiry, and that indifference or insincerity in the search after truth is one of the most degrading of sins. It is clear that a child brought up under the influences I have described is far more likely to succeed as a scientific man than one who was reared under the curb of dogmatic authority. Of two men with equal abilities, the one who had a truth-loving mother would be the more likely to follow the career of science; while the other, if bred up under extremely narrowing circumstances, would become as the gifted children in China, nothing better than a student and professor of some dead literature.

It is, I believe, owing to the favourable conditions of their early training, that an unusually large proportion of the sons of the most gifted men of science become distinguished in the same career. They have been nurtured in an atmosphere of free inquiry, and observing as they grow older that myriads of problems lie on every side of them, simply waiting for some moderately capable person to take the trouble of engaging in their solution, they throw themselves with ardour into a field of labour so peculiarly tempting. It is and has been, in truth, strangely neglected. There are hundreds of students of books for one student of nature; hundreds of commentators for one original enquirer. The field of real science is in sore want of labourers. The mass of mankind plods on, with eyes fixed on

the footsteps of the generations that went before, too indifferent
or too fearful to raise their glances to judge for themselves
whether the path on which they are travelling is the best, or
to learn the conditions by which they are surrounded and
affected. Hence, as regard the eminent sons of the scientific
men—twenty-six in number—there are only four whose eminence was not achieved in science. These are the two political
sons of Arago (himself a politician), the son of Haller, and the
son of Napier.

As I said before, the fathers of the ablest men in science
have frequently been unscientific. Those of Cassini and Gmelin
were scientific men; so, in a lesser degree, were those of
Huyghens, Napier, and De Saussure; but the remainder—
namely, those of Bacon, Boyle, De Candolle, Galilei, and
Leibnitz—were either statesmen or literary men.

As regards mathematicians, when we consider how many
among them have been possessed of enormous natural gifts,
it might have been expected that the lists of their eminent
kinsmen would have been yet richer than they are. There are
several mathematicians in my appendix, especially the Bernoulli family; but the names of Pascal, Laplace, Gauss, and
others of class G. or even X., are absent. We might similarly
have expected that the senior wranglers of Cambridge would
afford many noteworthy instances of hereditary ability shown
in various careers, but, speaking generally, this does not seem
to be the case. I know of several instances where the senior
wrangler, being eminently a man of mathematical genius, as
Sir William Thomson and Mr. Archibald Smith, is related to
other mathematicians or men of science, but I know of few
senior wranglers whose kinsmen have been eminent in other
ways. Among these exceptions are Sir John Lefevre, whose
brother is the ex-Speaker, Viscount Eversley, and whose son is
the present Vice-President of the Board of Trade; and Sir
F. Pollock, the ex-Chief Baron, whose kinships are described
in JUDGES. I account for the rarity of such relationships in
the following manner. A man given to abstract ideas is not
likely to succeed in the world, unless he be particularly eminent

in his peculiar line of intellectual effort. If the more moderately gifted relative of a great mathematician can discover laws, well and good; but if he spends his days in puzzling over problems too insignificant to be of practical or theoretical import, or else too hard for him to solve, or if he simply reads what other people have written, he makes no way at all, and leaves no name behind him. There are far fewer of the numerous intermediate stages between eminence and mediocrity adapted for the occupation of men who are devoted to pure abstractions, than for those whose interests are of a social kind.

APPENDIX TO MEN OF SCIENCE

Here, as in the previous chapter, I have confined myself to the names that are most prominent in biographical collections, or that otherwise came most readily in my way. I add the names of those in to whose lives I also inquired, who seem to have had no kinsmen of marked ability. They are eighteen in number, and as follow:—

Bacon, Roger; Berzelius; Blumenbach; Brahe, Tycho; Bramah; Brewster; Brown, Robert; Copernicus; Galen; Galvani; Guericke; Hooke; Kepler; Priestley; Réaumur; Count Rumford; Whewell; Dr. Young.

AMPÈRE, André Marie (1775–1836, æt. 61); eminent man of science—mathematician, electrician, and philologist. He was entirely self-taught, for his parents were in humble circumstances. Even in early boyhood, he read voraciously and showed a most tenacious memory. He was endowed with a vast vigour of brain, accompanied by a very shy and sensitive organisation. Thus, though his genius was universal, he became in after life a great oddity, and his pupils made fun of him. He wanted perseverance in any one direction; he was always flying off to new subjects. Arago thought that the discipline of a public school would have had a most salutary influence on his character.

AMPÈRE, André Marie—*continued*

S.   Jean Jacques Antoine, historian and literary man of considerable eminence and originality. Educated by his father, who left him free to follow the bent of his genius. He travelled much, and always with literary and scientific results. Was Professor of Modern French History in the College of France.

ARAGO, Dominique François; mathematician and astronomer. Writer on many scientific subjects; also a politician and strong republican. As a boy, he made great and almost unassisted progress in mathematics. Became Academician æt. 23. He had a good deal of brusqueness of manner and of self-assertion. His three brothers were distinguished in their different professions, as follows:—

B.   Jean, driven from France by an unjust accusation; became a noted General in the Mexican Service, and rendered great service in their War of Independence.

B.   Jacques; traveller, artist, and author. He led a restless, wandering life, and was a man of great energy and literary power and productiveness.

B.   Etienne; dramatic author of considerable repute, and a most prolific writer; was a hot republican. He held office under the provisional government of 1848; was exiled under Napoleon III.

S.   Emmanuel; barrister, elected, at the early age of thirty-four, "membre du conseil de l'ordre," politician and hot republican. He took a prominent part in the Revolution of 1848, but was silenced after the *coup d'état*.

S.   Alfred, a painter, Inspecteur-Général des Beaux Arts.

ARISTOTLE. Founder of the Peripatetic School, one of the ablest of men in science and philosophy, teacher of Alexander. He joined Plato's academy, who called him, æt. 17, "the intellect of his school." He had weak health, but marvellous industry. Was restless; taught as he walked—hence the name of the Peripatetic School. Was very particular about his dress. Was wealthy; lost his parents early in life.

ARISTOTLE—*continued*

F.   Nicomachus, friend and physician to Amyntas II, King
       of Macedonia; author of works, now lost, on medicine
       and science.

P.   Nicomachus. According to Cicero, he was considered by
       some to have been the author of the *Nicomachean Ethics,*
       generally attributed to Aristotle.

Up.   (? about the form of the U). Callisthenes, the philosopher
       who accompanied Alexander the Great to the East, an
       imprudent man, wanting in tact, but otherwise able.
       His mother, Hero, was Aristotle's cousin.

BACON, Francis; created Lord Bacon, Lord Chancellor. "The
       wisest, brightest, meanest of mankind" is an over-hard
       sentence on his most illustrious philosopher and states-
       man. His natural gifts were formed by the simple addi-
       tion of those of his mother to those of his father. It is
       doubtful whether or no he was very precocious, but
       Queen Elizabeth certainly took delight in his boyish wit,
       gravity, and judgment.

F.   Sir Nicholas Bacon, Lord Keeper of the Great Seal. He
       was the first Lord Keeper who ranked as a Lord Chan-
       cellor. He was a grave stately man, fond of science,
       gardening, and house-building. In all this, his son was
       just like him. Married twice.

f.   Anne Cooke, a member of a most gifted family, and her-
       self a scholar of no mean order. Eminent for piety, virtue,
       and learning. Exquisitely skilled in Latin and Greek.

[4 *u.*] The four sisters of his mother are all spoken of in terms
       of the highest praise.

g.   Sir Anthony Cooke is described by Camden as "vir
       antiquâ serenitate." Lloyd (*State Worthies*) says, "Con-
       templation was his soul, privacy his life, and discourse
       his element." Lord Seymour standing by when he chid
       his son, remarked, "Some men govern families with
       more skill than others do kingdoms," and thereupon
       recommended him to the government of his young
       nephew Edward VI. "Such the majesty of his looks and

gait, that awe governed,—such the reason and sweetness, that love obliged all his family: a family equally afraid to displease so good a head, and to offend so great." He taught his daughters all the learning of the day. I greatly regret I have been unable to obtain any information about Sir Anthony's ancestry or collateral relations.

*u*S.   Cecil, 1st E. of Salisbury, eminent minister under Elizabeth and James I. His father was the great Lord Burleigh.

B.   Anthony; had weak health, but a considerable share of the intellectual power which distinguished this remarkable family.

B.   (but by a different mother). Sir Nathaniel, Bart., a man of rare parts and generous disposition. He was a very good painter. Walpole considered him to have "really attained the perfection of a master." Peacham in his *Graphicæ* says, "None in my opinion deserveth more respect and admiration for his skill and practice in painting, than Master Nathaniel Bacon of Brome, in Suffolk, not inferior in my judgment, to our skilfullest masters."

B.   (by the same parents as the above). Sir Nathaniel of Stivekey. His father remarks of him, æt. 22 (when Lord Bacon was æt. 7), "Indeed of all my children he is of best hope in learning."

N.   (son of another brother). Nathaniel, antiquarian writer, Recorder of Bury, and Admiralty Judge. He was M.P. for Cambridge, and a sturdy republican.

BERNOULLI, Jacques. The first who rose to fame in a Swiss family that afterwards comprised an extraordinary number of eminent mathematicians and men of science. They were mostly quarrelsome and unamiable. Many were long-lived; three of them exceeded eighty years of age. Jacques was destined for the Church, but early devoted himself to mathematics, in which he had accidentally become initiated. He had a bilious, melancholic temperament. Was sure but slow. He taught his brother Jean, but adopted, too long, a tone of superiority towards him; hence quarrels and rivalry. Jacques was a mathematician of the highest order in originality and power. Member of French Academy.

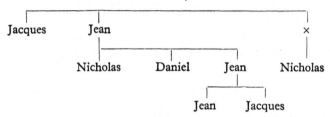

B. Jean, destined for commerce, but left it for science and chemistry. Member of French Academy. (*Eloge* by D'Alembert.) He was the ancestor of the five following:

N. Nicholas, *d.* æt. 31. He was also a great mathematical genius. Died at S. Petersburg, where he was one of the principal ornaments of the then young Academy.

N. Daniel, physician, botanist, and anatomist, writer on hydrodynamics; very precocious. Obtained ten prizes, for one of which his father had competed; who never forgave him for his success. Member of the French Academy. (Condorcet's *Eloge*.)

N. Jean, jurisconsult, mathematician and physicist. Obtained three prizes of the Academy, of which he was a member. Professor of eloquence and an orator. Would have been a great mathematician if he had not loved oratory more. He was destined for commerce, but hated it. (D'Alembert's *Eloge*.)

NS. Jean, astronomer, mathematician, and philosopher. Wrote many works and some travels.

NS. Jacques, physician and mathematician. Drowned when bathing, æt. 30.

NS. Nicholas (son of a third brother), mathematician, member of the French Academy.

There were yet two others, descendants of the same family, but I do not know the precise degree of their kinship.

BERNOULLI, Jacques
(?)   Christophe (1782–1863), Professor of Natural History
      at the University of Basle, author of many works on
      science and on statistics.
(?)   Jerome (1745–1829), chemist and pharmacist by trade,
      but he had a passion for natural history, and by æt. 20
      had made a considerable collection of mineralogy, which
      he afterwards improved until it became one of the most
      complete in Switzerland.
BOYLE, Hon. Robert. "The Christian philosopher." Eminent
      in natural science, especially in chemistry; a scholar and
      a theologian. He also takes rank as a religious statesman,
      from his efforts in causing Christianity to be propagated
      among the natives of India and North America. He was
      seventh son and fourteenth child. Was shy and diffident,
      and steadfastly refused the numerous offers of prefer-
      ment that were pressed upon him. He was a member of
      a very remarkable family, of whom I give a genealogical
      tree (see next page).
F.   Richard, 1st Earl of Cork, commonly called the Great
      Earl, Lord High Treasurer of Ireland; distinguished in
      the Great Rebellion by his energy and military skill. He
      made a large fortune by improving his Irish estates.
f.   Catherine. "The crown of all my" (the Earl's) "happi-
      ness. . . . Religious, virtuous, loving; the happy mother
      of all my hopeful children."
g.   Sir Geoffrey Fenton, Principal Sec. of State for Ireland.
US.   Michael Boyle, Bishop of Waterford.
US.   Richard Boyle, Archbishop of Tuam.
UP.   Michael Boyle, Archbishop of Armagh, and Lord
      Chancellor of Ireland.
4 B. All did well, all prosperously married. One inherited
      the title, and the others were created peers. The most
      eminent of these is Roger, 1st Earl of Orrery, Military
      Commander under Cromwell in Ireland, afterwards
      engaged in the restoration of Charles II, who ennobled
      him. Was offered, but refused, the Chancellorship.

THE BOYLE FAMILY; EARLS OF CORK, ORRERY, BURLINGTON, AND SHANNON, AND OTHER ACQUIRED TITLES

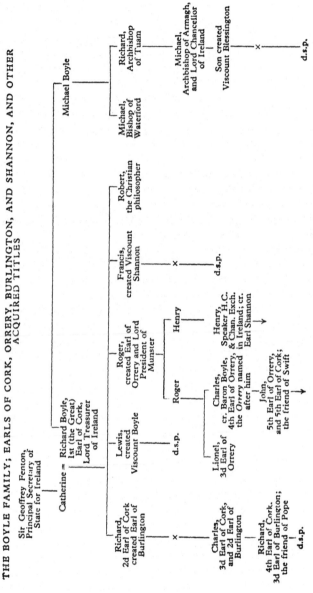

BOYLE, Hon. Robert—*continued*

[? *b.*] Also seven sisters married peers, and from the general accounts of the family I conclude, in the absence of knowledge of details, that some at least of them must have had considerable merits.

NS.   Chas. Boyle, 4th E. Orrery; scholar (*Epistles of Phalaris* controversy); diplomatist. The astronomical instrument the "Orrery" was named after him by its grateful inventor.

NS.   Henry Boyle, 1st Earl of Shannon; Speaker of House of Commons in Ireland, and Chanc. of the Exchequer there.

NP.   Richard Boyle, 4th Earl of Cork, encourager of the fine arts, the friend of Pope.

NP.   (But descended from another brother of the philosopher.) John Boyle, 5th Earl of Cork, the friend of Swift.

BRODIE, Sir Benjamin, Bart.; eminent surgeon; President of the Royal Society. The following relationships are taken from his Autobiography:—

[*G.*] "Had the reputation of being a person of very considerable abilities and I have formerly seem some of her MSS., which seemed to prove that this really was the case."

[F.]   "Was altogether remarkable for his talents and acquirements. He was well acquainted with general literature, and was an excellent Greek and Latin scholar. . . . He was endowed with a large share of energy and activity but. . . . I cannot doubt he was a disappointed person" (owing to politics). He attended to local business, and acquired a considerable local influence.

[B.]   "My elder brother became a lawyer, and has since obtained the highest place in his profession as a conveyancing barrister."

*u*S.   Lord Denman, the Lord Chief Justice (*see in* JUDGES). (His father was an eminent London physician.)

*u*P.   George Denman, Q.C., M.P.; the senior classic of his year (1842) in Cambridge.

S.   Sir Benjamin Brodie, second Bart.; Professor of Chemistry at Oxford.

BUCKLAND, William, D.D., Dean of Westminster; eminent geologist.

S.   Frank Buckland; naturalist; well-known popular writer on natural history, especially on pisciculture.

BUFFON, G. L., Comte de; naturalist. "Majestate naturæ par ingenium." Nature gave him every advantage in figure, bearing, features, strength, and general energy. Voltaire said he had "le corps d'un athléte l'âme d'un sage." He was educated for the law, but had an irresistible bias to science—at first to physics and mathematics, and finally to zoology.

ƒ.   From her he said that he derived his qualities. He always spoke with great affection of his mother.

S.   His abilities were considerable, and his attachment to his father was extreme. He was guillotined as an aristocrat.

CASSINI, Jean Dominique (1624–1712, æt. 87); celebrated Italian astronomer, whose name is chiefly connected with the discovery of the satellites of Saturn, with the rotations of the planets on their axes, and with the zodiacal light. He had an immense reputation in his day. Colbert induced him, by the offer of a pension, to settle in France, and to be naturalised as a Frenchman. He founded the Observatory of Paris. He was of a strong constitution, calm temper, and religious mind; was the first of a family of a remarkable series of long-lived astronomers.

S.   Jacques Cassini (1677–1756, æt. 79); author of *Theories on the Figures of the Earth*; succeeded his father in the French Academy.

P.   Cæsar F. Cassini de Thury ⎫
PS.⎱ His descendants   ⎬ *See below.*
PP.⎰   ⎭

CASSINI, de Thury, Cæsar François (1714–1784, æt. 70); showed early abilities in astronomy; was received into the Academy æt. 22; was author of the governmental survey of France; published many scientific memoirs.

I

CASSINI, de Thury, Cæsar François—*continued*

G.   Jean Dominique Cassini ⎱ *See below.*
F.   Jacques Cassini   ⎰

S.   Jacques Dominique (1747–1854, æt. 98); succeeded his father as director of the Observatory, and finished the "Carte Topographique de la France."

P.   Alex. Henri Gabriel (1781–1832, æt. 51); passionately fond of natural history; no taste for astronomy; wrote *Opuscules Philologiques*; was member of the Academy. He was a lawyer; President of the Cour Royale at Paris; and peer of France; *d.* prematurely of cholera.

CAVENDISH, Hon. Henry (1731–1810, æt. 79); celebrated chemist; founder of pneumatic chemistry.

gB.   William, Lord Russell; patriot; executed 1683. *See.*

CELSIUS, Oläus; a Swedish botanist, theologian, and orientalist. He is regarded as the founder of the study of natural history in Sweden, and was the master and patron of Linnæus. He wrote on the plants mentioned in Scripture; was professor of theology and of the Eastern languages at Upsala; *d.* æt. 86.

S.   Magnus Nicholas Celsius, mathematician and botanist; professor at Upsala.

P.   Andrew Celsius, astronomer. It was he who first employed the centigrade scale of the thermometer; professor at Upsala; *d.* æt. 43.

CONDORCET, Jean Caritat, Marquis de; secretary of the French Acadamy; also a writer on morals and politics. He was precocious in mathematical study, and had an insatiable and universal curiosity; was very receptive of ideas, but not equally original; had no outward show of being vain, simply because he had a superb confidence in his own opinions. He was deficient in brilliancy. His principal faculty was in combining and organising. Different people estimate his character very differently. St. Beuve shows him to have been malign and bitter, with a provoking exterior of benignity. He poisoned himself æt. 51, to avoid the guillotine.

CONDORSET, Jean Caritat, Marquis de—*continued*

[*f.*] His mother was very devout. She devoted him to the Virgin, when a child, to dress in white for eight years, like a young girl.

U. A distinguished bishop. (Arago's *Eloge.*)

(2 ?) He was also nearly connected with both the Archbishop of Vienne and with the Cardinal de Bernis, but I do not know in what degree.

CUVIER, George, Baron de; one of the most illustrious of naturalists. He became well known æt. 26; *d*. æt. 63. He had delicate health as a boy.

[*f.*] His mother was an accomplished woman, who took especial care in his early education.

B. Frederick, who early devoted himself to natural history, and was little inferior in research to George, though he never accomplished anything comparable in scientific value to his brother's works, except his *Teeth of Animals.*

D'ALEMBERT, Jean le Rond; mathematician and philosopher of the highest order. He was illegitimate; his mother abandoned him, and left him exposed in a public market, near the church of Jean le Rond, whence his Christian name; the origin of his surname is unknown. He showed, as a child, extraordinary eagerness to learn, but was discouraged at every step. The glazier's wife, in whose charge he had been placed by the authorities as a foundling, ridiculed his pursuits; at school he was dissuaded from his favourite mathematics; whenever he persuaded himself that he had done something original, he invariably found that others had found out the same thing before him. But his passion for science urged him on. He became member of the Academy æt. 24, and thenceforward his career was one of honour. He was totally free from envy, and very charitable. Never married, but had curious Platonic relations with Mdlle. de Espinasse. His father was said to be M. Destouches, a commissary of artillery.

D'ALEMBERT, Jean le Rond—*continued*

f.   Mdlle. de Tencin, novelist of high ability; originally a
nun, but she renounced her vows. She and both her
sisters were adventuresses of note. She allied herself
closely to her brother, the Cardinal de Tencin; loved
him passionately, and devoted herself to his advancement. She managed his house, which became a noted
centre for eminent men. She was anything but virtuous.
Fontanelle, the Secretary of the French Academy (*see
in* POETS *under* CORNEILLE), was one of her admirers,
previous to the birth of D'Alembert. Æt. 34 she threw
herself into political intrigue. After D'Alembert had
attained fame, it is stated that she for the first time
introduced herself to him as his mother; to whom he
replied, "You are only my step-mother; the glazier's
wife is my mother."

The maternal relatives of D'Alembert formed a curious
group. They were—

[*u.*] Madame Feriol, mother of Pont de Veyle and of D'Argental; and

[*u.*] Countess of Grolée; and the following brothers—

u.   Cardinal de Tencin, minister of state and nearly
premier.

*u*S.   Pont de Veyle, song-writer and dramatist; full of spirit,
but a selfish man. He was brought up by a pedant, who
roused in him a hatred of study.

*u*S.   Argental, Charles Aug. Feriol, Comte de; the confidant
and great admirer of Voltaire, who made him the
depositary of his writings. He was a polished literary
critic.

DARWIN, Dr. Erasmus, physician, physiologist, and poet.
His *Botanic Garden* had an immense reputation at the
time it was written; for, besides its intrinsic merits, it
chimed in with the sentiments and mode of expression
of his day. The ingenuity of Dr. Darwin's numerous
writings and theories is truly remarkable. He was a man
of great vigour, humour, and geniality.

DARWIN, Dr. Erasmus—*continued*

[F.] It is said that Dr. Darwin "sprang from a lettered and intellectual race, as his father was one amongst the earliest members of the Spalding Club."

S. Charles, student in medicine, died young and full of promise, from the effect of a wound when dissecting. He obtained the gold medal of Edinburgh University for a medical essay.

S. Dr. Robert Darwin, of Shrewsbury, was a physician of very large practice, and of great consideration in other respects.

P. Charles Darwin, the illustrious modern naturalist; author of the *Theory of Natural Selection.*

[2PS.] One of the sons of the above was second wrangler at Cambridge, 1868, and another was second in the Woolwich examination of the same year.

The number of individuals in the Darwin family who have followed some branch of natural history, is very remarkable—the more so because it so happens that the tastes appear (I speak from private sources of knowledge) to have been more personal than traditional. There is a strong element of individuality in the different members of the race which is adverse to traditional influence. Thus—

[S.] Sir Francis Darwin, a physician; was singularly fond of animals. His place in Derbyshire was full of animal oddities—half-wild pigs ran about the woods, and the like.

[P.] One of his sons is a well-known writer—though under a *nom de plume*—on natural history subjects, and on sporting matters.

I could add the names of others of the family who, in a lesser but yet decided degree, have shown a taste for subjects of natural history.

DAVY, Sir Humphry; chemist and philosopher. He was not precocious as a child, but distinguished himself as a youth. He published his first essays æt. 21. Was Professor of Chemistry at the Royal Institution æt. 23.

DAVY, Sir Humphry—*continued*

B.   Dr. John Davy, author of many memoirs on physiology. Inspector-General of Army Hospitals.

DE CANDOLLE, Augustin Pyrame; eminent Swiss botanist. His infancy resembled that of Cuvier; both had mothers who were intelligent and affectionate; both were of delicate health, and also of a most happy disposition. He had hydrocephalus, and nearly died of it æt. 7. Being unable to share the pursuits of other boys, he became studious, very fond of verse-making and of literature, but was not interested in science. He collected plants merely as subjects to draw from, but before long he became deeply interested in them. When æt. 15, his weakness of health ceased. His is almost a solitary instance of complete recovery from hydrocephalus. He then became very vigorous. He wrote a memoir æt. 20, that gained him some reputation. His essay, æt. 26, on being admitted Doctor of Medicine, was a very masterly one. Died æt. 63.

F.   Premier Syndic of Geneva on two occasions.

S.   Alphonse; also a Swiss botanist; Professor and Director of the Botanical Garden in Geneva.

EULER, Leonard; Swiss mathematician. His father taught him mathematics, but destined him for the Church; however, the younger Bernouli discovered his talents, and thereupon his father left him free to follow his bent. He wrote an important essay æt. 20. Lost one eye æt. 28, and became quite blind æt. 63. Died æt. 76. Was of a happy and pious disposition. Had three sons. Twenty-six grandchildren survived him.

[F.] Paul; a Calvinist clergyman of good mathematical abilities.

S.   Jean Albert; æt. 20, was Director of Observatory at Berlin.

S.   Charles; physician and mathematician.

S.   Christopher; astronomer. He served in Russia.

FORBES, Edward; naturalist of high achievement, and of yet higher promise; Professor of Natural History at Edinburgh, but died young, æt. 39, of kidney disease. He was a true genius and a man of rare social and conversational powers. In early childhood he showed that he had remarkable moral and intellectual gifts. While still a young student in Edinburgh, he travelled and wrote on the natural history of Norway. He was constantly on the move, sea-dredging and the like. Married, but had no children. The following is taken from Geikie's Life of him: "His immediate paternal ancestors were most of them characterised by great activity and energy. The men were fond of travel, fond of society and social pleasures, free-handed, and better at spending than saving money."

f. Gentle and pious, passionately fond of flowers—a taste that she transmitted to her son, the future Professor of Botany.

[3 u.] One died in Demerara, one in Surinam, and one was lost in Africa.

[2 B.] One died by drowning in Australia, and another was accidentally killed in America.

B. The other brother, an excellent mineralogist, was formerly engaged in the mines of South America.
A love of roving certainly runs in the blood of the Forbes family, and in none of them was it stronger than in that of the great naturalist.

FRANKLIN, Benjamin; philosophical, political, and miscellaneous writer, and a man of great force and originality of character. American patriot and statesman.

pS. Alexander Dallas Bache, superintendent of the United States Coast Survey; was professor of natural philosophy, also of chemistry and mathematics.

pS. Franklin Bache, M.D., author of many medical works; professor of chemistry.

[P.] W. T. Franklin, editor of his grandfather's works.

GALILEI, Galileo; illustrious physicist. Used, when a child, to construct mechanical toys. He discovered that the beats of the pendulum were isochronous, when a boy, before he knew any mathematics. He was intended for the profession of medicine, but he broke loose and took to mathematics. Became blind. Died æt 82.

F. Vicenzo was a man of considerable talent and learning. He wrote on the theory of music.

[B.] A brother seems to have attended to natural history.

[S.] His son, Vicenzo Galilei, was the first who applied to clockwork his father's invention of the pendulum.

GEOFFROY, St. Hilaire (Etienne); celebrated French naturalist. He was one of the *savans* who accompanied Napoleon to Egypt.

B. Château; a distinguished officer of engineers, much appreciated by Napoleon. Died after Austerlitz, of the fatigues of campaigning. Napoleon adopted his two sons, both of whom were authors, but of no particular importance.

S. Auguste; zoologist.

GMELIN, John Frederick; eminent German chemist, naturalist, and physician. He is the most prominent member of a family that has given at least five names to science:—

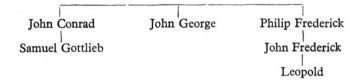

F. Philip Frederick; botanist and physician, who made scientific journeys in Europe, and wrote numerous monographs.

U. John George; botanist and physician, member of the St. Petersburg Academy, Siberian traveller, author of *Flora Siberica*.

[U.] John Conrad; a physician of repute.

GMELIN, John Frederick—*continued*

US. Samuel Gottlieb; scientific traveller in Astrakan and by the Caspian, where he was seized by Tartars, and died in confinement, æt. 29.

S. Leopold; chemist.

GREGORY, James; mathematician; inventor of the reflecting telescope; a man of very acute and penetrating genius. He was the most important member of a very important scientific family, partly eminent as mathematicians, and largely so as physicians. The annexed pedigree (p. 266) is necessary to explain their relationships, but I should add that I know it does not do full justice to the family. The talent came from the Andersons, of whom I wish I knew more. We may accept, at least, the following letters for the subject of this notice: *f.*, g., gB., B., 3N., NS., NS., S., 2 P., PS., and 2 Pp.

(See pedigree overleaf)

HALLER, Albert von (1708–1777, æt. 69); a Swiss physician, considered as the father of modern physiology. He was exceedingly precocious; the accounts of his early genius are as astonishing as any upon record. He was rickety, feeble, and delicate as a child. Was exceedingly laborious, having written about 200 treatises, including some good poetry. He suffered from gout, and took opium immoderately.

[F.] His father belonged to an hereditary pious family, and had the reputation of being an able lawyer.

g. One of the members of the Supreme Council of Switzerland.

S. Gottlieb Emmanuel; wrote various works on the history and literature of Switzerland.

HARVEY, William, M.D.; eminent physician; discoverer of the circulation of the blood; a good scholar. He was a little man with a round face, olive complexion, and small black eyes full of spirit. He became gouty, and acquired fanciful habits. He lay in bed thinking overmuch at night

PEDIGREE OF THE FAMILY OF GREGORY

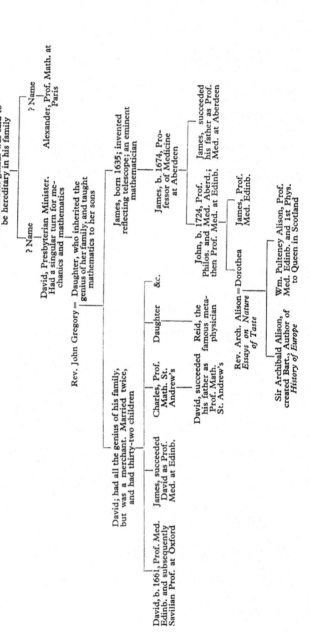

time, and slept ill. He and all his brothers were very choleric. Married, no children. His relationships show sterling ability.

[5 B.] Five of his brothers were merchants of weight and substance, chiefly trading in the Levant, and most of them made large fortunes. *The Merchants' Map of Commerce* is dedicated to all the brothers, who were remarkably attached to each other throughout their lives. They were also fondly attached to their mother, as shown by the very touching epitaph on her tombstone.

[N.? how many.] His nephews were prosperous merchants, and several made fortunes and achieved titles (?). (*Mem.* This is the statement in the biography prefaced to his works, published by the Sydenham Society.)

Up. (I believe.) Heneage Finch, created 1st Earl of Nottingham, Lord Chancellor. His father was also eminent (*see* FINCH, in JUDGES). William Harvey calles Heneage Finch "his loving cousin" in his will, and leaves him a legacy for his assistance in making it. I do not know the exact relationship. Earl Nottingham's mother was daughter of a William Harvey, and she was *not* a sister of the physician. There were forty-three years' difference of age between the physician and the Earl. It is probable that the Earl was first cousin once removed to Harvey, viz. the son of his father's brother's daughter.

HERSCHEL, Sir William; eminent astronomer; President of the Royal Society. Educated as a musician; came to England with the band of the Hanoverian Guards, then was organist at Bath. By æt. 41 he had acquired some knowledge of mathematics. Made his own telescopes, and became a renowned astronomer æt. 43. Died æt. 83.

[E.] Issac; son of a land-agent, but was so fond of music that he joined the military band of the Hanoverian Foot Guards: it was a band of select performers. He became a musician of some note, chiefly as a performer on the violin and oboe.

HERSCHEL, Sir William—*continued*

[B.]   Alexander; good performer on the violoncello; had also a strong turn for mechanics.

b.   Miss Caroline Herschel co-operated in the most helpful manner, with her brother, in all his astronomical work. She received the gold medal of the Royal Society. Died æt. 98.

S.   Sir John Herschel, also famous as an astronomer, and one of the foremost philosophers of the day.

[3 P.] Two of his grandsons have already made a name in the scientific world—Professor Alexander Herschel as a writer on meteorites, and Lieut. John Herschel, the first of his year at Addiscombe, who took charge of the expedition organised in 1868 by the Royal Society, to observe the total eclipse in India. The other son, William, a Bengal civilian, was first of his year at Haileybury.
       Musical gifts are strongly hereditary in the Herschel family.

HOOKER, Sir William; botanist; late Director and the promoter of the Royal Gardens at Kew; author of numerous works on systematic botany.

S.   Dr. Joseph Dalton Hooker, botanist and physicist, Director of the Royal Gardens at Kew; formerly naturalist to Sir J. Ross's Antarctic expedition, and afterwards traveller in the Sikkim Himalayas. His mother's father, g., was Dawson Turner, the botanist; and his cousins are, 2 *u*S., Giffard Palgrave, Arabian explorer and author of a work on Arabia, and Francis Palgrave, a well-known writer on literature, poetry, and art.

HUMBOLDT, Alexander, Baron von; scientific traveller and philosopher, and a man of enormous scientific attainments. He had an exceedingly vigorous constitution, and required very little sleep. His first work on natural history was published æt. 21; *d.* æt. 90, working almost to the last. He concluded his *Kosmos* æt. 82.

B.   Wilhelm von Humboldt, philologist of the highest order, classical critic, and diplomatist. The different tastes of the two brothers were conspicuous at the university where they studied together—Alexander for science, Wilhelm for philology.

HUNTER, John; the most eminent of English anatomists; Surgeon-General of the Army, Surgeon-Extraordinary to the King. His education was almost wholly neglected in his youth. He was a cabinet-maker between æt. 17 and 20; then he offered himself as assistant in the dissecting-room to his elder brother William (*see below*). He rapidly distinguished himself, and ultimately formed the famous Hunterian Museum.

B. William Hunter, President of the College of Physicians and Physician-Extraordinary to the Queen; whose reputation as an anatomist and surgeon, especially in midwifery, was of the highest order. He was of a sedate and studious disposition from youth; was first intended for the Church, but he took to medicine instead. He formed a splendid anatomical museum. He never married.

n. Matthew Baillie, M.D., an eminent physician, anatomist, and pathologist.

n. Joanna Baillie, authoress, dramatist; *d.* æt. 89.

HUYGHENS, Christian; Dutch astronomer and physicist; one of the eminent foreigners whom Colbert invited to Paris and pensioned there. He was very precocious; made great progress in mathematics as a boy; published a mathematical treatise æt. 22; *d.* æt. 68 of overwork. Never married.

F. Constantine, a mathematician and a scholar; author of *Monumenta Desultoria*; Secretary of three Princes of Orange in succession, and though a politician, he bravely avowed himself the friend of Descartes.

B. Constantine, succeeded his father in his royal secretaryship, and accompanied William III to England.

JUSSIEU, Antoine Laurent de; one of the greatest of botanists, author of the *Natural System*, and the most eminent member of a very eminent family of botanists. Became Professor in the Royal Garden æt. 22, and therefore chief to his uncle Bernard (*see below*), then 71 years old, who had refused the post, believing himself happier and more free where he was. There is some doubt how far he was the interpreter of Bernard's ideas and how far he was original. Became academician æt. 25. Had a strong constitution; was tall; had the appearance of a man of thought, always master of himself. Became blind: all the botanists of his family were very short-sighted. He was simple in his tastes, and had a long and healthy old age: *d.* æt. 88. He was descended from a family that had been notaries generation after generation. His grandfather broke through the tradition, and became a chemist at Lyons.

[G.] His grandmother had great influence over her numerous children for their good, in keeping them united and mutually helpful.

His father was one of a family of sixteen children, and the only one of them that married.

U. Antoine Jussieu. Had a love of absorbing plants even when a child; it became a passion when he was a youth, and drove him in a contrary direction to the path of life intended for him by his father. He became a student at Montpellier, had a rapid success, and æt. 23 succeeded Tournefort as Professor of Botany at Paris.

U. Bernard Jussieu, a great botanical genius, some say the greatest in this family. He, at first, had no taste for botany, not even when he was a youth, and had shared in a botanising excursion. Then he performed the duty of assistant demonstrator of botany to his brother Antoine, who persuaded him to follow that science as a profession, and he kept throughout life to the same subordinate post, for he preferred it. He was exceedingly attached to his brother. He became a most patient observer. He was a calm, composed man; very orderly; very temperate and simple in his habits. He was a virtuous, able, and kindly man. He had strong health, but he became blind, just as his nephew did after him: *d.* æt. 78.

JESSIEU, Antoine Laurent de—*continued*

U.   Joseph Jussieu. Was deficient in the steadiness of his eminent brothers, but had plenty of ability. He was successively, or rather simultaneously, botanist, engineer, physician, and traveller. He was botanist to the expedition sent to Peru under Condamine, whence he returned to Europe with a broken constitution: however, he lived to æt. 75.

S.   Adrien Jussieu, the only male heir of the family, succeeded his father as Professor of Botany. Married; had only two daughters; *d.* æt. 56, in 1853.

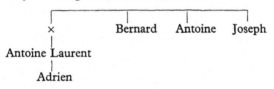

JUSSIEU, Bernard. *See above.*

2 B., N., NS.

LEIBNITZ, Gottfried Wilhelm; profound mathematician and metaphysician. He was very precocious, and read everything he could get. Was an excellent scholar, and became eminently proficient in law, philosophy, history, politics, and mathematics before æt. 22. He had a great taste for poetry, knew a vast deal by heart; even in his old age he could repeat all *Virgil*. He was strong, and seldom ailed, except in later life; had a great appetite, but drank little; was of prodigious activity—everything interested him equally; was a little subject to giddiness and to gout; *d.* æt. 68 of gout. Is said to have been vain and avaricious. Was never married.

[g.] Guillaume Schmuck, Professor of Jurisprudence at Leipsic.

F.   Professor of Morale (? Casuistry) at Leipsic.

u.   A renowned jurisconsult.

LINNÆUS (Von Linne), Carl; the great Swedish botanist, founder of the Linnæan system of classification of plants.

Was ill taught. He had the strongest predilection for botany, but his intellectual development in boyhood was slow. He began to be of high repute æt. 24. He had a curious want of power of learning languages; he could not speak French, and therefore always corresponded with foreigners in Latin. He was a man of impetuous character; had strong health, except some gout; slept but little. Was a poet by nature, though he never versified. He married; but "his domestic life does not bear examination, for it is well known that he joined his wife, a profligate woman, in a cruel persecution of his eldest son, an amiable young man, who afterwards succeeded to his botanical chair." (*Engl. Cycl.*)

S.   Charles, a botanist of distinction, though far from equalling his father.

NAPIER, John; Baron of Merchiston; inventor of logarithms.

F.   Master of the Mint of Scotland. He was only 16 years old when his son was born.

S.   Archibald, Privy Councillor to James VI, created Lord Napier.

This is an exceedingly able family. It includes the generals and admiral of the last generation (*see* COMMANDERS), and in this generation, Capt. Moncrieff (Moncrieff's battery), and Mr. Clerk Maxwell, second wrangler in 1854, and eminent in natural philosophy.

NEWTON, Sir Isaac; the most illustrious of English mathematicians and philosophers. Was exceedingly puny as a child; his life was then despaired of, but he grew to be strong and healthy. "The three grand discoveries which form the glory of his life, were conceived in his mind before the completion of his twenty-fourth year" (*Libr. Univ. Knowl.*): that is to say, the theories of gravitation, fluxions, and light. D. æt. 84.

Newton's ancestry appear to have been in no way remarkable for intellectual ability, and there is nothing of note that I can find out among his descendants, except what may be inferred from the fact that the two Huttons were connected with him in some unknown way, through the maternal line. The following paragraph is printed in the *Catalogue of Portraits* belonging to the Royal Society; it will be found under the description of a portrait of Sir Isaac Newton, which was presented by Mr. Charles Vignolles, the eminent engineer:—"The mother of James Hutton and the mother of Dr. Charles Hutton were sisters; and his grandmother and the mother of Sir Isaac Newton were also sisters." Mr. Vignolles, who is grandson of Dr. Charles Hutton, has kindly give me the history of the paragraph. It appears it was written on one of the few scraps of paper that he inherited from Dr. C. Hutton; it was in the handwriting of his aunt Miss Isabella Hutton, and appears to have been dictated by her father, Dr. C. Hutton. There is absolutely no other information obtainable. Now the word "his" in the paragraph is not grammatical; its interpretation is therefore ambiguous. It might be supposed to be intended to apply to Dr. C. Hutton, but a comparison of dates makes me doubt this. Sir Isaac was born in 1642, and Dr. C. Hutton in 1737, leaving a difference of 95 years to be bridged over by only one intervening generation. This is not absolutely impossible, but it is exceedingly incredible. It could have come to pass on some such extravagant hypothesis as the following, viz. that Newton's mother may have been only 20 when her son was born; also—which is just possible—that her sister may have been 35 years her junior. Also, that this sister may have been as much as 40 years old when her daughter was born, and that that daughter may also have been 40 years old when she gave birth to Dr. C. Hutton. As $40 + 40 + 35 - 20 = 95$, this hypothesis would satisfy the dates. However, I strongly suspect that Miss Hutton, writing from her father's not very clear dictation in his old age (he *d.* æt. 83), had omitted a phrase which I will supplement in brackets, and had thereby unintentionally struck out one or even two intervening

generations. Thus, "The mother of Dr. James Hutton
and the mother of Dr. Charles Hutton were sisters;
[they were children (or ? grandchildren) of Mr. —
Hutton;] and his grandmother and the mother of Sir
Isaac Newton were also sisters." This reading would
satisfy the possessive pronoun "his," it would satisfy
the dates, and it would also account for the exact nature
of the relationship not having been a matter of distinct
family tradition. If, on the other presumption, the
mothers of the Huttons had been first cousins to Sir
Isaac, the Huttons would assuredly have often alluded
to the fact; it is a simple form of kinship, easy to remember, and would have become well known to their contemporaries, especially to those who were Fellows of the
Royal Society, of which Dr. Charles Hutton was the
secretary; and it would never have been overlooked by
the biographers, either of Sir Isaac or of the Huttons. In
the biographies of the Huttons, Newton is simply spoken
of as having been their ancestor by the maternal line.

*uP*p. Charles Hutton, LL.D., was the well-known mathematician, Secretary to the Royal Society, and Professor at
Woolwich.

*uP*p. James Hutton was the geologist and chemist, and
founder of modern geology; a man whose reputation
was very great in his day, and whose writings some of
our modern leading geologists consider as extraordinarily
good and far from obsolete.

[n.] John Conduit; succeeded Sir Isaac as Master of the
Mint.

OERSTED, Hans Christian; Danish physicist and chemist,
discoverer of electro-magnetism; *d.* æt. 74.

B. Anders Sandöe Oersted, Premier of Denmark and
author; *d.* æt. 82.

N. Anders Sandöe (also); S. American traveller and
naturalist.

PLINY the Elder, naturalist. A most industrious compiler and
a student of extraordinary devotion, but curiously devoid

of critical ability. He was parsimonious of his time; slept little; was grave and noble. Lost his life in visiting Vesuvius during an eruption.

n. Pliny the Younger (he took the name of his mother's family), author of the *Epistles*. Very precocious; a man of great accomplishments, a great orator, a patron of men of learning, and an able statesman.

PORTA, Giovanni Baptista; an Italian philosopher of high eminence in his day, 1550–1615. Inventor of the camera obscura. He was a youthful prodigy, and became universally accomplished. He wrote well on many subjects besides science. He founded societies, and gave a notable impulse to the study of natural science. Unmarried.

B. A younger brother shared his ardour for study.

SAUSSURE, H. B. de; Swiss geologist and physicist. Carefully educated; was appointed Professor at Geneva æt. 22. His constitution became injured by the effects of Alpine exploration, also by anxiety on money matters. Died æt. 59.

F. Agriculturist and author of works on agriculture and statistics.

S. Nicholas Theodore; naturalist and chemist. Died æt. 78. He was first associated with his father in his pursuits, but afterwards followed an independent line of inquiry.

STEPHENSON, George; eminent engineer. The father of railways. A big, raw-boned youth, who educated himself. By steady but slow advances, he became engineer to a colliery at £100 a year, æt. 41. His first steam-engine was made æt. 43. He gained the prize for the best design for a locomotive æt. 49, and thenceforward his way to fortune was short. He invented the whole system of railway labour, its signals, "navvies," rails, stations, and locomotives; and his success was gained in the teeth of all kinds of opposition and absurd objections.

S. Robert; precocious and industrious. Became the foremost engineer of his day.

VOLTA, Alexander; an Italian physicist of the highest order, best known by his electrical (Voltaic) researches. Napoleon desired to make him the representative of Italian science, and pushed him forward in many ways, but Volta had no ambition of that kind. He was a man of noble presence, strong and rapid intelligence, large and just ideas, affectionate and sincere character. His scholars idolised him. He distinguished himself early at college. Began to write on electricity æt. 24. During the last six years of his life, he lived only for his family. Died æt. 82.

[S.]   One of his two sons died æt. 18, full of promise.

WATT, James; inventor of the steam-engine and of much else. He had a share in the discovery of the composition of water. Was very delicate as a child; was precocious, fond of experiment; read with avidity and indiscriminately. Æt. 21, he had attracted the notice of the authorities of the University of Glasgow, as being an ingenious and philosophical workman. His progress to fortune was slow and mainly due to his fortunate association with Boulton, who supplied energy, concentration of purpose, daring, administrative skill and capital. Watt ailed continually, and he was very irresolute until he approached old age, when his vigour became more and more remarkable. Few men had read so much as Watt, or remembered what they had read with such accuracy. He had a prodigious and orderly memory, and singular clearness in explaining. As an inventive genius he has never been surpassed.

[G.]   A humble teacher of mathematics, and something of an oddity. Mr. Muirhead says of him, in his *Life of Watt*, "It is curious to observe how decidedly a turn for scientific pursuit seems, in some measure at least, to have been common to every male of that family, so as to have become almost the birthright of both the grandsons of Thomas Watt, 'the old mathematician.' And it may be added that the same inclination still continued to 'run in their veins' till the line of direct male descent itself became extinct by the death, without issue, of both the sons of the illustrious improver of the steam-engine." (Page 17).

[F.] A man of zeal and intelligence, for twenty years town councillor, treasurer, and baillie of Glasgow.

[*f*.] Agness Muirhead was a superior woman, of good understanding, fine womanly presence, orderly, and ladylike. An old woman described her from recollection, "as a braw braw woman, none now to be seen like her."

[u.] John Muirhead seems to have been of kindred disposition to Watt's father; the two were closely united in many adventures.

[B.] Died at sea, æt. 21. (*See* above, the allusion to the two grandsons.)

S. Gregory died æt. 27. Was of great promise as a man of science, and intimately attached to Sir Humphry Davy. Is well known to geologists by his experiment of fusing stones and making artificial basalt.

[S.] James died unmarried, æt. 79. Had great natural abilities, but he was a recluse, and somewhat peculiar in his habits.

WOLLASTON, William Hyde, M.D.; a very ingenious natural philosopher and experimentalist, known chiefly by his invention of the goniometer which gave an accurate basis to the science of crystallography, and by that of the camera lucida. Also by his discovery of the metal palladium.

"A peculiar taste for intellectual pursuits of the more exact kind appears to have been hereditary in the family."

POETS

The Poets and Artists generally are men of high aspirations, but, for all that, they are a sensuous, erotic race, exceedingly irregular in their way of life. Even the stern and virtue-preaching Dante is spoken of by Boccaccio in most severe terms.[1] Their talents are usually displayed early in youth, when they are first shaken by the tempestuous passion of love. Of all who have a place in the appendix to this chapter, Cowper is the only one who began to write in mature life; and none of the others who are named in the heading to my appendix, except possibly Camoens and Spenser, delayed authorship till after thirty. It may be interesting, and it is instructive, to state a few facts in evidence of their early powers.

Béranger, a printer's compositor, taught himself and began to publish at 16. Burns was a village celebrity at 16, and soon after began to write: Calderon at 14. Campbell's *Pleasures of Hope* was published when he was 20. Goldoni produced a comedy in manuscript that amazed all who saw it, at 8. Ben Jonson, a bricklayer's lad, fairly worked his way upwards through Westminster and Cambridge, and became famous by his *Every Man in his Humour*, at 24. Keats, a surgeon's apprentice, first published at 21 and died at 25. Metastasio improvised in public when a child, and wrote at 15. Tom Moore published under the name of Thomas Little, and was famous at 23. Ovid wrote verses from boyhood. Pope published his *Pastorals* æt. 16, and translated the *Iliad* between 25 and 30. Shakespeare must have begun very early, for he had written almost all his historical plays by the time he was

[1] See Preface to the Translation of the *Inferno*, by Rossetti, p. xix.

34. Schiller, a boy of promise, became famous through his *Brigands* at 23. Sophocles, at the age of 27, beat Æschylus in the contest for the theatrical prize.

I now annex the usual tables.

TABLE I

SUMMARY OF RELATIONSHIPS OF 24 POETS GROUPED INTO 20 FAMILIES

One relation (or two in family)

	Byron	*s.*		Milman	F.
	Chaucer	S.		Racine	S.
2.	Chenier	B.	2.	Tasso	F.
	Goethe	*f.*		Vega	S.
	Heine	U.			

Two or three relations (or three or four in family)

	Æschylus	2 B		Dibdin	S. N.
2.	Ariosto	B. N.		Dryden	S. *UP.*
	Aristophanes	3 S.		Hook	F. B. N.
2.	Corneille	B. n.		Milton	F. B.
	Cowper	G. GB.			

Four or more relations (or five or more in family)

Coleridge	S. *s.* 3 N. P. 2 NS.
Wordsworth	B. 3 N.

The results of TABLE II are surprising. It appears that, if we except the kindred of Coleridge and Wordsworth, who have shown various kinds of ability, almost all the relations are in the first degree. Poets are clearly not founders of families. The reason is, I think, simple, and it applies to artists generally. To be a great artist, requires a rare and, so to speak, unnatural correlation of qualities. A poet, besides his genius, must have the severity and steadfast earnestness of those whose dispositions afford few temptations to pleasure, and he must, at the same time, have the utmost delight in the exercise of his senses and affections. This is a rare character, only to be formed by

TABLE II[1]

Degrees of Kinship					A	B	C	D
Name of the degree	Corresponding letters							
1 degree Father	4 F.	...	...	...	4	20	1	60
Brother	8 B.	...	...	...	8	40	150	26
Son	9 S.	...	...	...	9	45	100	45
2 degrees Grandfather	1 G.	0 g.	...	...	1	5	200	2·5
Uncle	1 U.	0 n.	...	...	1	5	400	1·25
Nephew	9 N.	1 n.	...	...	10	50	400	12·5
Grandson	1 P.	0 p.	...	...	1	5	200	2·5
3 degrees Great-grandfather	0 GF.	0 gF.	0 *GF.*	0 *g*F.	0	0	400	0
Great-uncle	1 GB.	0 gB.	0 *GB.*	0 *g*B.	1	5	800	6
First-cousin	0 US.	0 uS.	0 *US.*	0 *u*S.	0	0	800	0
Great-nephew	2 NS.	0 nS.	0 *NS.*	0 *n*S.	2	10	800	1
Great-grandson	0 PS.	0 pS.	0 *PS.*	0 *p*S.	0	0	400	0
All more remote	1	...	...	...	1	5	...	...

some happy accident, and is therefore unstable in inheritance. Usually, people who have strong sensuous tastes go utterly astray and fail in life, and this tendency is clearly shown by numerous instances mentioned in the following appendix, who have inherited the dangerous part of a poet's character and not his other qualities that redeem and control it.

APPENDIX TO POETS

I have examined into the relationships of the following 56 poets. Of some of them—as of those of Ferdusi, Terence, and Sappho—there seems to exist no record at all, and my information is very scanty about many of the others. Nevertheless I find that the 20 poets whose names are printed in *italics*, have

[1] See, for explanation, the footnote to the similar table on page 102.

had eminent kinsfolk, and that some of the remainder afford minor proofs of hereditary ability; thus the father of Burns and the mother of Schiller were far from mediocrity; Southey's aunt, Miss Tyler, was passionately fond of the theatre. We may fairly conclude that at least 40 per cent. of the Poets have had eminently gifted relations.

LIST OF POETS

Æschylus; Alfieri; Anacreon; *Ariosto*; *Aristophanes*; Béranger; Burns; *Byron*; Calderon; Campbell; Camoens; *Chaucer*; *Chenier*; *Coleridge*; *Corneille*; *Cowper*; Dante; *Dibdin*; *Dryden*; Euripides; Ferdusi; La Fontaine; *Goethe*; Goldoni; Gray; *Heine*; *Hook*; Horace; Ben Jonson; Juvenal; Keats; Lucretius; Metastasio; *Milman*; *Milton*; Molière; Moore; Oehlenschläger; Ovid; Petrarch; Plautus; Pope; Praed (but see Appendix); *Racine*; Sappho; Schiller; Shakespeare; Shelley; Sophocles; Southey; Spencer; *Tasso*; Terence; *Vega*; Virgil; Wieland; *Wordsworth*.

ÆSCHYLUS, great Greek tragedian; also highly renowned as a warrior, and all his family were distinguished for bravery. He began early to write, but was æt. 41 before he gained his first prize for drama. He afterwards gained sixteen; *d.* æt. 69.

B.   Cynægeirus distinguished himself so highly at Marathon, together with Æschylus, that their feats were commemorated by a descriptive painting.

B.   Ameinias was noted as having commenced the attacks on the Persian ships at Salamis.

[n.]   Philocles was victorious over the "King Œdipus" by Sophocles, but probably with a posthumous tragedy of Æschylus.

[2 S]   Euphorion and Bion were said to have gained four victories with posthumous pieces of Æschylus. What may have been their share and that of Philocles in the completion of these plays is unknown; but at all events from and by means of these persons arose what was called the tragic school of Æschylus, which continued for the space of 125 years.

ARIOSTO, Ludovico; author of the epic *Orlando Furioso*, and of many excellent satires. He wrote dramas as a boy, and showed an early disposition for poetry, but was educated for the law, which he abandoned under an overpowering impulse towards literature. Never married; had two illegitimate sons.

B.   Gabriel; a poet of some distinction. He finished the comedy of *La Scholastica*, which his brother had left uncompleted at his death. He wrote several poems, and left a MS. volume of Latin verses, which were published posthumously.

N.   Orazio was an intimate friend of Tasso. He wrote the *Argomenti*, and other works.

ARISTOPHANES, Greek comedian of the highest order; author of fifty-four comedies, of which only eleven have reached us. His genius showed itself so early, that his first play—and it won the second prize—was written when he was under the age prescribed by law for competitors. It was therefore submitted under a borrowed name.

3. S. His three sons—Philippus, Araros, and Nicostratus—were all poets of the middle comedy.

BYRON, Lord. Very ill educated at home; did not show genius when at Harrow; his *Hours of Idleness* were published æt. 19, and the *English Bards and Scotch Reviewers*, which made him famous, æt. 21; *d.* æt. 36.

[G.]   Hon. Admiral Byron, circumnavigator; author of the *Narrative*.

[F.]   Captain Byron; imprudent and vicious.

[*f.*]   Was strange, proud, passionate, and half-mad. "If ever there were a case in which hereditary influences, arising out of impulse, passions, and habits of life, could excuse eccentricities of character and extremes of conduct, this excuse must be pleaded for Byron, as having descended from a line of ancestry distinguished on both sides by everything calculated to destroy all harmony of character, all social concord, all individual happiness." (Mrs. Ellis.)

s. Ada, Countess of Lovelace; had remarkable mathematical gifts.

CHAUCER, Geoffrey; wrote the *Court of Love* æt. 18. Illustrious poet; father of English poetry and, in some sense, of the English language also.

S. Sir Thomas; was Speaker of the House of Commons and ambassador to France.

CHENIER, André Marie de; eminent French poet. His mother was Greek and inspired him with a passionate taste for Greek literature. He was guillotined æt. 32. It was he who touched his forehead on the scaffold, and said regretfully, just before his execution, "Pourtant j'avais quelque chose là."

B. Marie-Joseph; also a poet. He wrote dramas and lyrical pieces. Among the latter was the *Chant du Départ*, which nearly rivalled the *Marseillaise*. He was a leading politician under the Republic and the Empire. His first play was acted at æt. 20, and was hissed.

COLERIDGE, Samuel Taylor; poet and metaphysician; was filled with poetry and metaphysics æt. 15; always slothful and imprudent. He had warm friendships, but was singularly regardless of duties, and somewhat querulous; of a peculiarly hesitating disposition; opium eater. Fully eight members of this family—indeed, nearly all of its male representatives—have been gifted with rare abilities.

S. Hartley, poet; a precocious child, who had been a visionary boy. His imaginative and colloquial powers were extraordinary. He was morbidly intemperate.

s. Sara; had in a remarkable degree the intellectual characteristics of her father. She was authoress and principal editor of her father's works. She married her cousin, H. Nelson Coleridge, and was mother of Herbert. *See below.*

COLERIDGE, Samuel Taylor—*continued*

S.   The Rev. Derwent Coleridge, author, Principal of St.
        Mark's College, Chelsea; is the remaining child of the
        poet.

N.   Sir John Taylor Coleridge, judge, eminent in early life as
        an accomplished scholar and man of letters.

N.   Edward Coleridge, Master at Eton, now fellow.

N.   Henry Nelson Coleridge, scholar; a well-known writer
        of many articles in periodicals; married his cousin Sara.
        See above.

P. also BP. Herbert Coleridge, philologist.

[NS.]   Henry, late Fellow of Oriel College; now Roman
        Catholic.

NS.   Sir John Duke Coleridge, Solicitor-General.

CORNEILLE, Pierre; French dramatist; creator of the
        dramatic art in France; was brought up to the bar, but
        left it for poetry under an overpowering impulse. His
        first publication was a comedy, æt. 23; *d.* æt. 78.

B.   Thomas, also a poet, who worked with Pierre, his elder
        and only brother. Their dispositions and way of life
        were in singularly close sympathy. Thus their difference
        of ages being nineteen years, they married sisters the
        difference of whose ages was the same. Their respective
        families lived in the same house. They wrote about an
        equal number of plays, and their writings were alike in
        character. Thomas had the greater facility in authorship,
        but his style was inferior in energy to that of his brother.
        He succeeded Pierre at the Academy; *d.* æt. 84.

n.   Fontenelle, son of the only sister; the celebrated Secre-
        tary of the French Academy for nearly forty years. His
        real name was Bovier. He says, "Mon père était une
        bête, mais ma mère avait de l'esprit; elle était quiétiste."
        His was a mixed character—partly that of a man of
        society of a frivolous and conventional type, and partly
        that of the original man of science and free-thinker. The
        Fontenelle of the opera and the Fontenelle of the
        Academy of Sciences seemed different people. Some

biographers say he had more brain than heart; others admire his disposition. He almost died from weakness on the day of his birth. He was a precocious child. At college the note attached to his name was, "Adolescens omnibus partibus absolutus"—a youth perfectly accomplished in every respect. He began public life by writing plays, in order to imitate his uncles, but his plays were hissed. Then he took to science, and became academician æt. 34. He lived to extreme old age, becoming deaf and losing much of his memory; but he was "aussi spirituel que jamais" to the last; *d.* one month short of æt. 100. *See* D'ALEMBERT *in* SCIENCE.

[*BPP.*] (?) Charlotte Corday, the heroic assassin of Marat; born about 150 years, or probably five generations, later than the Corneille family; was a direct descendant of the mother of Fontenelle.

COWPER, William; a poet, whose writings have a singularly quiet charm, and are full of kindly and delicate feeling. He was past middle age when he began to publish; his first success was æt. 54. He had a morbid constitutional timidity in youth, and insanity with religious terrors hung over his later life. He contended bravely against them, but ultimately they overpowered him.

G. The judge, Sir Spencer Cowper.

GB. The Lord Chancellor, Earl Cowper.

DIBDIN, Charles; writer of more than 900 naval ballads. He was intended for the Church, but a love of music so predominated that he connected himself with the stage. His first opera was acted at Covent Garden when he was æt. 16. He afterwards became manager of theatres, but was improvident, and consequently much embarrassed in later life.

[F.] Was a considerable merchant.

[*f.*] Was æt. 50 when he was born, and he was her eighteenth child.

S. Thomas; was apprenticed to an upholsterer, but he joined a party of strolling players, and took to the stage.

He wrote and adapted a vast number of pieces—none of much original merit.

N. Rev. Thomas F. Dibdin, famous bibliographer; founder of the Roxburghe Club, for the purpose of reprinting scarce books.

DRYDEN, John; dramatist, satirist, and critic. He held the highest standing among the wits of his day. Æt. 17 he wrote good verses; he published *Astræa Redux* æt. 29, but was not recognised as a writer of the first order till æt. 50.

S. John; wrote a comedy.

UP. Jonathan Swift, D.D., Dean of St. Patrick's, satirist and politician. *See under* LITERATURE.

GOETHE, John Wolfgang; poet and philosopher. One of the greatest men of genius the world has produced. His disposition, like that of Lord Bacon, appears to have been mainly formed by the simple addition of those of his ancestors. He was an exceedingly precocious child, for he wrote dialogues and other pieces that were both original and good between the ages of 6 and 8. He was an eager student in boyhood and youth, though desultory in his reading. His character then was proud and fantastic. Goethe describes his hereditary peculiarities in a pretty poem,[1] of part of which I give a translation from his *Life* by Lewes:—"From my father I inherit my frame and the steady guidance of my life; from dear little mother my happy disposition and love of story-telling.

[1] "Vom Vater hab'ich die Statur,
        Des Lebens ernstes Führen;
   Von Mütterchen die Frohnatur,
        Und Lust zu fabuliren.

   "Urahnherr war der Schönsten hold,
        Das spukt so hin und wieder;
   Urahnfrau liebte Schmuck und Gold.
        Das zuckt wohl durch die Glieder.

   "Sind nun die Elemente nicht,
        Aus dem Complex zu trennen,
   Was ist den an dem ganzen Wicht
        Original zu nennen?"

My ancestor was a 'ladies' man,' and that haunts me now and then; my ancestress loved finery and show, which also runs in the blood." To go more into particulars, I take the substance of the two following paragraphs from Lewes's *Life of Goethe*.

f. One of the pleasantest figures in German literature, and one standing out with greater vividness than almost any other. She was the delight of children, the favourite of poets and princes. After a lengthened interview an enthusiastic traveller exclaimed, "Now do I understand how Goethe has become the man he is." The Duchess Amalia corresponded with her as an intimate friend; a letter from her was a small jubilee at the Weimar court. She was married æt. 17 to a man for whom she had no love, and was only 18 when the poet was born.

[F.] "Was a cold, stern, formal, somewhat pedantic, but truth-loving, upright-minded man." From him the poet inherited the well-built frame, the erect carriage, and the measured movement, which in old age became stiffness, and was construed into diplomacy or haughtiness; from him also came that orderliness and stoicism which have so much distressed those who cannot conceive genius otherwise than as vagabond in its habits. The lust for knowledge, the delight in communicating it, the almost pedantic attention to details, which are noticeable in the poet, are all traceable in the father.

Goethe married unsuitably, and had a son of no note, who died before him.

HEINE, Heinrich; German poet, essayist, and satirist of the highest order. Was intended for commerce, but took a disgust to it, and followed literature, as pupil and friend of A. W. Schlegel. He first published æt. 25, but his writings were little appreciated by the public till æt. 28. He became partially paralysed æt. 47, and *d.* æt. 56. Was of Jewish parentage.

U. Salomon Heine, German philanthropist; who raised himself from poverty to the possession of nearly two millions sterling, and who gave immense sums to public institutions.

[US.] The son of Salomon; succeeded him in the management of his affairs.

HOOK, Theodore. Was a remarkably clever boy, who sang well and composed songs. He had great success æt. 17. His constitution was naturally excellent, but he ruined it by dissipation; *d.* æt. 53 of a broken constitution. Was unmarried, but had six illegitimate children.

F. James Hook, a musical composer of extraordinary fertility and of considerable reputation in his day.

B. Dr. James Hook, Dean of Worcester, accomplished scholar; eminent as a political pamphleteer.

N. Dr. Walter Farquhar Hook, Dean of Chichester, theologian, author, and preacher.

MILMAN, Henry Hart; Dean of St. Paul's; scholar, critic, poet, historian, and divine. *Fall of Jerusalem, History of the Jews,* &c. Very successful at Oxford. Singularly handsome. *D.* æt. 77.

F. Eminent Physician, President of the College of Physicians.

MILTON, John; most illustrious English poet, scholar, and republican writer. Was handsome and of girlish beauty when a youth. Had written *Arcades, Comus, L' Allegro,* and *Il Penseroso* before æt. 31. Became blind about æt. 40. He abandoned poetry for twenty years, during the time he was engaged in political life. *Paradise Lost,* and *Regained* were not written till after that period. *D.* æt. 66. *Paradise Lost* did not become famous till long after the poet's death.

F. A man of considerable musical genius, whose chants are still in use.

B. A judge, whose creed, politics, and character were the opposite of those of the poet's, and whose abilities were far inferior.

PRAED, Mackworth; a man of a thoroughly poetic disposition, though of more elegance than force.

PRAED, Mackworth—*continued*

[3 n.] Sir George Young, Bart., and his brothers; an able family of scholars.

RACINE, Jean; French dramatist, and author of other writings. Orphan æt. 4; received æt. 16 into a school attached to Port Royal, where he made astonishing progress, but he soon broke quite away from the ideas and studies of that place and devoted himself to works of imagination and to writing verses; for this he was severely reprimanded.

S.   Louis; was a poet by nature, but never pursued poetry to his full desire, on account of remonstrances. He had high gifts; *d.* æt. 70.

TASSO, Torquato; Italian poet; was exceedingly precocious. His father said of him, æt. 16, that he showed himself worthy of his mother. Æt. 17 he had written *Rinaldo*; *d.* æt. 51, just after his release from a cruel imprisonment for seven years, and on the eve of his intended coronation at the Capitolas prince of poets.

[*f.*]   Porzia di Rossi was a gifted woman in every respect.

F.   Bernardo Tasso, poet; author of *L'Amadiji*, &c.; orator. He was left in embarrassed circumstances in his youth, and for a long time led a wandering and necessitous life.

VEGA, Lope de; Spanish poet of extraordinary fertility. He wrote 497 plays, and much other matter besides. He was very precocious. He ran away from home, and afterwards entered the army. He made a considerable fortune by his pen; *d.* æt. 73.

S.   A natural son by Marcela; æt. 14 made some figure as a poet, but, entering the navy, lost his life in a battle when still quite young.

WORDSWORTH, William; poet. His epitaph by Keble is so grand and just, that I reprint an extract from it here:—
"A true Philosopher and Poet, who, by the special gift and calling of Almighty God, whether he discoursed on Man or Nature, failed not to lift up the heart to holy

K

things; tired not of maintaining the cause of the poor and simple; and so, in perilous times, was raised up to be the chief minister, not only of noblest poesy, but of high and sacred truth."

He does not appear to have been precocious as a boy; he was a hot republican in his youth; did not attain rank as a poet till manhood, about æt. 40. He was a principal member of the "Lake" school of poets; *d.* æt. 82.

B.   Rev. Dr. Christopher Wordsworth, master of Trinity College, Cambridge; author of *Ecclesiastical Biography*, &c. He had the three following sons, nephews of the poet:—

N.   John; excellent scholar, Cambridge, 1827; *d.* young.

N.   Rev. Christopher, Bishop of Lincoln; senior classic, Cambridge, 1830; formerly public orator of Cambridge, and Head Master of Harrow; voluminous author.

N.   Charles, Bishop of Dunkeld; also an excellent scholar.

MUSICIANS

The general remarks I made in the last chapter on artists, apply with especial force to Musicians. The irregularity of their lives is commonly extreme; the union of a painstaking disposition with the temperament requisite for a good musician is as rare as in poets, and the distractions incident to the public life of a great performer are vastly greater. Hence, although the fact of the inheritance of musical taste is notorious and undeniable, I find it exceedingly difficult to discuss its distribution among families. I also found it impossible to obtain a list of first-class musicians that commanded general approval, of a length suitable to my purposes. There is excessive jealousy in the musical world, fostered no doubt by the dependence of musicians upon public caprice for their professional advancement. Consequently, each school disparages others; individuals do the same, and most biographers are unusually adulatory of their heroes, and unjust to those with whom they compare them. There exists no firmly-established public opinion on the merits of musicians, similar to that which exists in regard to poets and painters, and it is even difficult to find private persons of fair musical tastes, who are qualified to give a deliberate and dispassionate selection of the most eminent musicians. As I have mentioned at the head of the appendix to this chapter, I was indebted to a literary and artistic friend in whose judgment I have confidence, for the selection upon which I worked.

The precocity of great musicians is extraordinary. There is no career in which eminence is achieved so early in life as in that of music.

I now proceed to give the usual tables.

TABLE I

SUMMARY OF RELATIONSHIPS OF 26 MUSICIANS
GROUPED INTO 14 FAMILIES

One relation (or two in family)

2. Gabrielli	N.	Hillier	S.
2. Haydn	B.		

Two or three relations (or three or four in family)

Bononcini	B. S.	Keiser	F. *s.*
Dussek	F. B. *s.*	Mendelssohn	G. F. *b.*
Eichhorn	2 S.	Meyerbeer	2 B.

Four or more relations (or five or more in family)

2. Amati, Andrea	2 S. B. P.
9. Bach	G. F. U. GN. 2 GB. 3 S.
2. Benda Giorgio	3 B. 4 N. S.
Mozart	F. *b.* 2 S.
Palestrina	4 S.

TABLE II

14 FAMILIES

In first degree	5 F. 9 B. 16 S.
In second degree	2 G. 1 U. 5 N. 1 P.
In third degree	2 GB.
All more remote	1.

The nearness of degree of the eminent kinsmen is just as
remarkable as it was in the case of the poets, and equally so in
the absence of eminent relations through the female lines.

Mendelssohn and Meyerbeer are the only musicians in my
list whose eminent kinsman have achieved their success in
other careers than that of music.

APPENDIX TO MUSICIANS

I am indebted to a friend for a list of 120 musicians, who
appeared to him to be the most original and eminent upon
record. They were made for quite another object to my own,
and I therefore am the more disposed to rely on the justice of
my friend's choice. Twenty-six of these, or about 1 in 5, have
had eminent kinsmen, as is shown in the following catalogue.
The illustrious musicians are only 7 in number; namely *Sebastian Bach*, Beethoven, Handel, *Haydn*, *Mendelssohn*, *Mozart*,
and Spohr. The four who are *italicised* are instances of hereditary genius.

ALLEGRI, Gregorio (1580–1652, æt. 72); composer of the
      Miserere sung at the S. Sixtine at Rome in Lent; a man
      of kindly and charitable disposition, who used to visit the
      prisons daily, and give what he could to the prisoners.
?   Exact relation. Correggio Allegri and his family. *See*
      PAINTERS.
AMATI; a family of eminent makers of violins, who lived in
      Cremona, and were the first introducers of that instru-
      ment into Italy. They are six in number; indeed, there
      is a seventh—Joseph of Bologna, who was living in 1786,
      but whose relationship to the others is unknown.

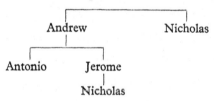

Those of the family that showed the most original power
are Andrea (B, 2 S., P.) and Antonio (F., U., B., N.).
BACH, Sebastian; a transcendent musical genius (1685–1750,
      æt. 65). He was very precocious, and arrived at the full
      maturity of his powers æt. 22. His home life was simple
      and quiet. He was a good husband, father, friend, and

citizen. He was very laborious; and became blind from over-study.

The Bachs were a musical family, comprising a vast number of individuals, and extending through eight generations. It began in 1550, it culminated in Sebastian (6 in the genealogical table) and its last known member was Regina Susanna, who was alive in 1800, but in indigent circumstances. There are far more than twenty *eminent* musicians among the Bachs; the biographical collections of musicians give the lives of no less than fifty-seven of them (see Fétis' *Dictionary of Musicians*). It was the custom of the family to meet in yearly reunions, at which the entertainments were purely musical. In or about A.D. 1750 as many as 120 Bachs attended one of these meetings. A complete genealogy of the family is to be found in Korabinsky's *Beschreibung der Königlichen Ungarischen Haupt Frey, und Krönungstadts Presburg*, t. i. p. 3; also a genealogical tree in No. 12 of the Leipsic *Musical Gazette*, 1823. I give a modified copy of this, for it is otherwise impossible to convey the lines of descent in a sufficiently intelligible manner. Every person mentioned in the list ranks as a sterling musician, except where the contrary is distinctly stated.

F. J. Ambrose, a distinguished organist.

U. J. Christopher, a twin child with Ambrose. These two were so exceedingly alike in feature, address, and style, that they were the wonder of all who saw and heard them. It is added that their wives could not distinguish them except by their dresses.

G. Christopher (3).

2 GB. Henry (2) and John (4).

[GG.] Weit Bach (1), the founder of the family, was a baker at Presburg, who sang to the guitar; was obliged to leave his town because he was a Protestant. He settled in Saxe Gotha.

GN. J. Christopher (5), one of the greatest musicians of Germany; a laborious student.

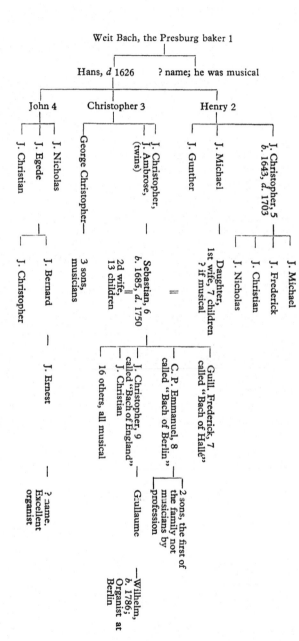

PEDIGREE OF THE BACHS

Weit Bach, the Presburg baker 1

Hans, *d* 1626   ? name; he was musical

John 4   Christopher 3   Henry 2

John 4:
- J. Christian
- J. Egede
- J. Nicholas

Christopher 3:
- George Christopher
- J. Christopher, (twins)
- J. Ambrose,

Henry 2:
- J. Michael
- J. Gunther

- J. Michael
- J. Frederick
- J. Christian
- J. Nicholas
- J. Christopher, 5 *b.* 1643, *d.* 1703

- J. Christian
- J. Bernard
- J. Nicholas

- Daughter, 1st wife, 7 children ? if musical
- J. Christian

3 sons, musicians

Sebastian, 6 *b.* 1685, *d.* 1750 ‖ 2d wife, 13 children

J. Ernest

=

Guill. Frederick, 7 called "Bach of Halle"

C. P. Emmanuel, 8 called "Bach of Berlin"

J. Christopher, 9 called "Bach of England"

J. Christian

16 others, all musical

? name, Excellent organist

2 sons, the first of the family not musicians by profession

Guillaume

—Wilhelm, *b.* 1786; Organist at Berlin

BACH, Sebastian—*continued*

S.   Guillaume Frederick (7), called "Bach of Hallé" a
       man of great power and very learned; died indigent.

S.   C. P. Emmanuel (8), called "Bach of Berlin;" the
       founder of our pianoforte music; whom Haydn, and
       likewise Mozart, regard as their direct predecessor and
       teacher. (Lady Wallace, *Letters of Musicians.*)

S.   J. Christopher (9), called "Bach of England;" a charm-
       ing composer.

       I have not met with any notice of the Bach musical
       genius being transmitted through a female line.

BEETHOVEN, Ludwig von. I insert the name of this great
       composer on account of his having formerly been reputed
       the illegitimate son of Frederick the Great of Prussia.
       However, recent biographers consider this allegation to
       be absolutely baseless, and therefore, although I mention
       the report, I do not accept its truth. His mother's
       husband was a tenor singer of the Elector's Chapel at
       Cologne. His two brothers were undistinguished. He had
       a nephew of some talent, who did not turn out well, and
       was cause of great grief to him.

       Beethoven began to publish his own musical composi-
       tions æt. 13.

BENDA, Francesco (1709–1786, æt. 77); was the elder member
       of a very remarkable family of violinists. His father was a
       poor weaver, but musical, and taught his sons to play.
       The following tables shows how its eight principal
       members were related:—

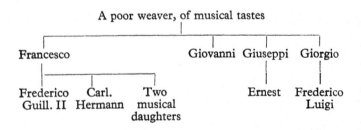

A poor weaver, of musical tastes

| Francesco | | | Giovanni | Giuseppi | Giorgio |

| Frederico Guill. II | Carl. Hermann | Two musical daughters | | Ernest | Frederico Luigi |

Francesco was the founder of a school of violinists, and was himself the ablest performer on that instrument in his day.

B. Giovanni, pupil of Francesco; *d.* æt. 38.

B. Giuseppi; succeeded Francesco as master of the concerts of the King of Prussia; *d.* æt. 80.

B. Giorgio, the most eminent member of this interesting family. He had vast musical powers, but was fantastic, and wasted his time in reverie. It is said that, after his wife had died in his arms, he rushed to the piano to express his grief; but soon, becoming interested in the airs he was originating, he forgot both his grief and the cause of it so completely, that, when his servant interrupted him to ask about communicating the recent event to the neighbours, Giorgio jumped up in a puzzle, and went to his wife's room to consult her.

N. Frederick Luigi (son of Giorgio), musician; husband of Madame Benda, director of concerts.

S. Frederick Guillaume, a worthy pupil of his father, and a composer.

S. Carl Hermann, who nearly approached his father as a violinist.

[2s.] Two musical daughters.

N. Ernest Fred., son of Giuseppi; promised to be an artist of the first order, but *d.* of fever æt. 31.

BONONCINI, Giovanni Maria (1640–?); composer and writer on music.

[B.] But the relationship is not established. Domenichino, a musician at the court of Portugal, who lived to beyond 85 years of age.

B. Antonio, composer of Church music.

S. Giovanni; composed a very successful opera—*Camilla*— æt. 18. He was a rival in England of Handel, but had to yield.

DUSSEK, Ladislas (1761–1812, æt. 51); played on the piano æt. 5; a very amiable and noble character; exceedingly careless about his own money; equally celebrated as a performer and as a composer. He greatly advanced the power of the piano. Married Miss Corri (? Currie), a musician.

F.　Giovanni; excellent organist.

B.　Francesco; very good violinist.

s.　Olivia; inherited the talents of her parents; performer on the piano and harp.

EICHHORN, Jean Paul, 1787, and his two sons. Jean Paul was of humble birth. He showed remarkable aptitude for music, and without any regular instruction he became a good musician. He married twice; his son by the first wife was Ernest, and by the second, whom he married very shortly after the death of the first in childbirth, was Edward.

2 S.　These children were known as "the Brothers Eichhorn." They both had marvellous musical powers from the tenderest years, and played instinctively. Thenceforward their father used them cruelly, to make as much money as he could, and compelled them to perform continually in public. Thus they lost all opportunity for that study and leisure which are required for the development of the highest artistic powers.

Edward was not equal in musical ability to his brother.

GABRIELLI, Andrea (about 1520–1576, æt. about 66); an esteemed composer of music.

N.　Jean Gabrielli, a great and original artist, wholly devoted to musical labours; eulogised in the highest terms by his contemporaries and scholars.

HAYDN, Francis Joseph. His disposition to music was evident from the earliest childhood. He was born in low circumstances, and gradually struggled upwards. His father was a village organist and wheelwright. He married, but not happily, and was soon separated from his wife who had no children by him.

B.　Jean Michael. Joseph Haydn considered him to be the best composer of Church music of his day. He was an excellent organist.

HILLER, Jean Adam (Hüller), (1728–?); a most eager student of music; had a wretched hypochondriacal state of ill-health in early manhood, which somewhat disappeared in later life. He had an honourable reputation both for his musical compositions and writings upon music.

S.   Frederick Adam Hiller (1768–1812, æt. 44); a first-rate violinist. He died when he was rising to a great reputation.

KEISER, Reinhard (1673–1739, æt. 66); one of the most illustrious of German composers. He showed originality in his earliest musical efforts. He was a most fertile writer; in forty years he wrote 116 operas, and much else besides; but copies were seldom made of his works, and they are exceedingly rare.

F.   A distinguished musician and composer of Church music.

s.   His daughter was an excellent singer.

MENDELSSOHN, Bartholdy; had an early and strong disposition towards music; first published æt. 15.

G.   Moses Mendelssohn, a celebrated Jewish philosopher, who wrote, among other matters, on the æsthetics of music. He was precocious.

F.   Abraham Mendelssohn, a rich banker in Berlin. His son says to him, "I often cannot understand how it is possible to have so acute a judgment with regard to music without being yourself technically informed." (*Letters*, ii. 80.)

[2 U.]   His uncles were well-informed men. One was associated with Abraham in the bank; he wrote on Dante; also on the currency. The other was a hard student.

b.   Very musical; as a pianist she was Mendelssohn's equal, and of high genius. She was also very affectionate.

MEYERBEER, James (the name is really Beer); was exceedingly precocious. He played brilliantly æt. 6, and was amongst the best pianists of Berlin æt. 9. He began to publish compositions æt. 19, and *d*. æt. 70.

B.   William Meyerbeer, the astronomer—Map of the Moon.

B.   Michael Beer, a poet of high promise, who died young.

MOZART, J. C. Wolfgang; was exceedingly precocious as a child—quite a prodigy in music. He played beautifully æt. 4, and composed much of real merit between the ages of 4 and 6. He overworked himself, and *d*. æt. 35.

F. Leopold Mozart; famous violinist. His method, which he published, was considered for fifty years to be the best work of its kind. He composed a great deal.

b. Was a hopeful musician as a child, an excellent pianist, but she did not succeed in after-life.

S. Charles Mozart; cultivated music as an amateur, and played with distinguished talent, but nothing more is recorded of him.

S. Wolfgang Amedée; born four months after his father's death; was a distinguished performer, and has composed a good deal, but has not risen to high eminence as a composer.

PALESTRINA, Jean Pierluigi de (b. ?—died 1594); composer of Church music; one of the most illustrious of names in the history of music, yet nothing is known of his parentage or family, and even the dates of his birth and death are doubtful. He married young.

44 S. His three eldest sons—Ange, Rodolphe, and Sylla—died in their youth. They seem to have had their father's abilities, judging from such of their compositions as are preserved among Palestrina's works. The fourth son—Hygin—edited his father's musical compositions.

PAINTERS

Among painters, as among musicians, I think no one doubts that artistic talent is, in some degree, hereditary. The question is rather, whether its distribution in families, together with the adjuncts necessary to form an eminent painter, follows much the same law as that which obtains in respect to other kinds of ability. It would be easy to collect a large number of modern names to show how frequently artistic eminence is shared by kinsmen. Thus, the present generation of the Landseers consists of two Academicians and one Associate of the Royal Academy, who were all of them the sons of an Associate. The Bonheur family consists of four painters. Rosa, Juliette, Jules, and Auguste, and they are the children of an artist of some merit. Very many more instances could easily be quoted. But I wish to adduce evidence of the inter-relationship of artists of a yet higher order of merit, and I therefore limit my inquiry to the illustrious ancient painters, especially of Italy and the Low Countries. These are not numerous—only, as well as I can make out, about forty-two, whose natural gifts are unquestionably more than "eminent"; and the fact of about half of them possessing eminent relations, and of some of them, as the Caracci and the Van Eycks, being actually kinsmen, is more important to my argument than pages filled with the relationships of men of the classes F or E of artistic gifts. It would be interesting to know the number of art students in Europe during the last three or more centuries, from whom the forty-two names I have selected are the most illustrious. It is assuredly very great, but it hardly deserves much pains in investigation, because it would afford a minimum, not a true indication of the artistic superiority of the forty-two over the rest of the world: the reason being, that the art students are themselves a selected class. Lads follow painting as a profession usually because they are instinctively drawn to it, and not as a career in which they were placed by accidental circumstances. I should estimate the average of the forty-two painters to rank far above the average of class F, in the natural gifts necessary for high success in art.

In the following table I have included ten individuals that do not find a place in the list of forty-two; namely, Isaac Ostade; Jacopo and Gentile Bellini; Badille, Agostino Caracci, William Mieris; David Teniers; W. Van der Velde the elder; and Francesco da Ponte, both the elder and the younger. The average rank of these men is far above that of a modern Academician, though I have not ventured to include them in the most illustrious class. I have kept Claude in the latter, notwithstanding recent strictures, on account of his previously long-established reputation.

TABLE I

SUMMARY OF RELATIONSHIPS OF 26 GREAT PAINTERS, GROUPED INTO 14 FAMILIES

One relation (or two in family)

Allegri	S.	2. Ostade	B.
(Correggio, *see*		Potter	F.
Allegri)			

Two or three relations (or three or four in family)

3. Bellini	F. B.	Robusti	S. *s.*
2. Cagliari (and		2. Teniers	F. B.
Badille)	u. S.	(Tintoretto, *see*	
3. Caracci	2 US. UP.	Robusti)	
2. Eyck	B. *b.*	2. Velde, Van der	F. S.
2. Mieris	2 S.	(Veronese, *see*	
Murillo	2 u. uS.	Cagliari)	

Four or more relations (or five or more in family)

(Bossano, *see* Ponte)	
3. Ponte	S. 4P.
(Titian, *see* Vecelli)	
Vecelli	B. 2 S. UP. 2 UPS.

TABLE II

14 FAMILIES

In first degree	4 F. 5 B. 9 S.
In second degree	3 u. 4 P.
In third degree	2 US. 1 uS.
All more remote	4.

The rareness with which artistic eminence passes through more than two degrees of kinship, is almost as noticeable here as in the cases of musicians and poets.

APPENDIX TO PAINTERS

I have procured a list of 42 ancient painters of the Italian, Spanish, and Dutch schools, which includes, I believe, all who are ranked by common consent as illustrious. Eighteen of them have eminent relations, and 3 of the remainder—namely, Claude, Parmegiano, and Raffaelle—have kinsmen worthy of notice: these are printed in *italics* in the following list, the remainder are in ordinary type.

ITALIAN SCHOOLS. *Allegri*, "*Correggio*"; (Andrea del Sarto, *see* Vannucchi); (*Bassano*, see *Ponte*); *Bellini*; Buonarotti, Michael Angelo; *Cagliari*, "*Paolo Veronese*"; *Caracci, Annibale*; *Caracci, Ludovico*; Cimabue; (*Claude*, see *Gelée*); (*Correggio*, see *Allegri*); (Domenichino, *see* Zampieri); (*Francia*, *see* Raibollini); *Gelée, Claude "Lorraine*"; Giorgione; Giotto; (Guido, *see* Reni); Marratti, Carlo; *Mazzuoli*, "*Parmegiano*"; (Michael Angelo, *see* Buonarotti); (*Parmegiano*, see *Mazzuoli*); (Perugino, *see* Vannucci); Piombo, Sebastian del; *Ponte*, "*Bassano*"; Poussin; (*Raffaelle*, see *Sanzio*); Raibollini, Francia; Reni, Guido; *Robusti*, "*Tintoretto*"; Rosa, Salvator; *Sanzio, Raffaelle*; (*Titan*, see *Vecelli*); Vannucci, Andrea, "del Sarto"; Vannucci, Perugino; *Vecelli, Titian*; (*Veronese*, see *Cagliari*); Vinci, Leonardo da.

SPANISH SCHOOLS. *Murillo*; Ribiera, Spagnoletto; Velasquez.

DUTCH SCHOOLS. Dow, Gerard; Dürer, Albert; *Eyck, H.*; *Eyck, J. V.*; Holbein; *Mieris*; *Ostade*; *Potter, Paul*; Rembrandt; Rubens; *Ruysdael*; *Teniers*; *Vandyck*; *Velde, Van der*.

ALLEGRI, Antonio da CORREGGIO (1494–1534, æt. 40); one of those rare examples of a man of innate and daring genius who, without a precursor and without a technical education, became a great painter. Very little is known of his parentage.

S.   Pomponeo Allegri, only son; his father died when he was only 12, but he painted in his father's style. His fresco in Parma Cathedral is full of Correggiesque expression.

[p.]   Antonio Pelegrino, called "Il Pittore."

?   (I do not know the relation.) Gregorio Allegro, the musician. *See*.

BASSANO. *See* PONTE.

BELLINI, Giovanni (1422–1512, æt. 90); was the first Venetian painter in oil, and the instructor of the two greatest painters of Venice—Giorgione and Titian. He was himself the first Venetian painter, when in his prime.

F.   Jacopo Bellini, one of the most reputable painters of the early period at which he lived. He was eminent for his portraits.

B.   Gentile Cav. Bellini, painter of very high reputation. The large pictures in the great Council Chamber of Venice are by him. The Senate gave him honour, and a stipend for life.

CAGLIARI, Paolo, called "Paolo Veronese" (1532–1588, æt. 56). His genius showed itself early. It was said of him that, in the spring of life, he bore most excellent fruit. He was the most successful among painters of ornament and of scenes of sumptuous and magnificent parade.

[F.]   Gabrielle Cagliari, sculptor.

u.   Antonio Badile, the first of the Venetian painters that entirely emancipated himself from the Gothic style.

CAGLIARI, Paolo—*continued*

S. Carletto Cagliari; inherited the inventive genius of his father, and gave most flattering promise of future excellence, but died æt. 26.

[S.] Gabrielle Cagliari, a painter, but not a successful one, who afterwards abandoned the profession and followed commerce.

CARACCI, Lodovico (1555–1619, æt. 64); the principal founder of the school that bears the name of his family. His genius was slow in declaring itself; his first master having counselled him to abandon art, and his fellow-pupils having nicknamed him, from his slowness, "the Ox." But the slowness was more apparent than real; it arose from profound reflection, as distinguished from vivacity. His powers were extraordinary.

US. Agostino Caracci (1558–1601, æt. 43); an excellent painter, but chiefly eminent as an engraver. His powers showed themselves in boyhood. He was an accomplished man of letters and science, and had the gifts of a poet.

US. Annibale Caracci (1560–1609, æt. 49). This great artist was the younger brother of Agostino. He had received from nature the gifts of a great painter, and they were carefully cultivated by Lodovico. Annibale had more energy than Agostino, but a far less cultured mind; he was even averse to literature.

[US.] Francesco Caracci, a third brother of great pretensions as a painter, but of disproportionate merit.

UP. Antonio Caracci, a natural son of Annibale; had much of his father's genius, and became an able designer and painter. His constitution was weak, and he died æt. 36.

[B.] Paolo Caracci, a painter, but without original power.

CLAUDE. *See* GELÉE.

CORREGGIO. *See* ALLEGRI.

EYCK, John van (1370–1441); the discoverer of oil painting. His pictures were held in the highest estimation at the time in which he lived.

EYCK, John van—*continued*

B.   Hubert van Eyck, equally eminent as a painter. In fact,
       the two brothers worked so much in conjunction that
       their works are inseparable.

[F.]   An obscure painter.

b.   Marguerite. She was passionately devoted to painting.

GELÉE, CLAUDE (called LORRAINE), (1600–1682, æt. 82).
       This eminent landscape painter began life as an appren-
       tice to a pastrycook, then travelling valet, and afterwards
       cook to an artist. His progress in painting was slow, but
       he had indomitable perseverance; was at the height of
       his fame æt. 30. He never married; he was too devoted
       to his profession to do so.

[B.]   A carver in wood.

MAZZUOLI, Francesco, called "Il Parmegiano" (1504–1541,
       æt. 37). This great colourist and graceful and delicate
       painter made such great progress as a student, though
       ill-taught, that æt. 16 his painting was the astonishment
       of contemporary artists. According to Vasari, it was said
       at Rome that "the soul of Raffaelle had passed into the
       person of Parmegiano." It is stated that when at the
       height of his fame he became seized with the mania of
       alchemy, and wasted his fortune and health in searching
       for the philosopher's stone.

[F. and 2Y.] Filippo Mazzuoli, and Michele and Pier Ilario,
       were all three of them artists, but obscure.

(?) US. Girolamo, son of Michele, and scholar of Parme-
       giano; he married a cousin, the daughter of Pier Ilario.
       He was a painter of some success. The ? is appended to
       his letter because it has been said that he was not a
       relation at all. It is singular to note the contradictions
       about the family concerns of the painters. There is less
       known of their domestic history than of any other class
       of eminent men except musicians.

[uP. (and also ? UP).] Alessandro, son of Girolamo, and his
       scholar. He was but an inferior artist.

MIERIS, Francis (the Elder), (1635–1681, æt. 46). "It is too much, with all his merits, to say he is superior to, or even equal with, Gerard Dow; his admirers should be content with placing him at the head of the next rank."

S. John Mieris; despaired of equalling his father in minuteness and delicacy, so he followed historical painting and portraiture; died æt. 30.

S. William Mieris; was an able artist æt. 18, and was scarcely inferior to his father in the exquisite finish of his pictures.

[P.] Francis Mieris (the Younger), son of William; a painter in the same style as his father, but decidedly inferior to him.

MURILLO, Bartolomé Estevan (1613–1685, æt. 72). Few have a juster claim to originality than this admirable Spanish painter. He showed early inclination to the art. He was naturally humble-minded and retiring, and remarkably good and charitable, even to his own impoverishment.

u. Juan del Castillo, a painter of considerable merit, and the instructor of some of the greatest artists in Spain, namely, Murillo, Alonzo Cano, and Pedro de Moya.

u. Augustin Castillo, a good painter.

uS. Antonio del Castillo, y Salvedra; eminent painter as regards composition and design, but inferior in colouring. He sank into a despondency after visiting Seville, where he first saw a collection of Murillo's pictures, so much superior to his own, and he died of it.

OSTADE, Adrian van (1610–1685, æt. 75); eminent painter of Dutch domestic scenes and grotesque subjects.

B. Isaac van Ostade; began by copying his brother's style without much success, but afterwards he adopted a manner of his own, and became a well-known painter. He died in the prime of life.

PARMEGIANO. *See* MAZZUOLI.

PONTE, Francesco da (the Elder), (1475–1530, æt. 55); the head of the family of the Bassanos, and the founder of the school distinguished by their name.

PONTE, Francesco da (the Elder)—*continued*

S.　　Giacomo da Ponte (called Il BASSANO), (1510–1592, æt. 82); eminent artist; had extraordinary invention and facility of execution. He had four sons, as follow, all well-known painters:—

P.　　Francesco da Ponte (the Younger); had eminent talents. He had attacks of melancholy, and committed suicide æt. 49.

P.　　Giovanni Battista da Ponte, noticeable as a most precise copyist of the works of his father, Giacomo.

P.　　Leandro da Ponte; celebrated portrait painter.

P.　　Girolamo da; excellent copyist of his father's works.

POTTER, Paul; admirable Dutch painter of animals; before he was æt. 15, his works were held in the highest estimation.

F.　　Peter Potter, landscape painter, whose works are now rare, but they must have been of considerable merit, judging from the prints engraved from them by P. Nolpe.

RAFFAELE. *See* SANZIO.

ROBUSTI, Giacomo (called Il TINTORETTO). This distinguished Venetian painter showed an artistic bent from infancy, and far outstripped his fellow-students. He was a man of impetuous genius and prompt execution.

s.　　Marietta Robusti (Tintoretto); acquired considerable reputation as a portrait painter, and her celebrity was not confined to her native country.

S.　　Domenico Robusti (Tintoretto); followed the traces of his father, but with unequal strength. He was also a good portrait painter. and painted many of the historical personages of his time.

RUYSDAEL, Jacob (born about 1636); Dutch landscape painter. He showed extraordinary artistic ability æt. 14, but did not at first follow painting as a profession. He began life as a surgeon.

[B.]　Solomon Ruysdael, the elder brother, twenty years older than Jacob, was a landscape painter of feeble powers.

SANZIO, RAFFAELE, di Urbino. This illustrious artist has, by the general approbation of mankind, been considered as the prince of painters.

[F.] Giovanni Sanzio, a painter whose powers were moderate, but certainly above the average.

TENIERS, David (the Younger), (1610–1694, æt. 84). This celebrated Dutch painter followed the same style and adopted the same subjects as his father, such as village festivals and the like, but his compositions are by far the more varied and ingenious, and the superior in every way.

F. David Teniers (the Elder), (1582–1649, æt. 67). His pictures were very original in style, and universally admired. They would have been considered among the happiest efforts in that class of drawings if they had not been greatly surpassed by the inimitable productions of his son.

B. Abraham Teniers. He painted in the same style as his brother and father, but though a fair artist he was much inferior to both of them.

TITIAN. *See* VECELLI.

VANDYCK, Sir Anthony (1599–1641); admirable portrait painter, second only to Titian.

[F.] A painter on glass; a man of some property.

[*f*.] His mother was skilful in embroidery, which she wrought with considerable taste, from designs both of landscape and figures.

VECELLI, Tiziano da Cadore (TITIAN), (1477–1576); the great founder of the true principles of colouring. Showed considerable ability at the age of 18, and he painted until his death, by the plague, æt. 99.

There are eight or nine good painters in this remarkable family: Bryan mentions six of them in his Dictionary, but it seems that he is not quite accurate as to their relationships. The annexed genealogical tree is compiled from Northcote's descriptions. All those whose names appear in the diagram are painters. The connecting links indicated by crosses are, singularly enough, every one of them lawyers.

B. and 2 S. Titian's brother, Francesco, and two sons, Pomponio and Horatio, had all of them great abilities. The brother was chiefly engaged in military duties, and was never able to make a profession of painting. The sons wanted the stimulus of poverty, but there is no doubt of their large natural capacities for art.

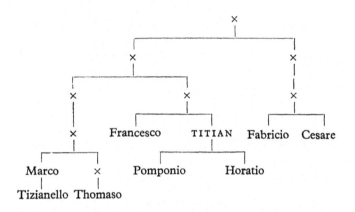

[*f.*]   Lucia; was a very able woman.

UP., 2 UPS. The other relationships, though distant, are interesting as showing the persistent artistic quality of the Vecelli race.

VELDE, William van der (the Younger), (1633–1707). Is accounted the best marine painter that ever lived. Walpole says of him that he is "the greatest man that has appeared in this branch of painting: the palm is not less disputed with Raphael for history than with Vandervelde for sea-pieces." He was born at Amsterdam.

F.   William van der Velde (the Elder), (1610–1693, æt. 83); admirable marine painter, born in Leyden. He taught his son, by whom he was surpassed.

VELDE, William van der (the Younger)—*continued*

S. Also named William, and also a painter of the same subjects as his father and grandfather.

There are three other eminent painters of the same family, name, towns, and period; but I find no notice of their relationships. Thus the two brothers, Esias and John van der Velde, were born in Leyden about 1590 and 1595, and Adrian van der Velde was born in Amsterdam in 1639.

VERONESE, Paul. *See* CAGLIARI.

I am now about to push my statistical survey into regions where precise inquiries seldom penetrate, and are not very generally welcomed. There is commonly so much vagueness of expression on the part of religious writers, that I am unable to determine what they really mean when they speak of topics that directly bear on my present inquiry. I cannot guess how far their expressions are intended to be understood metaphorically, or in some other way to be clothed with a different meaning to what is imposed by the grammatical rules and plain meaning of language. The expressions to which I refer are those which assert the fertility of marriages and the establishment of families to be largely dependent upon godliness.[1] I may even take a much wider range, and include those other expressions which assert that material well-being generally is influenced by the same cause.[2]

I do not propose to occupy myself with criticising the interpretation of these or similar passages, or by endeavouring to show how they may be made to accord with fact; it is the business of theologians to do these things. What I undertake is simply to investigate whether or no the assertions they contain, according to their *primâ facie* interpretation, are or are not in accordance with statistical deductions. If an exceptional providence protects the families of godly men, it is a fact that we must take into account. Natural gifts would then have to be conceived as due, in a high and probably measurable degree, to ancestral piety, and, in a much lower degree than I might

[1] For example—as to fertility, Ps. cxxvii. 1, 3, 5; cxiii. 8; and as to founding families, xxiv. 11, 12.

[2] For example—as to general prosperity, Ps. i. 4; as to longevity, xxxiv. 12–14; and as to health, xci. 3, 6, 10.

otherwise have been inclined to suppose, to ancestral natural peculiarities.

All of us are familiar with another and an exactly opposite opinion. It is popularly said that the children of religious parents frequently turn out badly, and numerous instances are quoted to support this assertion. If a wider induction and a careful analysis should prove the correctness of this view, it might appear to strongly oppose the theory of heredity.

On both these accounts, it is absolutely necessary, to the just treatment of my subject, to inquire into the history of religious people, and learn the extent of their hereditary peculiarities, and whether or no their lives are attended by an exceptionally good fortune.

I have taken considerable pains to procure a suitable selection of Divines for my inquiries. The Roman Catholic Church is rich in ecclesiastical biography, but it affords no data for my statistics, for the obvious reason that its holy personages, of both sexes, are celibates, and therefore incapable of founding families. A collection of the Bishops of our Church would also be unsuitable, because, during many generations, they were principally remarkable as administrators, scholars, polemical writers, or courtiers; whence it would not be right to conclude, from the fact of their having been elevated to the Bench, that they were men of extraordinary piety. I thought of many other selections of Divines, which further consideration compelled me to abandon. At length I was fortunately directed to one that proved perfectly appropriate to my wants.

Middleton's *Biographia Evangelica*, 4 vols. 8vo., 1786, is exactly the kind of work that suits my inquiries. The biographies contained in it are not too numerous, for there are only 196 of them altogether, extending from the Reformation to the date of publication. Speaking more precisely, the collection includes the lives of 196 Evangelical worthies, taken from the whole of Europe, who, with the exception of the four first—namely, Wickliffe, Huss, Jerome of Prague, and John of Wesalia—died between 1527 and 1785. This leaves 192 men during a period of 258 years; or 3 men in every 4—a sufficiently rigorous, but not too rigorous, selection for my purposes. The biographies are written in excellent English, with well-weighed epithets; and though the collection is, to some extent, a compilation of other men's writings, it may justly be viewed as an integral work, in which a proportionate prominence has been given to the lives of the more important men, and not as a combination of separate memoirs, written without reference to one another. Middleton assures the reader, in his preface, that no bigoted partiality to sects will be found in his collection; that his whole attention has been paid to truly great and gracious characters of all those persuasions which hold the distinguishing principles of the Gospel. He does not define what, in his opinion, those principles are, but it is easy to see that his leaning is strongly towards the Calvinists, and he utterly reprobates the Papists.

I should further say, that, after reading his work, I have gained a much greater respect for the body of Divines than I had before. One is so frequently scandalised by the pettiness, acrimony, and fanaticism shown in theological disputes, that an inclination to these failings may reasonably be suspected in men of large religious profession. But I can assure my readers, that Middleton's biographies appear, to the best of my judgment, to refer, in by the far greater part, to exceedingly noble characters. There are certainly a few personages of very doubtful reputation, especially in the earlier part of the work, which covers the turbid period of the Reformation; such as Cranmer, "saintly in his professions, unscrupulous in his dealings, zealous for nothing, bold in speculation, a coward and a time-server in action, a placable enemy, and a lukewarm friend." (Macaulay.) Nevertheless, I am sure that Middleton's collection, on the whole, is eminently fair and trustworthy.

The 196 subjects of Middleton's biographies may be classified as follow: 22 of them were martyrs, mostly by fire; the latest of these—Homel, a pastor in the Cevennes in the time of Louis XIV—was executed, 1683, under circumstances of such singular atrocity, that, although they have nothing to do with my subject, I cannot forbear quoting what Middleton says about them. Homel was sentenced to the wheel, where "every limb, member, and bone of his body were broken with the iron bar, forty hours before the executioner was permitted to strike him upon the breast, with a stroke which they call '*le coup de grâce*,' the blow of mercy—that death-stroke which put an end to all his miseries." Others of the 196 worthies, including many of the martyrs, were active leaders in the Reformation, as Wickliffe, Zuinglius, Luther, Ridley, Calvin, Beza; others were most eminent administrators, as Archbishops Parker, Grindal, and Usher; a few were thorough-going Puritans, as Bishop Potter, Knox, Welch, the two Erskines, and Dr. J. Edwards; a larger number were men of an extreme, but more pleasing form of piety, as Bunyan, Baxter, Watts, and George Herbert. The rest, and the majority of the whole list may be described as pious scholars.

As a general rule, the men in Middleton's collection had considerable intellectual capacity and natural eagerness for study, both of which qualities were commonly manifest in boyhood. Most of them wrote voluminously, and were continually engaged in preachings and religious services. They had evidently a strong need of utterance. They were generally, but by no means universally, of religious parentage, judging by the last 100 biographies of Middleton's collection, the earlier part of the work giving too imperfect notices of their ancestry to make it of use to analyse it. It would appear that, out of 100 men, only 41 had one or more eminently religious parents, nothing whatever being said of the parentage of the other 59. The 41 cases are divided thus:[1]—in 17 cases (*a*) the father was a minister; in 16 cases (*b*), the father not being a minister, both

[1] (*a*) Lewis de Dieu, Alting, Manton, T. Gouge, Owen, Leighton, Claude, Hopkins, Fleming, Burkitt, Halyburton, M. Henry, Clarke, Mather, Evans, Edwards, Hervey.

(*b*) Donne, Downe, Taylor, Whately, W. Gouge, Janeway, Winter, Flavel, Spener, Witsius, Shower, Doddridge, G. Jones, Davies, Guyse, Gill.

(*c*) G. Herbert, Hall, P. Henry, Baily, Whitefield.

(*d*) Wilkins (mother's father, J. Dod), Toplady (two maternal uncles, clergymen).

(*e*) Hale.

parents were religious; in 5 cases (*c*) the mother only is mentioned as pious; in 2 cases (*d*) the mother's near relatives are known to have been religious; in 1 case (*e*) the father alone is mentioned as pious.

There is no case in which either or both parents are distinctly described as having been sinful, though there are two cases (*f*.)[1] of meanness, and one (g.)[2] of overspending.

The condition of life of the parents is mentioned in 66 cases —more than one-third of the whole. They fall into the following groups:—

4. *Highly connected*—Hamilton; George, Prince of Anhalt; John à Lasco; Herbert.

8. *Ancient families* (not necessarily wealthy)—Jewell, Deering, Gilpin, Hildersham, Ames, Bedell, Lewis de Dieu, Palmer.

15. *Well connected*—Œcolampadius, Zuinglius, Capito, Farel, Jones, Bugenhagius, Bullinger, Sandys, Featley, Dod, Fulke, Pool, Baxter, Griffith Jones, Davies.

23. *Professional*—Melancthon and Toplady, officers in army; Gataker, Usher, and Saurin, legal; seventeen were ministers (see list already given); Davenant, merchant.

6. *In Trade*—Two Abbots, weaver; Twisse, clothier; Bunyan, tinker; Watts, boarding-school; Doddridge, oil-man.

4. *Poor*—Huss, Ball, Grynæus, Fagius, Latimer.

6. *Very poor*—Luther, Pellican, Musculus, Cox, Andreas, Prideaux.

There is, therefore, nothing anomalous in the parentage of the Divines; it is what we should expect to have found among secular scholars, born within the same periods of our history.

The Divines are not founders of influential families. Poverty was not always the reason of this, because we read of many whose means were considerable. W. Gouge left a fair fortune to his son T. Gouge wherewith he supported Welsh and other charities. Evans had considerable wealth, which he wholly lost by speculations in the South Sea Bubble; and others are mentioned who were highly connected, and there-

---

[1] *f*. Bullinger, Fulke. [2] g. Baxter.

fore more or less well off. The only families that produced men of importance are those of Saurin, whose descendant was the famous Attorney-General of Ireland; of Archbishop Sandys, whose descendant after several generations became the 1st Lord Sandys; and of Hooker, who is ancestor of the eminent botanists, the late and present Directors of the Kew Botanical Gardens. The Divines, as a whole, have had hardly any appreciable influence in founding the governing families of England, or in producing our judges, statesmen, commanders, men of literature and science, poets or artists.

The Divines are but moderately prolific. Judging from the later biographies, about one-half of them were married, and there were about 5, or possibly 6, children to each marriage. That is to say, the number actually recorded gives at the rate of $4\frac{1}{2}$, but in addition to these occurs, about once in 6 or 7 cases, the phrase "many children." The insertion of these occasional unknown, but certainly large numbers, would swell the average by a trifling amount. Again, it is sometimes not clear whether the number of children who survived infancy may not be stated by mistake as the number of births, and, owing to this doubt, we must further increase the estimated average. Now in order that population should not decrease, each set of 4 adults, 2 males and 2 females, must leave at least 4 children who live to be adults, behind them. In the case of the Divines, we have seen that only one-half are married men; therefore each married Divine must leave 4 adults to succeed him, if his race is not to decrease. This implies an average family of more than 6 children, or, as a matter of fact, larger families than the Divines appear to have had.

Those who marry, often marry more than once. We hear in all of 81 married men; 3 of these, namely, Junius, Gataker, and Flavel, had each of them 4 wives; Bucer and Mather had 3; and 12 others had 2 wives each. The frequency with which the Divines became widowers is a remarkable fact, especially as they did not usually marry when young. I account for the early deaths of their wives, on the hypothesis that their constitutions were weak, and my reasons for thinking so are twofold. First, a very large proportion of them died in childbirth, for seven such deaths are mentioned, and there is no reason to suppose that all, or nearly all, that occurred have been recorded by Middleton. Secondly, it appears, that the wives of the Divines were usually women of great piety; now it will be shown a little further on, that there is a frequent correlation between an unusually devout disposition and a weak constitution.

The Divines seem to have been very happy in their domestic life. I know of few exceptions to this rule: the wife of T. Cooper was unfaithful, and that of poor Hooker was a termagant. Yet in many cases, these simple-hearted worthies had made their proposals under advice, and not through love. Calvin married on Bucer's advice; and as for Bishop Hall, he may tell his own story, for it is a typical one. After he had built his house, he says, in his autobiography. "The uncouth solitariness of my life, and the extreme incommodity of my single housekeeping, drew my thoughts after two years, to condescend to the necessity of a married estate, which God no less strangely provided for me, for walking from the church on Monday in the Whitsun week with a grave and reverend minister, Mr. Grandidge, I saw a comely and modest gentlewoman standing at the door of that house where we were invited to a wedding-dinner, and inquiring of that worthy friend whether he knew her, 'Yes,' quoth he, 'I know her well, and have bespoken her for your wife.' When I further demanded an account of that answer, he told me she was the daughter of a gentleman whom he much respected, Mr. George Winniffe, of Bretenham; that out of an opinion had of the fitness of that match for me, he had already treated with her father about it, whom he found very apt to entertain it, advising me not to neglect the opportunity, and not concealing the just praises of the modesty, piety, good disposition, and other virtues that were lodged in that seemly presence. I listened to the motion as sent from God; and at last, upon due prosecution, happily prevailed, enjoying the company of that meet-help for the space of forty-nine years."

The mortality of the Divines follows closely the same order in those who are mentioned in the earlier, as in the later volumes of Middleton's collection, although the conditions of life must have varied in the periods to which they refer. Out of the 196, nearly half of them die between the ages of 55 and 75; one quarter die before 55, and one quarter after 75: 62 or 63 is the average age at death, in the sense that as many die before that age as after it. This is rather less than I have deduced from the other groups of eminent men treated of in this volume. Dod, the most aged of all the Divines, lived till he was 98. Nowell and Du Moulin died between 90 and 95; and Zanchius, Beza, and Conant, between 85 and 90. The diseases that killed them are chiefly those due to a sedentary life, for, if we exclude the martyrs, one quarter of all the recorded cases were from the stone or strangury, between which diseases the doctors did not then satisfactorily discriminate; indeed, they murdered Bishop Wilkins by mistaking the one for the other. There are five cases of plague, and the rest consist of the following groups in pretty equal proportions, viz. fever and ague, lung disease, brain attacks, and unclassed diseases.

As regards health, the constitutions of most of the Divines were remarkably bad. It is, I find, very common among scholars to have been infirm in youth, whence, partly from inaptitude to join with other boys in their amusements, and partly from unhealthy activity of the brain, they take eagerly to bookish pursuits. Speaking broadly, there are three eventualities to these young students. They die young; or they strengthen as they grow, retaining their tastes and enabled to indulge them with sustained energy; or they live on in a sickly way. The Divines are largely recruited from the sickly portion of these adults. There is an air of invalidism about most religious biographies, that also seems to me to pervade, to some degree, the lives in Middleton's collection.

He especially notices the following fourteen or fifteen cases of weak constitution:—

1. Melancthon, *d.* æt. 63, whose health required continual management. 2. Calvin, *d.* æt. 55, faint, thin, and consumptive, but who nevertheless got through an immense amount of work. Perhaps we may say 3. Junius, *d.* æt. 47, a most infirm and

sickly child, never expected to reach manhood, but he strengthened as he grew, and though he died young, it was the plague
that killed him; he moreover survived four wives. 4. Downe,
d. æt. 61, a Somersetshire vicar, who through all his life, "in
health and strength, was a professed pilgrim and sojourner"
in the world. 5. George Herbert, *d.* æt. 42, consumptive, and
subject to frequent fevers and other infirmities, seems to have
owed the bent of his mind very much to his ill-health, for
he grew more pious as he became more stricken, and we can
trace that courageous, chivalric character in him which developed itself in a more robust way in his ancestors and
brothers, who were mostly gallant soldiers. One brother was a
sailor of reputation; another carried twenty-four wounds on
his person. 6. Bishop Potter, *d.* æt. 64, was of weak constitution, melancholic, lean, and puritanical. 7. Janeway, *d.* æt. 24,
found "hard study and work by far an overmatch for him."
8. Baxter, *d.* æt. 76, was always in wretched health; he was
tormented with a stone in the kidney (which by the way, is said
to have been preserved in the College of Surgeons). 9. Philip
Henry, *d.* æt. 65, called the "heavenly Henry," when a young
clergyman, was a weakly child; he grew stronger as an adult,
but ruined his improved health by the sedentary ways of a
student's life, alternating with excitement in the pulpit, where
"he sweated profusely as he prayed fervently." He died of
apoplexy. 10. Harvey, *d.* æt. 30, was such a weakly, puny
object, that his father did not like his becoming a minister,
"lest his stature should render him despicable." 11. Moth,
d. æt. ? seems another instance. Hardly any personal anecdote
is given of him, except that "God was pleased to try him
many ways," which phrase I interpret to include ill-health.
12. Brainerd, *d.* æt. 29, was naturally infirm, and died of a
complication of obstinate disorders. 13. Hervey, *d.* æt. 55,
though an early riser, was very weakly by nature; he was
terribly emaciated before his death. 14. Guise, *d.* æt. 81, a
great age for those times, was nevertheless sickly. He was hectic
and overworked in early life, afterwards ill and lame, and lastly
blind. 15. Toplady, *d.* æt. 38, struggled in vain for health and

a longer life, by changing his residence at the sacrifice of his hopes of fortune.

In addition to these fifteen cases of constitutions stated to have been naturally weak, we should count at least twelve of those that broke down under the strain of work. Even when the labour that ruined their health was unreasonably severe, the zeal which goaded them to work beyond their strength may be considered as being, in some degree, the symptom of a faulty constitution. Each case ought to be considered on its own merits; they are as follow:—1. Whitaker, *d.* æt. 48, laid the seeds of death by his incredible application. 2. Rollock, *d.* æt. 43, the first Principal of the University of Edinburgh, died in consequence of over-work, though the actual cause of his death was the stone. 3. Dr. Rainolds, *d.* æt. 48, called "the treasury of all learning, human and divine," deliberately followed his instinct for over-work to the very grave, saying that he would not "propter vitam vivendi perdere causas," —lose the ends of living for the sake of life. 4. Stock, *d.* æt. ? "spent himself like a taper, consuming himself for the good of others." 5. Preston, *d.* æt. 41, sacrificed his life to excessive zeal; he is quoted as an example of saying, that "men of great parts have no moderation." He died an "old" man at the age of 41. 6. Herbert Palmer, *d.* æt. 46, after a short illness; "for, having spent much of his natural strength in the service of God, there was less work for sickness to do." 7. Baily, *d.* æt. 54, who was so holy and conscientious, "that if he had been at any time but innocently pleasant in the company of his friends, it cost him afterwards some sad reflections" (preserve me from the privilege of such companions!); lost his health early in life. 8. Clarke, *d.* æt. 62, was too laborious, and had in consequence a fever æt. 43, which extremely weakened his constitution. 9. Ulrich, *d.* æt. 48, had an "ill habit of body, contracted by a sedentary life and the overstraining of his voice in preaching." 10. Isaac Watts, *d.* æt. 74, a proficient child, but not strong; fell very ill æt. 24, and again æt. 38, and from this he never recovered, but passed the rest of his life in congenial seclusion, an inmate of the house of Sir T. Abney, and afterwards of his

L

widow. 11. Davies, *d.* æt. 37, a sprightly boy and keen rider; grew into a religious man of so sedentary a disposition, that after he was made President of Yale College in America, he took hardly any exercise. He was there killed by a simple cold, followed by some imprudence in sermon-writing, his vital powers being too low to support any physical strain. 12. T. Jones, *d.* æt. 32: "Before the Lord was pleased to call him, he was walking in the error of his ways;" then he was afflicted "with a disorder that kept him very low and brought him to death's door, during all which time his growth in grace was great and remarkable."

This concludes my list of those Divines, 26 in number, who were specially noted by Middleton as invalids. It will be seen that about one-half of them were infirm from the first, and that the other half became broken down early in life. It must not be supposed that the remainder of the 196 were invariably healthy men. These biographies dwell little on personal characteristics, and therefore their silence on the matter of health must not be interpreted as necessarily meaning that the health was good. On the contrary, as I said before, there is an air as of the sick-room running through the collection, but to a much less degree than in religious biographies that I have elsewhere read. A gently complaining, and fatigued spirit, is that in which Evangelical Divines are very apt to pass their days.

It is curious how large a part of religious biographies is commonly given up to the occurrences of the sick-room. We can easily understand why considerable space should be devoted to such matters, because it is on the death-bed that the believer's sincerity is most surely tested; but this is insufficient to account for all we find in Middleton and elsewhere. There is, I think, an actual pleasure shown by Evangelical writers in dwelling on occurrences that disgust most people. Rivet, a French divine, has strangulation of the intestines, which kills him after twelve days' suffering. The remedies attempted, each successive pang, and each corresponding religious ejaculation is recorded, and so the history of his bowel-attack is protracted through forty-five pages, which is as much space as is allotted to the entire biographies of four average Divines. Mede's death, and its cause, is described with equal minuteness, and with still more repulsive details, but in a less diffused form.

I have thus far shown that 26 Divines out of the 196, or one-eighth part of them, were certainly invalids, and I have laid much stress on the hypothesis that silence about health does not mean healthiness; however, I can add other reasons to corroborate my very strong impression that the Divines are, on the whole, an ailing body of men. I can show that the number of persons mentioned as robust are disproportionately few, and I would claim a comparison between the numbers of the notably weak and the notably strong, rather than one between the notably weak and the rest of the 196. In professions where men are obliged to speak much in public, the constitutional vigour of those who succeed is commonly extraordinary. It would be impossible to read a collection of lives of eminent orators, lawyers, and the like, without being impressed with the largeness of the number of those who have constitutions of iron; but this is not at all the case with the Divines, for Middleton speaks of only 12, or perhaps 13 men who were remarkable for their vigour.

Two very instructive facts appear in connexion with these vigorous Divines: we find, on the one hand, that of the 12 or 13 who were decidedly robust, 5, if not 6, were irregular and wild in their youth; and, on the other hand, that only 3 or 4 Divines are stated to have been irregular in their youth, who were not also men of notably robust constitutions. We are therefore compelled to conclude that robustness of constitution is antagonistic, in a very marked degree, to an extremely pious disposition.

First as to those who were both vigorous in constitution and wild in youth; they are 5 or 6 in number. 1. Beza, *d. æt.* 86; "was a robust man of very strong constitution, and what is very unusual among hard students, never felt the headache"; he yielded as a youth to the allurements of pleasure, and wrote poems of a very licentious character. 2. Welch, *d.* æt. 53; was of strong robust constitution and underwent a great deal of fatigue; in youth he was a border-thief. 3. Rothwell, *d.* æt. 64; was handsome, well set, of great strength of body and activity; he hunted, bowled, and shot; he also poached a little. Though he was a clergyman he did not reform till late, and still the "devil assaulted him" much and long. He got on particularly well with his parishioners in a wild part of the north of England. 4. Grimshaw, *d.* æt. 55; was only once sick for the space of sixteen years, though he "used his body with less consideration than a merciful man would use his beast." He was educated religiously, but broke loose, æt. 18, at Cambridge. At the age of 26, being then a swearing, drunken parson, he was partly converted, and æt. 34 his "preaching began to be profitable"; then followed twenty-one years of eminent usefulness. 5. Whitefield, *d.* æt. 56; had extraordinary activity, constantly preaching and constantly travelling. He had great constitutional powers, though, "from disease," he grew corpulent after æt. 40. He was extremely irregular in early youth, drinking and pilfering (Stephen, *Eccl. Biog.*). [6.] It is probable that Trosse ought to be added to this list. He will again be spoken of in the next category but one.

Next, as to those who were vigorous in constitution but not irregular in youth; they are 7 in number. 1. Peter Martyr, *d.* æt. 62; a large healthy man of grave, sedate, and well-composed countenance. His parts and learning were very uncommon. 2. Mede, *d.* æt. 52; was a fine, handsome, dignified man. Middleton remarks that his vitals were strong, that he did not mind the cold, and that he had a sound mind in a sound body. He was a sceptic when a student at college, but not wild. 3. Bedell, *d.* æt. 72; a tall, graceful, dignified man; a favourite even with Italian papists; suffered no decay of his natural powers till near his death. 4. Leighton, *d*, æt. 70 of a sudden attack of pleurisy. He looked so fresh up to that time that age seemed to stand still with him. 5. Burkitt, *d.* æt. 53 of a malignant fever, but "his strength was such that he might have been expected to live till 80." He was turned to religion when a boy, by an attack of smallpox. 6. Alix, *d.* æt. 76; had an uncommon share of health and spirits; he was a singularly, amiable, capable, and popular man. 7. Harrison, *d.* æt. ?; a strong, robust man, full of flesh and blood; humble, devout, and of bright natural parts. This concludes the list. I have been surprised to find none of the type of Cromwell's "Ironsides."

Lastly, as to those who were irregular in youth but who are not mentioned as being vigorous in constitution. They are 3 or 4 in number, according as Trosse is omitted or included. 1. William Perkyns, *d.* æt. 43; a "cheerful, pleasant man;" was wild and a spendthrift at Cambridge, and not converted till æt. 24. 2. Bunyan; vicious in youth, was converted in a wild, irregular way, and had many backslidings throughout his career. 3. Trosse, *d.* æt. 82. His biography is deficient in particulars about which one would like to be informed, but his long life, following a bad beginning, appears to be a sign of an unusually strong constitution, and to qualify him for insertion in my first category. He was sent to France to learn the language, and he learnt also every kind of French rascality. The same process was repeated in Portugal. The steps by which his character became remarkably changed are not recorded, neither are his personal characteristics. [4.] T. Jones, *d.* æt. 32, has already been included among the invalids, having been wild in youth but rendered pious by serious and lingering ill-health.

I now come to the relationships of the Divines. Recollecting that there are only 196 of them altogether, that they are selected from the whole of Protestant Europe at the average rate of 2 men in 3 years, the following results are quite as remarkable as those met with in the other groups.

Seventeen out of the 196 are interrelated. Thus Simon Grynæus is uncle of Thomas, who is father of John James, and there are others of note in this remarkable family of peasant origin. Whitaker's maternal uncle was Dr. Nowell. Robert Abbot, Bishop of Salisbury, is brother to Archbishop Abbot. Downe's maternal uncle was Bishop Jewell. Dod's grandson (daughter's son) was Bishop Wilkins. William Gouge was father of Thomas Gouge. Philip Henry was father to Matthew Henry. Ebenezer Erskine was brother to Ralph Erskine.

There are 8 others who have remarkable relationships, mostly with religious people, namely:—Knox's grandson (the son of a daughter who married John Welch) was Josiah Welch, "the cock of the conscience." F. Junius had a son, also called Francis, a learned Oxonian; by his daughter, who married J. G. Vossius, he had for grandchildren, Dionysius and Isaac Vossius, famous for their learning. Donne was descended through his mother from Lord Chancellor Sir John More and Judge Rastall. Herbert was brother to Lord Herbert of Cherbury, and had other eminent and interesting relationships. Usher's connexions are most remarkable, for his father, father's brother, mother's father, mother's brother, and his own brother, were all very eminent men in their day. The mother's brother of Lewis de Dieu was a professor at Leyden. The father and grandfather of Mather were eminent ministers. The father and three brothers of Saurin were remarkably eloquent.

It cannot be doubted from these facts that religious gifts are, on the whole, hereditary; but there are curious exceptions to the rule. Middleton's work must not be considered as free from omissions of these exceptional cases, for neither he nor any other biographer would conceive it to be his duty to write about a class of facts, which are important for us to obtain; namely, the cases in which the sons of religious parents turned out badly. I have only lighted on a single instance of this apparent perversion of the laws of heredity in the whole of Middleton's work, namely that of Archbishop Matthew, but it is often said that such cases are not uncommon. I rely mostly for my belief in their existence, upon social experiences of modern date, which could not be published without giving pain to innocent individuals. Those of which I know with certainty are not numerous, but are sufficient to convince me of there being a real foundation for the popular notion. The notoriety of some recent cases will, I trust, satisfy the reader, and absolve me from entering any further into details.

The summary of the results concerning the Divines, to which I have thus far arrived, is: That they are not founders of families who have exercised a notable influence on our history, whether that influence be derived from the abilities, wealth, or social position of any of their members. That they are a moderately prolific race, rather under, than above the average. That their average age at death is a trifle less than that of the eminent men comprised in my other groups. That they commonly suffer from over-work. That they have usually wretched constitutions. That those whose constitutions were vigorous, were mostly wild in their youth; and conversely, that most of those who had been wild in their youth and did not become pious till later in life, were men of vigorous constitutions. That a pious disposition is decidedly hereditary. That there are also frequent cases of sons of pious parents who turned out very badly; but I shall have something to say on what appears to me to be the reason for this.

I therefore see no reason to believe that the Divines are an exceptionally favoured race in any respect; but rather, that they are less fortunate than other men.

I now annex my usual tables.

TABLE I

SUMMARY OF RELATIONSHIPS OF 33 OF THE DIVINES OF MIDDLETON'S BIOGRAPHIA EVANGELICA GROUPED INTO 25 FAMILIES.

One relation (or two in family)

Clarke	F.	Knox	p.
2. Dod (and Wilkins)	p.	Leighton	F.
(Downe, *see* Jewell)		(Nowell, *see* Whitaker)	
2. Erskine	B.	Welch	S.
Guise	S.	Whitaker (and Nowell)	u.
Hildersham	S.	(Wilkins, *see* Dod)	
Hospinian	u.	Witsius	u.
2. Jewell (and Downe)	n.		

Two or three relations (or three or four in family)

2.	Abbot	2B.	2.	Henry, H.	
	Dieu de	F. u.		(and M.)	S. *f.*
	Donne	g. gF.		Lasco, A.	B. U.
	Gilpin	gB. NP. NPPS.		Mather	F. G. g.
				Saurin	3B.

Four or more relations (or five or more in family)

2.	Gouge, W. (and T.)	*f.* 2u. S.
3.	Grynæus, T. (also S. and J.)	U. US. 4S.
	Herbert	F. *f.* g. B. US. 2UP.
	Junius	F. S. 2p.
	Usher	F. U. g. u. B.

TABLE II[1]

Degrees of Kinship					A	B
Name of the degree	Corresponding letter					
1 degree Father	7 F.	...	...	...	7	28
Brother	9 B.	...	...	...	9	36
Son	10 S.	...	...	...	10	40
2 degrees Grandfather	1 G.	4 g.	...	...	5	20
Uncle	3 U.	7 u.	...	...	10	40
Nephew	0 N.	1 n.	...	...	1	4
Grandson	0 P.	4 p.	...	...	4	16
3 degrees Great-grandfather	0 GF.	1 gF.	0 *GF.*	0 *g*F.	1	4
Great-uncle	0 GB.	1 gB.	0 *GB.*	0 *g*B.	1	4
First-cousin	2 US.	0 uS.	0 *US.*	0 *u*S.	2	8
Great-nephew	0 NS.	0 nS.	0 *NS.*	0 *n*S.	0	0
Great-grandson	0 PS.	0 pS.	0 *PS.*	0 *p*S.	0	0
All more remote	...	...	...	...	4	16

[1] For explanation, see page 102.

A comparison of the relative influences of the male and female lines of descent, is made in the following table:—

IN THE SECOND DEGREE

$1G.+3U.+0N.+0P. =$ 4 kinships through males
$4g. +7u. +1n. +4p. =$ 16 kinships through females

IN THE THIRD DEGREE

$0GF.-0GB.-2US.-0NS.-0PS. =$ 2 kinships through males
$1gF. -1gB. -0uS. -0nS. -0pS. =$ 2 kinships through females

This table shows that the influence of the female line has an unusually large effect in qualifying a man to become eminent in the religious world. The only other group in which the influence of the female line is even comparable in its magnitude, is that of scientific men; and I believe the reasons laid down when speaking of them, will apply, *mutatis mutandis,* to the Divines. It requires unusual qualifications, and some of them of a feminine cast, to become a leading theologian. A man must not only have appropriate abilities, and zeal, and power of work, but the postulates of the creed that he professes must be so firmly ingrained into his mind, as to be the equivalents of axioms. The diversities of creeds held by earnest, good, and conscientious men, show to a candid looker-on, that there can be no certainty as to any point on which many of such men think differently. But a divine must not accept this view; he must be convinced of the absolute security of the groundwork of his peculiar faith,—a blind conviction which can best be obtained through maternal teachings in the years of childhood.

I will now endeavour to account for the fact, which I am compelled to acknowledge, that the children of very religious parents occasionally turn out extremely badly. It is a fact that has all the appearance of being a serious violation of the law of heredity, and, as such, has caused me more hesitation and

difficulty than I have felt about any other part of my inquiry.
However, I am perfectly satisfied that this apparent anomaly
is entirely explained by what I am about to lay before the
reader, premising that it obliges me to enter into a more free
and thorough analysis of the religious character than would
otherwise have been suitable to these pages.

The disposition that qualifies a man to attain a place in a
collection like that of the *Biographia Evangelica*, can best be
studied by comparing it with one that, while it contrasts with
it in essentials, closely resembles it in all unimportant respects.
Thus, we may conclude from our comparison all except those
whose average moral dispositions are elevated some grades
above those of men generally; and we may also exclude all
except such as think very earnestly, reverently, and conscien-
tiously upon religious matters. The remainder range in their
views, and, for the most part, in the natural disposition that
inclines them to adopt those views, from the extremest piety
to the extremest scepticism. The *Biographia Evangelica* affords
many instances that approach to the former ideal, and we may
easily select from history men who have approached to the
latter. In order to contrast, and so understand the nature of
the differences between the two ideal extremes, we must lay
aside for a while our own religious predilections—whatever
they may be—and place ourselves resolutely on a point
equidistant from both, whence we can survey them alternately
with an equal eye. Let us then begin, clearly understanding
that we are supposing both the sceptic and the religious man
to be equally earnest, virtuous, temperate, and affectionate—
both perfectly convinced of the truth of their respective tenets,
and both finding moral content in such conclusions as those
tenets imply.

The religious man affirms, that he is conscious of an indwelling Spirit of grace, that consoles, guides, and dictates,
and that he could not stand if it were taken away from him.
It renders easy the trials of his life, and calms the dread that
would otherwise be occasioned by the prospect of death. It
gives directions and inspires motives, and it speaks through

the voice of the conscience, as an oracle, upon what is right and what is wrong. He will add, that the presence of this Spirit of grace is a matter that no argument or theory is capable of explaining away, inasmuch as the conviction of its presence is fundamental in his nature, and the signs of its action are as unmistakeable as those of any other actions, made known to us through the medium of the senses. The religious man would further dwell on the moral doctrine of the form of creed that he professes; but this we must eliminate from the discussion, because the moral doctrines of the different forms of creed are exceedingly diverse, some tending to self-culture and asceticism, and others to active benevolence; while we are seeking to find the nature of a religious disposition, so far as it is common to all creeds.

The sceptic takes a position antagonistic to that which I have described, as appertaining to the religious man. He acknowledges the sense of an indwelling Spirit, which possibly he may assert to have himself experienced in its full intensity, but he denies its objectivity. He argues that, as it is everywhere acknowledged to be a fit question for the intellect to decide whether other convictions, however fundamental, are really true, or whether the evidences of the senses are, in any given case, to be depended on, so it is perfectly legitimate to submit religious convictions to a similar analysis. He will say that a floating speck in the vision, and a ringing in the ears, are capable of being discriminated by the intellect from the effects of external influences; that in lands where mirage is common, the experienced traveller has to decide on the truth of the appearance of water, by the circumstances of each particular case. And as to fundamental convictions, he will add, that it is well known the intellect can successfully grapple with them, for Kant and his followers have shown reasons—to which all metaphysicians ascribe weight—that Time and Space are, neither of them, objective realities, but only forms, under which our minds, by virtue of their own constitution, are compelled to act. The sceptic, therefore, claiming to bring the question of the objective existence of the Spirit of grace under intellectual examination, has decided—whether rightly or not has nothing to do with our inquiries—that it is subjective, not objective. He argues that it is not self-consistent in its action, inasmuch as it prompts different people in different ways, and the same person in different ways at different times; that there is no sharp demarcation between the promptings that are avowedly natural, and those that are considered supernatural; lastly, that convictions of right and wrong are misleading, inasmuch as a person who indulges in them, without check from the reason, becomes a blind partisan, and partisans on hostile sides feel them in equal strength. As to the sense of consolation, derived from the creature of a fond imagination, he will point to the experiences of the nursery, where the girl tells all its griefs to its doll, converses with it, takes counsel with it, and is consoled by it, putting unconsciously her own words into the mouth of the doll. For these and similar reasons, which it is only necessary for me to state and not to weigh, the thorough-going ideal sceptic deliberately crushes those very sentiments and convictions which the religious man prizes above all things. He pronounces them to be idols created by the imagination, and therefore to be equally abhorred with idols made by the hands, of grosser material.

Thus far, we have only pointed out an intellectual difference —a matter of no direct service in itself, in solving the question on which we are engaged, but of the utmost importance when the sceptic and religious man are supposed to rest contentedly in their separate conclusions. In order that a man may be a contented sceptic of the most extreme type, he must have confidence in himself, that he is qualified to stand absolutely alone in the presence of the severest trials of life, and of the terrors of impending death. His nature must have sufficient self-assertion and stoicism to make him believe that he can act the whole of his part upon earth without assistance. This is the ideal form of the most extreme scepticism, to which some few may nearly approach, but it is questionable if any have ever reached. On the other hand, the support of a stronger arm, and of a consoling voice, are absolute necessities to a man who has a religious disposition. He is conscious of an incongruity in his nature, and of an instability in his disposition, and he knows his insufficiency to help himself. But all humanity is more or less subject to these feelings, especially in sickness, in youth, and in old age, and women are more affected by them than men. The most vigorous are conscious of secret weaknesses and failings, which give them, often in direct proportion to their intellectual stoicism, agonies of self-distrust. But in the extreme and ideal form which we are supposing, the incongruity and instability would be extreme; he would not be fit to be a freeman, for he could not exist without a confessor and a master. Here, then, is a broad distinction between the natural dispositions of the two classes of men. The man of religious constitution considers the contented sceptic to be foolhardy and sure to fail miserably; the sceptic considers the man of an extremely pious disposition to be slavish and inclined to superstition.

It is sometimes said, that a conviction of sin is a characteristic of a religious disposition; I think, however, the strong sense of sinfulness in a Christian, to be partly due to the doctrines of his intellectual creed. The sceptic, equally with the religious man, would feel disgust and shame at his miserable weakness in having done yesterday, in the heat of some impulse, things which to-day, in his calm moments, he disapproves. He is sensible that if another person had done the same thing, he would have shunned him; so he similarly shuns the contemplation of his own self. He feels he has done that which makes him unworthy of the society of pure-minded men; that he is a disguised pariah, who would deserve to be driven out with indignation, if his recent acts and real character were suddenly disclosed. The Christian feels all this, and something more. He feels he has committed his faults in the full sight of a pure God; that he acts ungratefully and cruelly to a Being full of love and compassion, who died as a sacrifice for sins like those he has just committed. These considerations add extreme poignancy to the sense of sin, but it must be recollected that they depend upon no difference of character. If the sceptic held the same intellectual creed, he would feel them in precisely the same way as the religious man. It is not necessarily dulness of heart that keeps him back.

It is also sometimes believed that Puritanic ways are associated with strong religious professions; but a Puritan tendency is by no means an essential part of a religious disposition. The Puritan's character is joyless and morose; he is most happy, or, to speak less paradoxically, most at peace with himself when sad. It is a mental condition correlated with the well-known Puritan features, black straight hair, hollowed cheeks, and sallow complexion. A bright, blue-eyed, rosy-cheeked, curly-headed youth would seem an anomaly in a Puritanical assembly. But there are many Divines mentioned in Middleton, whose character was most sunny and joyful, and whose society was dearly prized, showing distinctly that the Puritan type is a speciality, and by no means an invariable ingredient in the constitution of men who are naturally inclined to piety.

The result of all these considerations is to show that the chief peculiarity in the moral nature of the pious man is its conscious instability. He is liable to extremes—now swinging forwards into regions of enthusiasm, adoration, and self-sacrifice; now backwards into those of sensuality and selfishness. Very devout people are apt to style themselves the most miserable of sinners, and I think they may be taken to a considerable extent at their word. It would appear that their disposition is to sin more frequently and to repent more fervently than those whose constitutions are stoical, and therefore of a more symmetrical and orderly character. The *amplitude* of the moral oscillations of religious men is greater than that of others whose *average* moral position is the same.

The table (p. 75) of the distribution of natural gifts is necessarily as true of morals as of intellect or of muscle. If we class a vast number of men into fourteen classes, separated by equal grades of morality as regards their natural disposition, the number of men per million in the different classes will be as stated in the table. I have no doubt that many of Middleton's Divines belong to class G., in respect to their active benevolence, unselfishness, and other amiable qualities. But men of the lowest grades of morals may also have pious aptitudes; thus among prisoners, the best attendants on religious worship are often the worst criminals. I do not, however, think it is always an act of conscious hypocrisy in bad men when they make pious professions, but rather that they are deeply conscious of the instability of their characters, and that they fly to devotion as a resource and consolation.

These views will, I think, explain the apparent anomaly why the children of extremely pious parents occasionally turn out very badly. The parents are naturally gifted with high moral characters combined with instability of disposition, but these peculiarities are in no way correlated. It must, therefore, often happen that the child will inherit the one and not the other. If his heritage consist of the moral gifts without great instability, he will not feel the need of extreme piety; if he inherits great instability without morality, he will be very likely to disgrace his name.

APPENDIX TO DIVINES

(BIOGRAPHIA EVANGELICA)

Selected from the 196 names contained in Middleton's *Biographia Evangelica*. An * means that the name to which it is attached appears also in the alphabetical list; that, in short, it is one of Middleton's 196 selections.

ABBOT, George, Archbishop of Canterbury (1562–1633, æt. 71). Educated at Guildford Grammar School, then at Balliol College: became a celebrated preacher. Æt. 35 elected Master of University College, when the differences first began between him and Laud; these subsisted as long as they lived, Abbot being Calvinist and Laud High Church. Made Bishop of Lichfield æt. 45; then of London; and, æt. 49, Archbishop of Canterbury. He had great influence in the affairs of the time, but was too unyielding and too liberal to succeed as a courtier; besides this, Laud's influence was ever against him. He had great natural parts, considerable learning, charity, and public spirit. His parents were pious; his father was a weaver.

B.   Robert Abbot,★ Bishop of Salisbury. *See below.*

B.   Maurice, Lord Mayor of London and M.P.

[N.]   George, son of Maurice, wrote on the Book of Job.

ABBOT, Robert, Bishop of Salisbury (1560–1617, æt. 57). His preferment was remarkably owing to his merit, particularly in preaching. King James I highly esteemed him for his writings. Æt. 49 he was elected Master of Balliol College, which throve under his care. Three years afterwards he was made professor of Divinity, and æt. 55 Bishop of Salisbury. Died two years later through gout and stone brought on by his sedentary life. In contrasting his character with that of his younger brother, the Archbishop, it was said, "George was the more plausible preacher, Robert the greater scholar: gravity did frown in George and smile in Robert."

B.   George Abbot,★ Archbishop of Canterbury. *See above.*

B.   Maurice, Lord Mayor of London and M.P.

[N.]   George, son of Maurice, wrote on Job.

CLARKE, Matthew (1664–1726, æt. 62); an eminent minister among the Dissenters. An exceedingly laborious man, who quite overtasked his powers.

F.   Also Matthew Clarke, a man of learning. He spoke Italian and French with uncommon perfection. Was ejected from the ministry by the Uniformity Act. Dr. Watts wrote the epitaph of Matthew Clarke, junior, which begins with "a son bearing the name of his venerable father, nor less venerable himself."

DIEU, Lewis de (1590–?). "In practical godliness and the knowledge of divinity, science of all kinds, and the languages, he was truly a star of the first magnitude." Married, and had eleven children.

D I E U , Lewis de—*continued*

F. Daniel de Dieu, minister of Flushing, a man of great merit. He was uncommonly versed in the Oriental languages, "and could preach with applause in German, Italian, French, and English."

u. David Colonius, professor at Leyden.

D O D , John (1547–1645, æt. 98). This justly famous and reverend man was the youngest of seventeen children. Educated at Cambridge. He was a great and continual preacher, eminent for the frequency, aptness, freeness, and largeness of his godly discourse; very unworldly; given to hospitality. He married twice, each time to a pious woman.

p. John Wilkins,* D.D., Bishop of Chester (1614–1672, æt. 58), a learned and ingenious prelate. Educated at Oxford, where he was very successful, and where, æt. 34, he was made Warden of Wadham College by the Committee of Parliament appointed for reforming the University. Married Robina, widow of P. French and sister of Oliver Cromwell, who made him Master of Trinity College, Cambridge, whence he was ejected by Charles II. Æt. 54 he was made Bishop of Chester. He was indefatigable in study, and tolerant of the opinions of others. He was an astronomer and experimentalist of considerable merit, and took an active part in the foundation of the Royal Society.

I know nothing of his descendants, nor even if he had any. The Cromwell blood had less influence than might have been expected (*see* C R O M W E L L). A daughter of Robina Cromwell, by her first husband, married Archbishop Tillotson, and left issue, but undistinguished.

D O N N E , John, D.D., Dean of St. Paul's (1573–1631, æt. 58). "He was rather born wise than made so by study." He is the subject of one of Isaac Walton's biographies. The recreations of his youth were poetry; the latter part of his life was a continual study. He early thought out his religion for himself, being thoroughly converted from

Papacy through his own inquiries æt. 20. His mind was liberal and unwearied in the search of knowledge. His life was holy and his death exemplary.

[gU.] ? Sir Thomas More, the Lord Chancellor, from whose family he was descended through his mother. Sir Thomas being born ninety-three years before him was, I presume, his great-grandfather or great-great-uncle.

g. ? William Rastall, the worthy and laborious judge who abridged the statues of the kingdom. Rastall was a generation younger than Sir Thomas More, and was therefore probably a grandfather or great-uncle of Dr. Donne.

gF. ? John Rastall, father of the judge, printer and author.

DOWNE, John, B.D. *See under* JEWELL.

u. John Jewell,* Bishop of Salisbury.

ERSKINE, Ebenezer (about 1680–1754, æt. 74); originator of the Scottish secession. This pious minister preached freely against the proceedings of the Synod of Perth, for which he was reprimanded, and afterwards, owing to his continued contumacy, he was expelled from the Scottish Church. Hence the famous Secession.

B. Ralph Erskine.* *See below.*

ERSKINE, Ralph (1685–1752, æt. 67); also became a seceder. He did not simply follow his brother, but raised a separate religious tempest against himself. He wrote controversial tracts, was a strict Calvinist, and published sonnets that "breathe a warm spirit of piety, though they cannot be mentioned as finished poetical compositions." He laboured in preaching and writing till almost the time of his death. He left a large family (his father was one of thirty-three children), of whom three sons were ministers of the Secession, but died in the prime of life.

B. Ebenezer Erskine.* *See above.*

EVANS, John, D.D. (1680–1730, æt. 50). His vivacity, joined with great judgment, made a very uncommon mixture. His industry was indefatigable. He was descended from a race of ministers for four generations, and, excepting one interruption, quite up to the Reformation: say six generations in all.

GILPIN, Bernard (1517–1583, æt. 66); the "Apostle of the North." Was one of several children. He showed extraordinary genius in childhood, and an early disposition to seriousness and contemplative life; but as he grew older he became practical and energetic, and none the less pious. He was greatly beloved. In beginning his career he suffered from religious persecution, and if Queen Mary had lived a little longer, there is little doubt but that he would have been martyred. He remained rector of Houghton during the whole of his later life, refusing a bishopric. He built a school, and picked up intelligent boys and educated them, and became their friend and guardian in after-life. He had extraordinary influence over the wild border-people of his neighbourhood, going fearlessly among them. He was affluent and generous; a hater of slander and a composer of differences. He was tall and slender, careless of amusement, and rather abstemious. Was unmarried. His relationships are good, but distant.

gB. Bishop Tonstall, one of the most enlightened Churchmen of his time.

NP. Richard Gilpin, D.D., of Greystock, who was ejected thence by the Act of Uniformity.

NPPS. William Gilpin (*Forest Scenery*), an excellent pastor and good schoolmaster, was [PS.] to Richard and the biographer of Bernard Gilpin. I know nothing about the intervening relations; I wish I did, for I should expect to find that the Gilpin blood had produced other noteworthy results.

GOUGE, Thomas (1605–1681, æt. 76); educated at Eton and King's College, Cambridge; minister of St. Sepulchre's, in London, for twenty-four years. He originated the scheme, which he carried on for a while with his own funds, of finding employment for the poor by flax-spinning, instead of giving them alms as beggars; others afterwards developed the idea. He had a good fortune of his own, and finally applied almost the whole of it to charity in Wales, judging there was more occasion for help there than elsewhere. He contrived, with the further aid of subscriptions, to educate yearly from 800 to 1,000 poor Welsh children, and to procure and print a translation of the Bible into Welsh. Also, he took great pains with Christ's Hospital in London. He was humble and meek, and free from affected gravity and moroseness. His conversation was affable and pleasant; he had wonderful serenity of mind and evenness of temper, visible in his countenance; he was hardly ever merry, but never melancholy nor sad. He seemed always the same; ever obliging, and ever tolerant of difference of opinion.

F.   William Gouge.* *See below.*

[*p.*]   Mrs. Meliora Prestley, of Wild Hall, Hertford, whose name shows the continuance of a devout disposition in the family. She erected a monument to the Gouges in Blackfriars Church after the Fire.

There has been another eminent minister of the name of Gouge among the Dissenters, who died 1700, and on whom Dr. Watts wote a poem. I do not know whether he was a relation.

GOUGE, William, D.D. (1575–1653, æt. 78); was very religious from boyhood, and a laborious student at Eton and at Cambridge, sitting up late and rising early. He was singularly methodical in his habits; became minister of Blackfriars, London. He was continual in preaching and praying; very conscionable in laying out his time; temperate; of a meek and sweet disposition, and a great peacemaker. Devout people of all ranks sought his acquaintance. According to his portrait, his head was massive and square, his expression firm and benevolent. Married; had seven sons and six daughters; six sons lived to man's estate.

S.   Thomas Gouge.* *See above.*

GOUGE, William, D.D.—*continued*

[F.] Thomas, a pious gentleman living in London.

f. His mother "was the religious daughter" of one Mr. Nicholas Culverel, a merchant in London; her brothers were as follow:—

2u. The Revs. Samuel and Ezekiel Culverel, both of them famous preachers.

[2*u.*] Her two sisters were married to those famous divines, Dr. Chadderton, Master of Emmanuel College, and Dr. Whitaker,* the learned and devout Professor of Divinity in Cambridge.

GRYNÆUS, Simon (1493–1541, æt. 48); a most able and learned man; was son of a peasant in Suabia of I know not what name, that of Grynæus being of course adopted. He was a friend and fellow-student of Melancthon from boyhood; became Greek professor at Vienna, and afterwards adopted Protestantism. His change of creed led him into trouble, and compelled him to leave Vienna; was invited to and accepted the Greek chair in Heidelberg, and afterwards that of Basle. Æt. 38 he visited England, chiefly to examine the libraries, strongly recommended by Erasmus. He was made much of in this country by Lord Chancellor Sir Thomas More. Died at Basle of the plague. His claim to a place in the *Biographica Evangelica* is that he was a good man, a lover of the Reformation, and confidentially employed by the Reformers.

S. Samuel (1539–1599, æt. 60) inherited his father's abilities and studious tastes, for he was made Professor of Oratory at Basle æt. 25, and afterwards of civil law.

N. Thomas Grynæus.* *See below.*

4NS. Theophilus, Simon, John James,* and Tobias. *See for all these under* THOMAS GRYNÆUS.

GRYNÆUS, Thomas (1512–1564, æt. 52). This excellent man "eminently possessed the ornament of a meek and quiet spirit." Educated by his uncle Simon, he became so advanced that, while a mere youth, he was a public teacher at Berne; whence, wearied with the theological contentions of the day, and seeking a studious retirement, he removed to Rontela, near Basle, as minister of that place, where he performed "his duty with so much faithfulness, solemnity, and kindness of behaviour, that he was exceedingly endeared to his flock, and beloved by all those who had any concern for truth and knowledge." He died of the plague. It does not appear that he published any writings, but he left behind him a noble treasure for the Church in his four excellent sons, as follow:—

4 S. Theophilus, Simon, John James,* and Tobias; all of them eminent for their piety and learning; but John James (*see below*) was the most distinguished of the four. "He was indeed a burning and a shining light. Such a father and such sons are not often met with in the history of the world. Blessed be God for them!"

U. Simon Grynæus.* *See above.*

US. Thomas. *See above.*

GRYNÆUS, John James (1540–1617, æt. 77); succeeded his father in the pastoral charge of Rontela, where he changed from the Lutherans to the Zuinglians; was invited to Basle as Professor of Divinity, where he became happily instrumental in healing the differences between the above sects. Many noblemen and gentlemen came from other countries and boarded with him for the sake of his agreeable and profitable conversation. He was subsequently professor at Heidelberg, and thence retired to Basle as pastor. He used to be at his study, winter and summer, before sunrise, and to spend the day in prayer, writing, reading, and visiting the sick. He was remarkably patient under wrongs; was ever a most affectionate friend and relation to his family and all good men, and of the strictest temperance with respect to himself. He had great wit, tempered with gravity. His remarkable learning and worth was well appreciated by his contemporaries; and travellers from all parts, who had any concern for religion and science, constantly visited him. He became almost blind. Married, and had seven children, all of whom died before him, except one daughter. I know no more of this interesting family.

GB. Simon Grynæus.*

F. Thomas Grynæus;* *f.* was also a pious woman.

3B. *See under* THOMAS GRYNÆUS.

Thus we find three men, descended in as many generations from a simple husbandman, who have achieved a place among the 196 worthies selected on their own merits by Middleton, as the pick of two centuries and a half; and at least three others are mentioned by the same writer in terms of very high commendation.

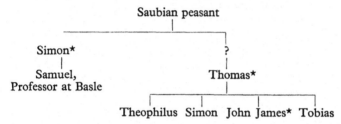

GUYSE, John (1680–1761, æt. 81); an eminent and excellent divine; minister at Hertford. His health was poor, and he was overworked and hectic, but his vigour was little abated till near his death. It was his constant study to make every one about him happy. He was thoroughly amiable, and had many excellent ministerial gifts.

[F. and *f.*] Parents very pious and worthy.

S. Rev. William; of excellent abilities and ministerial talents, who was for some time his assistant, but who died two years before him.

HENRY, Philip (1631–1696, æt. 56); educated at Westminster and Oxford. When a young clergyman, he went by the name of the "Heavenly Henry." He devoted his whole powers to the ministry. His constitution was but tender, yet by great carefulness in diet and exercise he enjoyed a fair amount of health. Married a Welsh lady of some fortune, and had one son and four daughters.

His father was named Henry, himself the son of Henry Williams, the father's Christian name becoming the son's surname, according to the old Welsh custom.

f. His mother was a very pious woman, who took great pains with him and with her other children.

S. Matthew Henry.* *See below.*

HENRY, Matthew (1662–1714, æt. 52); was a child of extraordinary pregnancy and forwardness. His father said of him, "Præterque ætatem nil puerile fuit,"—there was nothing of the child in him except his years; was but weakly when young, but his constitution strengthened as he grew. He could read a chapter in the Bible, very distinctly, when about three years old, and with some observation of what he read. He was very devoutly inclined. His father spared no pains to educate him. His labours in the ministry were many and great—first at Chester, and then at Hackney. He injured a naturally strong constitution by his frequent and fervent preaching, and by sitting over-long in his study. Married twice, and left many children. The order of his family was exemplary while he lived. I know nothing more of them.

F. Philip Henry.* *See above.*

HERBERT, Hon. George (1593–1635, æt. 42); educated by his mother till æt. 12, then at Westminster, where he was endeared to all; then he went to Cambridge, where he highly distinguished himself, and became orator to the University. He was eminent as a sacred poet; he was also an excellent musician, and composed many hymns and anthems. He selected a small ministerial charge, where he passed the latter years of his life in the utmost sanctity. In figure he was tall and very lean, but straight. He had the manners and mien of a perfect gentleman. He was consumptive, and subject to frequent fevers and illness. Married; no children; his nieces lived with him.

F. A man of great courage and strength, descended from a highly connected and very chivalrous family. He was a person of importance in North Wales, and given to wide hospitality.

f.   His mother was a lady of extraordinary piety, and of more than feminine understanding.

g.   Sir T. Bromley, privy councillor to Henry VIII.

B.   The first Lord Herbert of Cherbury; statesman, orator, cavalier, and sceptical philosopher.

[2B.] His other two brothers were remarkable men—both had great courage; one was a renowned duellist, and the other was a naval officer who achieved some reputation, and was considered to have deserved more.

US.   Sir Edward Herbert, Lord Keeper under Charles II (*see in* JUDGES).

2UP.   The two sons of the above were distinguished, one being a Chief Justice, and the other the admiral, cr. Lord Torrington.

HILDERSHAM, Arthur (1563–1632, æt. 69); was bred a Papist, but abandoned that creed; was fined 2,000*l.* for schism. He sojourned in many families, and always gained their esteem and love. He much weakened his constitution by his pains in preaching.

S.   Samuel, an excellent man, of whom Mr. Matthew Henry · makes honourable mention in the *Life* of his father, Mr. Philip Henry. Samuel wrote the *Life of Arthur Hildersham*. He died æt. 80.

HOOPER, John, Bishop of Gloucester (1495–1554, martyred æt. 59); originally a monk; became converted to the Reformation when in Germany. He was a great acquisition to that cause, for his learning, piety, and character would have given strength and honour to any profession. Was burnt at Gloucester.

[U.] J. Hooper, Principal of St. Alban Hall.

HOSPINIAN, Ralph (1547–1626, æt. 79); a learned Swiss writer.

u.   John Wolphius, professor at Zurich.

JEWELL, John, Bishop of Salisbury (1522–1571, æt. 49). This great man, "the darling and wonder of his age, the pattern for sanctity, piety, and theology," was one of the younger children in a family of ten. He was a lad of pregnant parts, and of a sweet and industrious nature and temper; was educated at Oxford, where his success was great. On Queen Mary's accession he had to take refuge on the Continent, æt. 31, escaping narrowly. He did not return till after her death, when, æt. 38, he was made bishop by Queen Elizabeth. He was an excellent scholar, and had much improved his learning during his exile; was a most laborious preacher. As bishop, he was exceedingly liberal and hospitable. It was his custom to have half a dozen or more intelligent poor lads in his house to educate them, and he maintained others at the University at his own expense: among these was Richard Hooker. He was a pleasant and amusing host; he had naturally a very strong memory. In body he was spare and thin, and he restlessly wore himself out by reading, writing, preaching, and travelling. His writings are famous; his *Apologia* was translated into English by the mother of Lord Bacon. His parents were of ancient descent, but not rich.

n. John Downe* (1576–1633, æt. 57) educated at Emmanuel College, Cambridge. He thence took a small college living in Devonshire. "Had his means been answerable to his worth, he had not lain in such obscurity as he did, but had doubtless moved and shined in a far higher and more extensive sphere. . . . The sharpness of his wit, the fastness of his memory" (this seems hereditary, like the "Porson" memory, which also went through the female line), "and the soundness of his judgment, were in him all three so rarely mixed as few men attain them single, in that degree he had them all. His skill in languages was extraordinary." He was very temperate and grave, but sociable and courteous, and a thoroughly good man and divine. His constitution was but crazy. Married happily, and had several children, who did well, judging from the phrase, "His civil wisdom appeared . . . in the education of his family . . . in his marriage and the marriages of his daughters."

JUNIUS, Francis (1545–1602, æt. 57). This extraordinary man was very infirm and weakly when a child, but he strengthened as he grew. Was singularly bashful. He read with avidity; went to Switzerland as a student, where he became a Reformer, and was persecuted. He was an excellent and most able man; the subject of numerous panegyrics. He died of the plague. Married four wives, and survived them all; had in all two sons and one daughter.

F.   A learned and a kind man.

S.   Francis, a very amiable and learned man, who spent most of his days in England, especially at Oxford.

2p.   Dionysius Vossius, the Orientalist, and Isaac Vossius, the learned Canon of Windsor; these were sons of the daughter of Junius, who married the learned John Gerard Vossius.

KNOX, John (1505–1572, æt. 67); a popular type of Puritanical bigotry. In his youth he was a successful student of scholastic divinity; was persecuted and exiled in his manhood; married twice—two sons and three daughters.

[2S.] Both his sons were fellows of St. John's College, Cambridge; the younger of them was University preacher.

p.   Josiah Welch, "the Cock of the Conscience." For him and his brothers, see under their father's name, JOHN WELCH.

LASCO, John à (?–1684); the Polish reformer. When the religious persecutions of the Continent had driven 380 exiles to England, they had their own laws, worship, and superintendent. The office of superintendent was held by A. Lasco.

B.   A diplomatist, and a man of considerable abilities.

U.   John à Lasco, Archbishop of Griesa in Poland. It was to him that Erasmus dedicated his edition of the works of St. Ambrose.

LEIGHTON, Robert, D.D., Archbishop of Glasgow (1614–1684, æt. 70); was bred up in the greatest aversion to the Church of England; became Master of the College at Edinburgh, then Archbishop. At æt. 70 he looked so fresh and well that age seemed to stand still with him; his hair black, and all his motions lively; but he caught pleurisy, and died suddenly of it.

F. Alexander Leighton, a Scotch physician, who wrote religious and political tracts, for which he got into trouble with the Star Chamber. He had his nose slit, his ears cut off, was publicly whipped, and imprisoned for eleven years. Died insane.

MATHER, Cotton, D.D., (1663–1727, æt. 64); born at Boston, in America; was a quick child, and always devoutly inclined; began to preach æt. 18. His application, and the labours he went through, are almost incredible; thus, as regards literature alone, he wrote 382 separate treatises.

F. and G. Dr. Increase Mather, his father, and Mr. Richard Mather, his grandfather, were eminent ministers.

g. John Cotton was a man of piety and learning.

[S.] Samuel; wrote his life.

MATTHEW, Tobie, D.D., Archbishop of York (1546–1628, æt. 82). This truly great man was an honour to his age. At Oxford "he took his degrees so ripe in learning and young in years as was half a miracle." He was "a most excellent divine, in whom piety and learning, art with nature strove."

[S.] Sir Tobie Matthew "had all his father's name, and many of his natural parts, but had few of his moral virtues, and fewer of his spiritual graces, being an inveterate enemy to the Protestant religion." I presume, from Middleton's taking so much notice of him, that he ought to be ranked as a person of importance and character.

NOWELL, Alexander, D.D., Dean of St. Paul's (1511–1601, æt. 90). Educated at Brasenose College, Oxford, of which he became a Fellow, and where he "grew very famous for piety and learning, and for his zeal in promoting the Reformation." On Queen Mary's accession he was marked out for Popish persecution, so he fled to Frankfort, whence he returned after her death, the first of the English exiles. He soon after obtained many and considerable preferments, and was made Dean of St. Paul's æt. 49; then Rector of Hadham in Yorkshire, where he became a frequent and painful preacher and a zealous writer. Æt. 84 he was elected Principal of Brasenose College, where, having enjoyed for a further term of six years the perfect use of his senses and faculties, he died. He was reckoned a very learned man and an excellent divine. His charity to the poor was great, especially if they had anything of the scholar in them; and his comfort to the afflicted either in body or mind was equally extensive. He wrote many religious works, especially a Catechism, which was highly esteemed, and which he was induced to write, by Cecil and other great men of the nation, on purpose to stop a clamour raised among the Roman Catholics, and the Protestants had no principles. His controversies were entirely with the Papists. He was so fond of fishing that his picture at Brasenose represents him surrounded with tackle.

n. William Whitaker,* D.D. (1547–1595, æt. 48). Educated by Dr. Nowell until he went to Trinity College, Cambridge, where he highly distinguished himself. He was elected Professor of Philosophy while quite young, and filled the chair with the greatest credit. Then he became a diligent student of religious writers and in a few years went through almost all the Fathers of the Church. He laboured with incredible application, but overdid his powers and strained his constitution. Æt. 31 he had obtained a very high reputation for theological knowledge, and shortly after was elected Professor of Divinity and Master of Queen's College. Æt. 38 he entered into controversies with the Papists, especially with Bellarmine. "He dealt peaceably, modestly, and gently, without taunting, bantering, wrath, deceit, or insidious language; so that you might easily see him to be no cunning and obstinate partisan, but a most studious searcher after divine truth." He was endowed with a most acute genius, happy memory, with as great eloquence as was ever in a divine, and with a most learned and polished judgment. He was a pious, holy man, of an even, grave demeanour, and very remarkable for patient bearing of injuries. He was extremely kind and liberal, in season and out of season, especially to young students who were poor. He was extremely meek, although so highly gifted and esteemed. Bishop Hall said, "Never man saw him without reverence, nor heard him without wonder." It was he who, at a conference of Bishops, drew up the famous ultra-predestinarian confession of faith, called the "Lambeth Articles." He married, first, the maternal aunt (u.) of William Gouge (*see*), and second, the widow of the learned Dr. Fenner, and by these two wives had eight children. It would be exceedingly interesting to know more of these children, especially those of the first wife, whose hereditary chances were so high. They appear to have turned out well, judging from Middleton's phrase that they "were carefully brought up in the principles of true religion and virtue." This, unfortunately, is all I know about them.

SAURIN, James (1677–1730, æt. 53). Served in the army as a cadet, but the profession was distasteful to him, and he left it to become a student in philosophy and divinity. He lived five years in England. He was an admirable scholar and preacher, and led a holy, unblemished life. Married, and had one son at least, who survived him.

[F.]   An eminent lawyer of Nismes, who was compelled to leave France on the revocation of the Edict of Nantes.

3 B.   They, as well as James, were trained up in learning by their father, and were all so remarkably eloquent "that eloquence was said to be hereditary in the family."
The eloquent Attorney-General of Ireland was a descendant.

USHER, James, D.D., Archbishop of Armagh (1580–1656, æt. 76). As a child he showed a remarkable attachment to books, and he became a great student as he grew older. He was the subject of universal admiration for his great erudition and wise and noble character. He was a first-rate man, and played a conspicuous part on many stages. His constitution was sound and healthy.

F.   Arnold Usher; was one of the six clerks of the Chancery in Ireland, and a man of parts and learning.

U.   Henry Usher, also Archbishop of Armagh, was highly celebrated for wisdom and knowledge.

g.   James Stanihurst; was three times Speaker of the House of Commons in Ireland, Recorder of Dublin, and Master in Chancery. He was highly esteemed for his wisdom and abilities.

u.   James Stanihurst; was a philosopher, historian, and poet.

B.   Ambrose Usher, who died in the prime of life, was a man of very extraordinary powers; he had attained great proficiency in the Oriental tongues.

[2 U.] The Archbishop was taught in his childhood by two *blind* aunts, who knew the Bible by heart, and so contrived to teach him to read out of it—Ingenious, persevering ladies!

James Usher was, therefore, a remarkable instance of hereditary ability associated with constitutional vigour, and apparently of a durable type. Unluckily for the world, he married an heiress,—an only daughter,—who appears, like many other heiresses, to have inherited a deficiency of prolific power, for she bore him only one daughter.

WELCH, John (1570–1623, æt. 53). He was profligate in his youth, and joined the border-thieves, but he repented and grew to be extremely Puritanical. The flesh upon his knees became "callous, like horn," from his frequent prayings upon them. He was "grievously tempted" throughout the whole of his life, and prayed and groaned at nights. His constitution was robust, and he underwent great fatigues. Married the daughter of John Knox★ (*see above*), and had three sons by her. The eldest son was accidentally shot when a youth.

[S.] The second son was shipwrecked, and swam to a desert island, where he starved and was afterwards found dead, on his knees, stiffened in a praying posture, with his hands lifted to heaven.

S. Josiah Welch, the third son, was "a man highly favoured of God, . . . and commonly called 'the Cock of the Conscience,' because of his extraordinary talent in awakening and arousing the conscience of sinners." He was extremely troubled with doubts about his own salvation. He was still young when he died.

WHITAKER, William D.D. *See under* NOWELL.★

u. Alexander Nowell,★ D.D.

WILKINS, John, D.D., Bishop of Chester. *See under* DOD.★

g. John Dod.★

WITSIUS, Herman, D.D. (1636–1708, æt. 72). Born in Friesland, a premature child. Was always puny in stature, but had vast intellectual abilities. Was Theological Professor at Utrecht. His fame was European. Till within a little before his death he could easily read a Greek Testament of the smallest type by moonlight.

[g.] A most pious minister.

u. The learned Peter Gerhard.

[2S., 3s.] His family consisted of two sons, who died young, and of three remarkably pious and accomplished daughters.

SENIOR CLASSICS OF CAMBRIDGE

The position of Senior Classic at Cambridge is of the same rank in regard to classical achievement as that of Senior Wrangler is to achievement in mathematics; therefore all that I said about the severity of the selection implied by the latter degree (see pp. 59–64) is strictly applicable to the former. I have chosen the Senior Classics for the subject of this chapter rather than the Senior Wranglers, for the reasons explained in p. 248.

The Classical Tripos was established in the year 1824. There have, therefore, been forty-six lists between that time and the year 1869, both inclusive. In nine cases out of these, two or more names were bracketed together at the head of the list as equal in merit, leaving thirty-six cases of men who were distinctly the first classics of their several years. Their names are as follow:—Malkin, Isaacson, Stratton, *Kennedy*, *Selwyn*, Soames, Wordsworth, *Kennedy*, *Lushington*, *Bunbury*, *Kennedy*, *Goulburn*, Osborne, Humphry, Freeman, Cope, *Denman*, Maine, *Lushington*, Elwyn, Perowne, Lightfoot, Roby, *Hawkins*, *Butler*, Brown, Clark, *Sidgwick*, Abbott, Jebb, Wilson, Moss, Whitelaw, Smith, Sandys, *Kennedy*. It will be observed that the name of Kennedy occurs no less than four times, and that of Lushington twice, in this short series. It will give the genealogies of these, and of a few others of which I have particulars, and which I have *italicised* in the above list, begging it at the same time to be understood that I do not mean to say that many of the remainder may not also be distinguished for the eminence of their kinsmen; I have not cared to make extensive and minute inquiries, because the following list is amply sufficient for my purpose. It is obvious that the descending relationships must be generally deficient, since the oldest of all the Senior Classics took his degree in

M

1824, and would therefore be only about sixty-seven at the present time. For the most part the sons have yet to be proved and the grandsons to be born.

There is no case in my list of only a single eminent relationship. There are four, namely Denman, Goulburn, Selwyn, and Sidgwick, of only two or three; all the others have four or upwards.

APPENDIX TO THE SENIOR CLASSICS OF CAMBRIDGE

Out of 36 senior classics (all bracketed cases being excluded) since the establishment of the Tripos in 1834, 14 find a place in the appendix; they are grouped into 10 families. The Kennedy family has supplied 1 in 9 out of the entire number of the senior classics.

BUNBURY, Edward H.; senior classic, 1833.

gF.   Henry, 1st Lord Holland, Secretary-at-War.

gR.   The Right Hon. Charles James Fox; illustrious statesman.

gB.   The 2nd Lord Holland; statesman and social leader. *See* FOX, *in* STATESMEN, for other relationships, including that of the Napier family.

[F.]   General Sir H. E. Bunbury, K.C.B., author.

BUTLER, Rev. H. Montagu, D.D.; senior classic, 1855; Head Master of Harrow.

F.   Rev. Dr. George Butler; Dean of Peterborough, previously Head Master of Harrow. He was senior wrangler in 1794, at which time there was no University test for classical eminence; however, the office he held is sufficient proof of his powers in that respect also.

[G.]   A man of considerable classical powers and literary tastes; was master of a school at Chelsea.

B.   The Rev. George Butler; Head Master of Liverpool College; 1st class, Oxford.

BUTLER, Rev. H. Montague—*continued*

B.   Spencer P. Butler; barrister; wrangler and 1st class in classics, Cambridge.

B.   The Rev. Arthur Butler; Head Master of Haileybury College; 1st class, Oxford.

DENMAN, Hon. George, Q.C., M.P.; senior classic, 1842.

F.   1st Lord Denman; Chief Justice Queen's Bench. (*See in* JUDGES.)

G.   Physician; a celebrated accoucheur.

GN.   Sir Benj. Brodie, Bart.; eminent surgeon. (*See* BRODIE, *in* SCIENCE.)

GOULBURN, Henry; senior classic, 1835. It was he who obtained the extraordinary distinction described in p. 63. He died young.

F.   Right Hon. H. Goulburn, Chancellor of the Exchequer.

[B.]   Also an able classical scholar.

U.   Edward Goulburn, Serjeant-at-Law; a man of well-known high accomplishments and ability.

US.   Rev. E. M. Goulburn, D.D., Dean of Norwich; formerly Head Master of Rugby; eminent preacher.

HAWKINS, F. Vaughan; senior classic, 1854; one of the youngest at the time of his examination, yet is reputed to have obtained one of the largest number of marks upon record.

F.   Francis Hawkins, M.D., Registrar of the College of Physicians.

U.   Edward Hawkins, D.D., Provost of Oriel College, Oxford.

U.   Cæsar Hawkins, Serjeant Surgeon to Her Majesty. This is the "blue ribbon" of the profession, being the highest post attainable by a surgeon.

GB.   Charles Hawkins, Serjeant Surgeon to George III.

GF.   Sir Cæsar Hawkins, 1st Bart., Serjeant Surgeon to George III.

GU.   Pennell Hawkins, Serjeant Surgeon to George III.

u.   Halford Vaughan, Professor at Oxford.

g.   Sir John Vaughan, Judge; Just C.P. (*See in* JUDGES.)

gB.   Rev. Edward Vaughan of Leicester; Calvinist theologian.

HAWKINS, F. Vaughan—*continued*

gB.   Peter Vaughan, Dean of Chester; Warden of Merton College, Oxford.

gB.   Sir Chas. Vaughan, Envoy Extraordinary to the United States.

GB.   Sir Henry Vaughan, assumed the name of Halford, 1st Bart.; the well-known physician of George III.

gN.   The Rev. Charles J. Vaughan, D.D., joint senior classic of Cambridge, 1838; eminent scholar; Head Master of Harrow; Master of the Temple; has refused two bishoprics. The rigid rule I have prescribed to myself, of reckoning only those who were sole senior classics, prevents my assigning a separate paragraph to Dr. Vaughan.

KENNEDY, Rev. Benjamin; senior classic, 1827; for many years Head Master of Shrewsbury School; professor of Greek at Cambridge. Educated at Shrewsbury, of which school he was head boy æt. 15; obtained the Porson prize at Cambridge æt. 18, before entering the University, and the Pitt University Scholarship æt. 19.

B.   Charles Rann Kennedy, barrister; senior classic, 1831.

B.   Rev. George Kennedy, senior classic, 1834; for many years one of the ablest of the private tutors at Cambridge.

B.   Rev. William Kennedy, Inspector of Schools; gained the Porson prize, 1835, but was incapacitated for competition in the classical tripos through his not having taken the previous, then essential, mathematical degree.

N.   W. R. Kennedy, son of the above; senior classic, 1868; was Newcastle scholar at Eton.

N.   J. Kennedy, has not yet (1869) arrived at the period for taking his degree. He was Newcastle scholar at Eton, and Bell University scholar at Cambridge.

F.   Benjamin Rann Kennedy. It is considered that he would have been an excellent scholar if he had had advantages. Had considerable poetic talent (poem on death of Princess Charlotte, quoted by Washington Irving in his *Sketch-book*). Was Master of King Edward's School, Birmingham.

KENNEDY, Rev. Benjamin—*continued*

G. Her maiden name was Maddox, a lady of considerable intellectual and poetic ability.

g. — Hall, engraver to George III; his portrait is in the Vernon Gallery; was a man of mark in his profession.

g. Her maiden name was Giles; she was the daughter of French emigrants; had excellent abilities, that were shared by others of her family, as follow:—

u. Rev. Dr. Hall, late Master of Pembroke College, Oxford; a man of considerable classical attainments.

Su. James Burchell, Under Sheriff of Middlesex; acting Judge of the Sheriff's Court for forty-five years; a man of eminent business capacity.

*u*S. William Burchell, most successful man of business; founder of important companies, as the first Electric Telegraph Company and the Metropolitan Railway.

LUSHINGTON, Edmund, senior classic, 1832; Professor at Glasgow.

GF. James Law, Bishop of Carlisle, author.

GB. The 1st Lord Ellenborough, Chief Justice of the King's Bench. (*See under* JUDGES.)

B. Henry Lushington, 4th classic of his year; Government Secretary at Malta.

B. Franklin Lushington, senior classic, 1846.

B. Charles H. Lushington, Secretary to Government in India.

The four following are descended from a second marriage; they have the Lushington, but not the Law, blood.

U. Stephen Rumbold Lushington, Privy Councillor; Governor of Madras; Secretary of the Treasury.

[U.] General Sir James Lushington, K.C.B.

[U.] Charles, Madras Civil Service; Member of Council.

US. Charles Hugh, Secretary to Government in India.

The branch of the Lushington family from which Sir Stephen Lushington, D.C.L., the eminent ex-Judge of the Admiralty, is descended, diverged from the one we are now considering, in the fifth ascending generation from the two senior classics. This branch also contains a considerable number of men of sterling ability, and very few others. There are fully eleven distinguished men within three grades of relationship to Sir Stephen Lushington.

SELWYN, Rev. Dr. William; senior classic, 1838; Margaret Professor of Divinity at Cambridge.

B.   The Bishop of Lichfield, formerly Bishop of New Zealand; 2d classic in 1831.

B.   Sir Jasper Selwyn, Judge; Lord Justice.

b.   Miss Selwyn, eminent for philanthropical labours. (Crimean War, "Home" at Birmingham.)

SIDGWICK, H.; senior classic, 1859.

B.   2d classic, 1863.

B.   Able scholar; Senior Tutor of Merton College, Oxford.

*G*nS., *G*UPS., and *gu*PS. Dr. Benson, Head Master of Wellington College, is related, though distantly, through the paternal and maternal lines, to Mr. Sidgwick, being both second and third cousin by the first, and third cousin by the second.

WORDSWORTH, Rev. Christopher, D.D., Bishop of Lincoln; senior classic, 1830. *See under* POETS for his relations, viz.:—

U.   The Poet.

F.   The Master of Trinity College, Cambridge.

2B.   Excellent scholars; one, the Bishop of Dunkeld.

OARSMEN

I propose to supplement what I have written about brain by two short chapters on muscle. No one doubts that muscle is hereditary in horses and dogs, but humankind are so blind to facts and so governed by preconceptions, that I have heard it frequently asserted that muscle is not hereditary in men. Oarsmen and wrestlers have maintained that their heroes spring up capriciously, so I have thought it advisable to make inquiries into the matter. The results I have obtained will beat down another place of refuge for those who insist that each man is an independent creation, and not a mere function, physically, morally, and intellectually, of ancestral qualities and external influences.

In respect to Oarsmen, let me assure the reader that they are no insignificant fraction of the community,—no mere waifs and strays from those who follow more civilised pursuits. A perfect passion for rowing pervades large classes. At Newcastle, when a great race takes place, all business is at a standstill, factories are closed, shops are shut, and offices deserted. The number of men who fall within the attraction of the career is very great; and there can be no doubt that a large proportion of those among them who are qualified to succeed brilliantly, obey the attraction and pursue it.

For the information in this and the following chapters, I am entirely indebted to the kind inquiries made for me by Mr. Robert Spence Watson of Newcastle, whose local knowledge is very considerable, and whose sympathies with athletic amusements are strong. Mr. Watson put himself into continual communication with one of the highest, I believe by far the highest, authority on boating matters, a person who had reported nearly every boating race to the newspapers for the last quarter of a century.

The list in the Appendix to this chapter includes the names of nearly all the rowing men of note who have figured upon the Tyne during the past six-and-twenty years. It also includes some of the rowers on the Thames, but the information about these is not so certain. The names are not picked and chosen, but the best men have been taken of whom any certain knowledge could be obtained.

It is not easy to classify the rowers, especially as many of the men have rarely, if ever, pulled in skiff matches, but formed part of crews in pair-oared, four-oared, or six-oared matches. Their performances have, however, been carefully examined and criticised by Mr. Watson and his assessor, who have divided them into four classes.

I have marked the names of the lowest with brackets [ ], and have attached to them the phrase "moderately good." These are men who have either disappointed expectations founded on early promise, or have not rowed often enough to show of what feats they are really capable. No complete failure is included. Few amateurs can cope with men of this class, notwithstanding the mediocrity of their abilities when judged by a professional standard.

The next ascending grade is also distinguished by brackets, [ ], but no qualifying expression is added to their names. They consist of the steady, reliable men who form good racing crews.

The two superior grades contain the men whose names are printed without brackets—whom, in short, I treat as being "eminently gifted." In order to make a distinction between the two grades, I add to the names of the men who belong to the higher of them, the phrase "very excellent oarsmen."

It is not possible to do more than give a rough notion of the places into which these four grades would respectively fall in my table (p. 75) of natural gifts. I have only two data to help me. The first is, that I am informed that in the early part of 1868, the Tyne Amateur Rowing Club, which is the most important institution of that kind in the north of England, had been fifteen years in existence and had comprised, in all, 377 members; that three of these, as judged by amateur standards of comparison, had been considered of surpassing excellence as skiff-rowers, and that the best of these three was looked upon as equal to, or perhaps a trifle better than, the least good of the brothers Matfin, who barely ranks as an "excellent" rower.

The other datum is the deliberate opinion of the authorities to whom I am indebted for the materials of this chapter, that not 1 man in 10 will succeed as a rower even of the lower of the two grades whose names are marked in my Appendix by brackets, and that not 1 in 100 rowers attains to excellence. Hence the minimum qualification for excellence is possessed by only 1 man in 1,000.

There is a rough accordance between these two data. A rowing club consists in part of naturally selected men. They are not men, all of whom have been taken at haphazard as regards their powers of rowing. A large part are undoubtedly mere conscripts from the race of clubable men, but there must always be a considerable number who would not have joined the club save for their consciousness of possessing gifts and tastes that specially qualified them for success on the water. To be the best oarsmen of the 377 men who are comprised in a crack rowing club, means much more than to be the best of 377 men taken at haphazard. It would be much nearer the truth to say, that it means being the best of all who might have joined the club, had they been so inclined and had appeared desirable members. Upon these grounds (see also my remarks in p. 54) it is a very moderate estimate to conclude that the qualifications for excellence as an oarsman, are only possessed by 1 man in 1,000.

The "very excellent" oarsmen imply, I presume, a much more rigorous selection, but I really have no data whatever on which to found an estimate. Many men who found they could attain no higher rank than "excellence," would abandon the unprofitable pursuit of match rowing for more regular and, as some would way, creditable occupations. We shall not be more than half a grade wrong if we consider the "excellent" oarsmen to rank in at least Class F of natural gifts, with respect to rowing ability, and the "very excellent" to fall well within it.

I do not propose to take any pains in analysing these relationships, for the data are inadequate. Rowing was comparatively little practised in previous generations, so we cannot expect to meet with evidence of ancestral peculiarities among the oarsmen. Again, the successful rowers are mostly single men, and some of the best have no children. It is important, in respect to this, to recollect the frequent trainings they have gone through. Mr. Watson mentions to me one well-known man, who has trained for an enormous number of races, and during the time of each training was most abstemious and in amazing health; then, after each trial was over, he commonly gave way, and without committing any great excess, remained for weeks in a state of fuddle. This is too often the history of these men.

There are in the Appendix only three families, each containing more than one excellent oarsman; they are Clasper, Matfin, and Taylor, and the total relationships existing towards the ablest member of each family are, 8 B. and 1 S.

There appears to be no intermarriage, except in the one case that is mentioned, between the families of the rowers; indeed there is much jealousy between the rival families.

APPENDIX TO OARSMEN

"I have not picked and chosen, but have simply taken all the best men I could hear anything certainly about."—*Extract from Mr. Watson's Letter.*

The 18 men whose names are printed in *italics* are described below as examples of hereditary gifts. The remaining 3 are not.

Candlish; Chambers; 5 *Clasper*; *Coombes*; Cooper; Kelly; *Maddison*; 2 *Matfin*; *Renforth*; *Sadler*; 5 *Taylor*; Winship.

CANDLISH, James; a Tyne man, married sister of Henry Clasper; has no children.

CANDLISH, James—*continued*

[B.] Thomas; a good but not a great rower; has always pulled as one of a crew. Unmarried.

[B.] Robert; moderately good; has not rowed very often.

CLASPER, Henry; very excellent oarsman. Is the most prominent member of a large and most remarkable family of oarsmen. He was for many years stroke of a four-oared crew, and frequently the whole crew, including the coxswain, were members of the Clasper family. For eight years this crew won the championship of the Tyne. Six times Henry Clasper pulled stroke for the crew winning the championship of the Thames, and Coombes declared that he was the best stroke that ever pulled. Up to the year 1859, when he was 47 years old, he had pulled stroke 78 times in pair or foar-oared matches, and his crew had been 54 times victorious. He had also pulled in 32 skiff matches and won 20 of them, and had been champion of Scotland upon the only two occasions on which he contested for it. Nearly all these matches were over a 4 or $4\frac{1}{2}$ mile course. He invented the light outrigger, and has been a very successful builder of racing boats.

Family of Clasper

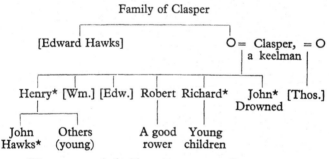

The names marked with an * are very excellent oarsmen
Those in brackets [ ] are similarly marked in the letterpress

S. John Hawks Clasper; very excellent oarsman. Has rowed more skiff matches than any man living. When he had contested 76 races, he had won 50 of them. He has brothers, but they are too young to have shown their powers.

B.   Richard Clasper; very excellent oarsman, known as the "Little Wonder." Was, when 37 years old, only 5 feet 2 inches high, and weighed 8 stone 6 lbs. In spite of this he was bow-oarsman to the brothers' crew, and a rare good one. He has rowed many skiff races with first-class men, and has scarcely ever been beaten, but is too light to contend for the championship.

B.   John Clasper; very excellent oarsman; was drowned when young (æt. 19). He had won several small matches, and one important match with a man called Graham, and his fine style and excellent performances (considering his age) caused him to be looked upon as a rower of extraordinary promise.

B.   Robert Clasper; able oarsman.

[N.] Son of the above; is a good rower.

[B.] William; never pulled but as one of a crew; he was recently drowned.

[B.] Edward; has the disadvantage of having lost a leg.

[B.] (half-brother). Thomas; moderately good.

[u.] Edward Hawks; a fair rower.

      The father of the Clasper family was a keelman.

COOMBES, Robert; very excellent oarsman.

[S.] David; a good match rower.

[B.] Thomas; has always pulled as one of a crew.

COOPER, Robert.

[S.] He pulls well, but is not old enough for matches.

MADDISON, Antony.

[B.] James; a good rower.

MATFIN, Thomas. Unmarried.

B.   William. Unmarried.

RENFORTH, James; Champion rower of England. Unmarried.

[B.] Stephen; a fair rower. Unmarried.

SADLER, Joseph. Unmarried.

[B.] William. Unmarried.

TAYLOR, James; very excellent oarsman, the ablest of a remarkable family. He has rowed 112 races, alone and in
crews; 13 of these were skiff matches, and of these he
won 10.

B.   Matthew; a good rower. (He has a son who is a clever
rower, but not old enough for matches.)

3 B.   Thomas, William, and John; all good rowers; they have
only pulled in crews. All unmarried.

WINSHIP, Edward; very eminent oarsman. He is not a skiff
rower, but always rows in two- or four-oared races. He
was one of the crew who won the "Champion Fours"
at the Thames National Regatta in 1854, 1859, 1861, and
1862, and the "Champion Pairs" at the same Regatta in
1855, 1856, 1860, 1861, and 1862.

[B.]   Thomas; a good rower, also in crews.

I am wholly indebted for the information contained in this chapter, as I was for that in the last, to Mr. Robert Spence Watson. With the assistance of a well-informed champion wrestler, that gentleman has examined into the history of those of the 172 men of whom anything could be learnt, who were either first or second at Carlisle or Newcastle since the establishment of the championship at those places; at the first, in 1809, and at the second, in 1839.

It is exceedingly difficult to estimate the performances of the ancestors of the present generation, because there were scarcely any prizes in former days; matches were then made simply for honour. We must not expect to be able to trace ancestral gifts among the wrestlers to a greater degree than among the oarsmen.

I should add, that I made several attempts to obtain information on wrestling families in the Lake districts of Westmoreland and Cumberland, but entirely without success; no records seem to have been kept of the yearly meetings at Keswick and Bowness, and the wrestling deeds of past years have fallen out of mind.

There are eighteen families in my Appendix, containing between them forty-six wrestlers, and the relationships existing towards the ablest wrestler of the family are 1 F, 21 B, 7 S, and 1 n.

APPENDIX TO WRESTLERS OF THE NORTH COUNTRY

BLAIR, Matthew; winner of Decies prize at Newcastle in 1859 champion of 11 stone men at Newcastle in 1862.

B. Robert; winner of Decies prize at Newcastle in 1857.

BLAIR, Matthew—*continued*

B. Joseph; winner of Decies prize in 1861; 2d 11 stone man at Newcastle in 1862, and at Carlisle, 1863.

DALEY, Charles; champion 10½ stone, Newcastle, 1839.

B. John; 2d 10 stone, Newcastle, 1840 and 1842.

[B.] William; moderately good.

EWBANK, Noble; champion of all weights at Newcastle, 1858, 1859, 1860; champion of picked men at Newcastle, 1859; champion of all weights, Carlisle, 1858.

F. Joseph; champion of all weights at Newcastle, 1847.

[B.] Joseph; only a second-rate wrestler.

GLAISTER, William; champion, Newcastle, 11 stone, 1850; 2d all weights, Newcastle, 1851; 2d all weights, Carlisle, 1856.

B. George; very good.

GOLIGHTLY, Frank; a famous wrestler in the last century.

B. Tom; champion at Melmerby.

GORDON, Robert; champion all weights, Carlisle, 1836 and 1846; 2d, 1837, 1839, 1840, 1845, and 1848; champion all weights at Newcastle, 1846.

B. William; a good wrestler.

[B.] Thomas; tolerably good.

n. Robert Lowthian; champion lightweights Newcastle, 1855 and 1860.

HARRINGTON, Joseph; champion lightweights at Newcastle, 1844, 1853, 1854; champion 11 stone, Newcastle, 1855; 2d all weights at Newcastle, 1845.

B. Charles; champion lightweights, Newcastle, 1848; 2d, 1849.

S. James Scott.

IRVING, George; champion all weights, Carlisle, 1827 and 1828.

S. George; very good lightweight wrestler.

IVISON, Henry; a first-class man, but in old times, when the competition was less severe than now.

S. John; 2d for all weights at Newcastle, in 1842; champion of 10½ stone men at Newcastle, 1844; 2d 9½ stone men at Newcastle, 1850.

IVISON, Henry—*continued*

S.   Henry; 2d lightweights at Newcastle, 1852; 2d 11 stone men, ditto, 1856.

[S.]   James.

JAMIESON, James; champion lightweights at Carlisle, 1838; twice threw the champion of all weights the same year; 2d 11½ stone, Newcastle, 1843; and 10½ stone, 1845.

3B.   Robert, William, and George. All good wrestlers; among them they won all the prizes at Brampton, so that the wrestling there had to be given up. They challenged any four men in England of their weight.

LITTLE, John; champion all weights, Carlisle.

B.   James; 2d all weights, Carlisle, 1834.

LONG, Rowland; wrestled for 30 years, and won nearly 100 prizes.

B.   John, the best champion at Carlisle.

LOWTHIAN. *See* GORDON.

NICHOL, John; 2d all weights, Carlisle, 1832 and 1836.

[B.]   James; a good, though not a first-rate wrestler.

PALMER, John; champion of all weights at Carlisle in 1851, and champion of lightweights the same year,—a most unusual success.

2B.   Matthew and Walter; twins, both very good; not champions, but often second in great matches.

ROBLEY, Joseph; a very good wrestler.

B.   John; also a good wrestler.

S.   William; 2d all weights at Newcastle, 1848; champion heavystone men, 1852.

ROBSON, Thomas; champion all weights at Newcastle, 1857; champion 11 stone, 1858.

B.   William; equally good.

TINIAN, John, champion at Penrith. As a wrestler, boxer, runner, leaper, cudgel and football player, he never met an equal; was the greatest hero in athletic exercises England ever produced. *Wrestliana,* by W. Litt (himself an excellent wrestler), Whitehaven, 1823.

TINIAN, John—*continued*

B.   Job; nearly equal to his brother; he threw William Richardson, who afterwards won 240 belts and was champion.

S.   John; a remarkably good wrestler.

S.   Joseph; a more powerful man than his father.

[2S.] Other sons were good wrestlers, but none remarkably so.

TWEDDELL, Joseph; champion 10 stone, Newcastle, 1842; 2d, ditto, 1841; champion 11½ stone, Newcastle, 1843.

B.   Thomas; champion 10 stone, Newcastle, 1841.

B.   Richard; 2d 11½ stone, Newcastle, 1841.

B.   William; 2d 10½ stone, Newcastle, 1846.

WEARMOUTH, Launcelot; champion 11 stone men at Newcastle, 1860.

B.   Isaac; 2d 9½ stone men at Newcastle, 1859.

PART THREE

COMPARISON OF
RESULTS

COMPARISON OF RESULTS

Let us now bring our scattered results side to side, for the purpose of comparison, and judge of the extent to which they corroborate one another—how far they confirm the provisional calculations made in the chapter on JUDGES from more scanty data, and where and why they contrast.

The number of cases of hereditary genius analysed in the several chapters of my book, amounts to a large total. I have dealt with no less than 300 families containing between them nearly 1,000 eminent men, of whom 415 are illustrious, or, at all events, of such note as to deserve being printed in small capitals at the head of a paragraph. If there be such a thing as a decided law of distribution of genius in families, it is sure to become manifest when we deal statistically with so large a body of examples.

In comparing the results obtained from the different groups of eminent men, it will be our most convenient course to compare the columns B of the several tables.[1] Column B gives the number of eminent kinsmen in various degrees on the supposition that the number of families in the group to which it refers is 100. All the entries under B have therefore the same common measure, they are all *percentages*, and admit of direct intercomparison. I hope I have made myself quite clear: lest there should remain any misapprehension, it is better to give an example. Thus, the families of Divines are only 25 in number, and in those 25 families there are 7 eminent fathers, 9 brothers, and 10 sons; now in order to raise these numbers to percentages, 7, 9, and 10 must be multiplied by the number of times that 25 goes into 100, namely by 4. They will then become 28, 36, and 40, and will be found entered as such, in

[1] *I.e.* in TABLES II on pp. 102, 154, 195, 220, 246, 280 and 328.

column B, p. 328; the parent numbers 7, 9, 10, appearing in the same table in the column A.

In the following table, the columns B of all the different groups are printed side by side; I have, however, thrown Painters and Musicians into a single group of Artists, because their numbers were too small to make it worth while to consider them apart. Annexed to these is a column B calculated from the whole of the families put together, with the intention of giving a general average; and I have further attached to it its appropriate columns C and D, not so much for particular use in this chapter as for the convenience of the reader who may wish to make comparisons with the other tables, from the different point of view which D affords.

The general uniformity in the distribution of ability among the kinsmen in the different groups, is strikingly manifest. The eminent sons are almost invariably more numerous than the eminent brothers, and these are a trifle more numerous than the eminent fathers. On proceeding further down the table, we come to a sudden dropping off of the numbers at the second grade of kinship, namely, at the grandfathers, uncles, nephews, and grandsons: this diminution is conspicuous in the entries in column D, the meaning of which has already been fully described in pp. 119–122. On reaching the third grade of kinship, another abrupt dropping off in numbers is again met with, but the first cousins are found to occupy a decidedly better position than other relations within the third grade.

We further observe, that while the proportionate abundance of eminent kinsmen in the various grades is closely similar in all the groups, the proportions deduced from the entire body of illustrious men, 415 in number, coincide with peculiar general accuracy with those we obtained from the large subdivision of 109 Judges. There cannot, therefore, remain a doubt as to the existence of a law of distribution of ability in families, or that it is pretty accurately expressed by the figures in column B, under the heading of "eminent men of all classes." I do not, however, think it worth while to submit a diagram like that in p. 123, derived from the column D in the

	Separate Groups								All Groups together		
Number of families, each containing more than one eminent man	85	39	27	33	43	20	28	25	300		
Total number of eminent men in all the families	262	130	89	119	148	57	97	75	977		
	JUDGES, p. 55	STATESMEN, p. 103	COMMANDERS, p. 140	LITERARY, p. 163	SCIENTIFIC, p. 188	POETS, p. 220	ARTISTS, pp. 231 231 and 241	DIVINES, p. 865	Illustrious and Eminent Men of all Classes		
	B	B	B	B	B	B	B	B	B	C	D
Father	26	33	47	48	26	20	32	28	31	100	31
Brother	35	39	50	42	47	40	50	36	41	150	27
	36	49	31	51	60	45	89	40	48	100	48
Grandfather	15	28	16	24	14	5	7	20	17	200	8
Uncle	18	18	8	24	16	5	14	40	18	400	5
Nephew	19	18	35	24	23	50	18	4	22	400	5
Grandson	19	10	12	9	14	5	18	16	14	200	7
Great-grandfather	2	8	8	3	0	0	0	4	3	400	1
Great-uncle	4	5	8	6	5	5	7	4	5	800	1
First-cousin	11	21	20	18	16	0	1	8	13	800	2
Great-nephew	17	5	8	6	16	10	0	0	10	800	1
Great-grandson	6	0	0	3	7	0	0	0	3	400	1
All more remote	14	37	44	15	23	5	18	16	31	?	...

last table, because little dependence can be placed on the
entries in C by the help of which that column had to be calculated. When I began my inquiries, I did indeed try to obtain
real and not estimated data for C by inquiring into the total

numbers of kinsmen in each degree, of every illustrious man, as well as of those who achieved eminence. I wearied myself for a long time with searching biographies, but finding the results very disproportionate to the labour, and continually open to doubt after they had been obtained, I gave up the task, and resigned myself to the rough but ready method of estimated averages.

It is earnestly to be desired that breeders of animals would furnish tables, like mine, on the distribution of different marked physical qualities in families. The results would be far more than mere matters of curiosity; they would afford *constants* for formulæ by which, as I shall briefly show in a subsequent chapter, the laws of heredity, as they are now understood, may admit of being expressed.

In contrasting the columns B of the different groups, the first notable peculiarity that catches the eye is the small number of the sons of Commanders; they being 31, while the average of all the groups is 48. There is nothing anomalous in this irregularity. I have already shown, when speaking of the Commanders, that they usually begin their active careers in youth, and therefore, if married at all, they are mostly away from their wives on military service. It is also worth while to point out a few particular cases where exceptional circumstances stood in the way of the Commanders leaving male issue, because the total number of those included in my lists is so small, being only 32, as to make them of appreciable importance in affecting the results. Thus, Alexander the Great was continually engaged in distant wars, and died in early manhood: he had one posthumous son, but that son was murdered for political reasons when still a boy. Julius Cæsar, an exceedingly profligate man, left one illegitimate son, by Cleopatra, but that son was also murdered for political reasons when still a boy. Nelson married a widow who had no children by her former husband, and therefore was probably more or less infertile by nature. Napoleon I was entirely separated from Marie Louise after she had borne him one son.

Though the great Commanders have but few immediate

descendants, yet the number of their eminent grandsons is as great as any other groups. I ascribe this to the superiority of their breed, which ensures eminence to an unusually large proportion of their kinsmen.

The next exceptional entry in the table is, the number of eminent fathers of the great scientific men as compared with that of their sons, there being only 26 of the former to 60 of the latter, whereas the average of all the groups gives 31 and 48. I have already attempted to account for this by showing, first, that scientific men owe much to the training and to the blood of their mothers; and, secondly, that the first in the family who has scientific gifts is not nearly so likely to achieve eminence, as the descendant who is taught to follow science as a profession, and not to waste his powers on profitless speculations.

The next peculiarity in the table is, the small number of eminent fathers, in the group of Poets. This group is too small to make me attach much importance to the deviation; it may be mere accident.

The Artists are not a much larger group than the Poets, consisting as they do of only 28 families, but the number of their eminent sons is enormous and quite exceptional. It is 89, whereas the average of all the groups is only 48. The remarks I made about the descendant of a great scientific man prospering in science, more than his ancestor, are eminently true as regards Artists, for the fairly-gifted son of a great painter or musician is far more likely to become a professional celebrity, than another man who has equal natural ability, but is not especially educated for professional life. The large number of artists' sons who have become eminent, testifies to the strongly hereditary character of their peculiar ability, while, if the reader will turn to the account of the Herschel family, p. 267, he will readily understand that many persons may have decided artistic gifts who have adopted some other more regular, solid, or lucrative occupation.

I have now done with the exceptional cases; it will be observed that they are mere minor variations in the law expressed by the general average of all the groups; for, if we say that to every 10 illustrious men, *who have any eminent relations at all,* we find 3 or 4 eminent fathers, 4 or 5 eminent brothers, and 5 or 6 eminent sons, we shall be right in 17 instances out of 24; and in the 7 cases where we are wrong, the error will consist of less than 1 unit in 2 cases (the fathers of the commanders and men of literature), of 1 unit in 4 cases (the fathers of poets, and the sons of judges, commanders, and divines), and of more than 1 unit in the sole case of the sons of artists.

The deviations from the average are naturally greater in the second and third grades of kinship, because the numbers of instances in the several groups are generally small; but as the proportions in the large subdivision of the 85 Judges correspond with extreme closeness to those of the general average, we are perfectly justified in accepting the latter with confidence.

The final and most important result remains to be worked out; it is this: if we know nothing else about a person than that he is a father, brother, son, grandson, or other relation of an illustrious man, what is the chance that he is or will be eminent? Column E in p. 102 gives the reply for Judges; it remains for us to discover what it is for illustrious men generally. In each of the chapters I have given such data as I possessed, fit for combining with the results in column D, in order to make the required calculation. They consist of the proportion of men whose relations achieved eminence, compared with the total number into whose relationships I inquired. The general result[1] is, that exactly one-half of the illustrious men have one or more eminent relations. Consequently, if we divide the entries in column D, of "eminent men of all classes," p. 375, by 2, we shall obtain the corresponding column E.

---

[1] Lord Chancellors, p. 106, 24 in 30; Statesmen of George III, p. 155, 33 in 53; Premiers, p. 163, not included in the "Statesmen," 8 in 16; Commanders, p. 197, 32 in 59: Literary Men, p. 221, 37 in 56; Scientific Men. pp. 244, 249, 65 in 83; Poets, p. 280, 40 in 100; Musicians, p. 293, 26 in 100; Painters, p. 303, 18 in 42; Divines, pp. 327, 335, 33 in 196; Scholars, p. 354, 14 in 36. These proportions reduced to decimals are $0 \cdot 8$, $0 \cdot 6$ and $0 \cdot 5$, $0 \cdot 5$, $0 \cdot 7$, $0 \cdot 8$, $0 \cdot 4$, $0 \cdot 3$, $0 \cdot 4$, $0 \cdot 2$, $0 \cdot 4$; giving a general average of $0 \cdot 5$ or one-half.

The reader may, however, suspect the fairness of my selection. He may recollect my difficulty, avowed in many chapters, of finding suitable selections, and will suspect that I have yielded to the temptation of inserting more than a due share of favourable cases. And I cannot wholly deny the charge, for I can recollect a few names that probably occurred to me owing to the double or treble weight given to them, by the cumulated performances of two or three persons. Therefore I acknowledge it to be quite necessary, in the interests of truth, to appeal to some wholly independent selection of names; and will take for that purpose the saints, or whatever their right name may be, of the Comtist Calendar. Many of my readers will know to what I am referring; how Auguste Comte, desiring to found a "Religion of Humanity," selected a list of names, from those to whom human development was most indebted, and assigned the months to the most important, the weeks to the next class, and the days to the third. I have nothing whatever to do with Comtist doctrines in these pages: his disciples dislike Darwinism, and therefore cannot be expected to be favourable to many of the discussions in this book; so I have the more satisfaction in the independence of the testimony afforded by his Calendar to the truth of my views. Again, no one can doubt that Comte's selections are entirely original; for he was the last man to pin his faith upon that popular opinion which he aspired to lead. Every name in his Calendar was weighed, we may be sure, with scrupulous care, though, I dare say, with a rather crazy balance, before it was inserted in the place which he assigned for it.

The Calendar consists of 13 months, each containing 4 weeks. The following table gives the representatives of the 13 months in capital letters, and those of the 52 weeks in ordinary type. I have not thought it worth while to transcribe` the representatives of the several days. Those marked with a ★ are included in my appendices, as having eminent relations; those with a † might have been so included. It will be observed that there are from 10 to 20 persons of whose kinships we know nothing or next to nothing, and therefore they should be struck out of the list—such as Numa, Buddha, Homer, Phidias, Thales, Pythagoras, Archimedes, Appollonius, Hipparchus, St. Paul. Among the remaining 55 or 45 persons, no less than 27, or one-half, have eminent relations.

1. *Theocracy, initial*	†MOSES,—Numa, Buddha, †Confucius, Mahomet.
2. *Ancient poetry*	HOMER,—*Æschylus, Phidia, *Aristophanes, Virgil.
3. *Ancient philosophy*	ARISTOTLE,—Thales, Pythagoras, Socrates, Plato.
4. *Ancient science*	ARCHIMEDES,—†Hippocrates, Apollonius, Hipparchus, *Pliny the Elder.
5. *Military civilisation*	*CÆSAR,—Themistocles, *Alexander, *Scipio, Trajan.
6. *Catholicism*	ST. PAUL,—†St. Augustine, Hildebrand, St. Bernard, Bossuet.
7. *Feudal civilisation*	*CHARLEMAGNE,—Alfred, Godfrey, Innocent III, St. Louis.
8. *Modern epic*	DANTE,—*Aristio, Raphael, *Tasso, *Milton.
9. *Modern industry*	GUTTENBERG,—Columbus, Vaucanson, *Watt, †Montgolfier.
10. *Modern drama*	SHAKESPEARE,—Calderon, *Corneille, Molière, *Mozart.
11 *Modern philosophy*	DESCARTES,—*St. Thomas Aquinas, *Lord Bacon, *Leibnitz, Hume.
12. *Modern politics*	FREDERICK THE GREAT,—Louis XI, *William the Silent, *Richelieu, *Cromwell.
13. *Modern science*	BICHAT,—*Galilei, *Newton, Lavoisier, Gall.

It is singularly interesting to observe how strongly the results obtained from Comte's selection corroborate my own. I am sure, then, we shall be within the mark if we consider column D in the table, p. 375, to refer to the eminent kinsmen, not of the large group of illustrious and eminent men, but of the more select portion of illustrious men only, and then calculate our column E by dividing the entries under D by 2.

For example, I reckon the chances of kinsmen of illustrious men rising, or having risen, to eminence, to be $15\frac{1}{2}$ to 100 in the case of fathers, $13\frac{1}{2}$ to 100 in the case of brothers, 24 to 100 in the case of sons. Or, putting these and the remaining proportions into a more convenient form, we obtain the following results. In first grade: the chance of the father is 1 to 6; of each brother, 1 to 7; of each son, 1 to 4. In second grade: of each grandfather, 1 to 25; of each uncle, 1 to 40; of each nephew, 1 to 40; of each grandson, 1 to 29. In the third grade, the chance of each member, is about 1 to 200, excepting in the case of first cousins, where it is 1 to 100.

The large number of eminent descendants from illustrious men must not be looked upon as expressing the results of their marriage with mediocre women, for the average ability of the wives of such men is above mediocrity. This is my strong conviction, after reading very many biographies, although it clashes with a commonly expressed opinion that clever men marry silly women. It is not easy to prove my point without a considerable mass of quotations to show the estimation in which the wives of a large body of illustrious men were held by their intimate friends, but the two following arguments are not without weight. First, the lady whom a man marries is very commonly one whom he has often met in the society of his own friends, and therefore not likely to be a silly woman. She is also usually related to some of them, and therefore has a probability of being hereditarily gifted. Secondly, as a matter of fact, a large number of eminent men marry eminent women. If the reader runs his eye through my Appendices, he will find many such instances. Philip II of Macedon and Olympias; Cæsar's *liaison* with Cleopatra; Marlborough and his most able wife; Helvetius married a charming lady, whose hand was also sought by both Franklin and Turgot; August Wilhelm von Schlegel was heart and soul devoted to Madame de Staël; Necker's wife was a blue-stocking of the purest hue; Robert

Stephens, the learned printer, had Petronella for his wife; the Lord Keeper Sir Nicholas Bacon and the great Lord Burleigh married two of the highly accomplished daughters of Sir Anthony Cooke. Every one of these names, which I have taken from the Appendices to my chapters on Commanders, Statesmen, and Literary Men, are those of decidedly eminent women. They establish the existence of a tendency of "like to like" among intellectual men and women, and make it most probable, that the marriages of illustrious men with women of classes E and D are very common. On the other hand, there is no evidence of a strongly marked antagonistic taste—of clever men liking really half-witted women. A man may be conscious of serious defects in his character, and select a wife to supplement what he wants, as a shy man may be attracted by a woman who has no other merits than those of a talker and manager. Also, a young awkward philosopher may accredit the first girl who cares to show an interest in him, with greater intelligence than she possesses. But these are exceptional instances; the great fact remains that able men take pleasure in the society of intelligent women, and, if they can find such as would in other respects be suitable, they will marry them in preference to mediocrities.

I think, therefore, that the results given in my tables, under the head of "Sons," should be ascribed to the marriages of men of class F and above, with women whose natural gifts are, on the average, not inferior to those of class B, and possibly between B and C.

I will now contrast the power of the male and female lines of kinship in the transmission of ability, and for that purpose will reduce the actual figures into percentages.

As an example of the process, we may take the cases of the Judges. Here—as will be observed in the first table the actual figures corresponding to the specified varieties of kinship are 41, 16, 19, 1, making a total of 77; now I raise these to what they would be if this total were raised to 100; in short, I multiply them by 100 and divide by 77, which converts them into 53, 21, 25, 1; and these are the figures inserted in the second table.

ACTUAL FIGURES

	Judges	Statesmen	Commanders	Literary	Scientific	Poets	Artists	Divines	Totals
G.+U.+&c.	41	19	12	18	20	12	13	4	139
GF.+GB.+&c.	16	4	5	7	12	3	4	2	53
g.+u.+&c.	19	10	6	9	9	1	3	16	73
gF.+gB.+&c.	1	3	2	0	4	0	0	0	10
Total	77	36	25	34	45	16	20	22	275

PERCENTAGES

	Judges	Statesmen	Commanders	Literary	Scientific	Poets	Artists	Divines	Total
G.+U.+N.+P.	53	53	48	53	44	75	65	18	51
GF.+GB.+US.+NS.+PS. }	21	11	20	21	27	19	20	9	19
Total by male lines	74	64	68	74	71	94	85	27	70
g.+u.+n.+p.	25	28	24	26	20	6	15	73	26
gF.+gB.+uS.+nS.+pS. }	1	8	8	0	9	0	0	0	4
Total by female	26	36	32	26	29	6	15	73	30
Male and female	100	100	100	100	100	100	100	100	100

It will be observed that the ratio of the total kinships, through male and female lines, is almost identical in the first five columns, namely, in Judges, Statesmen, Commanders, Men of Literature, and Men of Science, and is as 70 to 30, or more than 2 to 1. The uniformity of this ratio is evidence of the existence of a law, but it is difficult to say upon what that law depends, because the ratios are different for different varieties of kinship. Thus—to confine ourselves to those in the second grade, which are sufficiently numerous to give averages on which dependence may be placed—we find that the sum of the ratios of G., U., N., P. to those of g., u., n., p., is also a little more than 2 to 1. Now, the actual figures are as follow:—

$$21\,G. \quad 23\,U. \quad 40\,N. \quad 26\,P. = 110 \text{ in all.}$$
$$21\,g. \quad 16\,u. \quad 10\,n. \quad 6\,p. = 53 \text{ in all.}$$

The first idea which will occur is, that the relative smallness of the numbers in the lower line appears only in those kinships which are most difficult to trace through female descent, and that the apparent inferiority is in exact proportion to that difficulty. Thus the parentage of a man's mother is invariably stated in his biography; consequently, an eminent g. is no less likely to be overlooked than a G.; but a u. is more likely to be overlooked than a U., and an n. and p. much more likely than an N. and P. However, the solution suggested by these facts is not wholly satisfactory, because the differences appear to be as great in the well-known families of the Statesmen and Commanders, as in the obscure ones of the Literary and Scientific men. It would seem from this and from what I shall have to say about the Divines, that I have hunted out the eminent kinsmen in these degrees, with pretty equal completeness, in both male and female lines.

The only reasonable solution which I can suggest, besides that of inherent incapacity in the female line for transmitting the peculiar forms of ability we are now discussing, is, that the aunts, sisters, and daughters of eminent men do not marry, on the average, so frequently as other women. They would be likely not to marry so much or so soon as other women, because they would be accustomed to a higher form of culture and intellectual and moral tone in their family circle, than they could easily find elsewhere, especially if, owing to the narrowness of their means, their society were restricted to the persons in their immediate neighbourhood. Again, one portion of them would certainly be of a dogmatic and self-asserting type, and therefore unattractive to men, and others would fail to attract, owing to their having shy, odd manners, often met with in young persons of genius, which are disadvantageous to the matrimonial chances of young women. It will be observed, in corroboration of this theory, that it accounts for g. being as large as G., because a man must have an equal number of g. and G., but he need not have an equal number u., n., p., and U., N., P. Owing to want of further information, I am compelled to leave this question somewhat undecided. If my column c of the tables had been based on facts instead of on estimate, those facts would have afforded the information I want.

In the case of Poets and Artists, the influence of the female line is enormously less than the male, and in these the solution I have suggested would be even more appropriate than in the previous groups.

Among the Divines we come to a wholly new order of things. Here, the proportions are simply inverted, the female influence being to the male as 73 to 27, instead of as, in the average of the first five columns, 30 to 70. I have already, in the chapter on Divines, spoken at so much length about the power of female influence in nurturing religious dispositions, that I need not recur to that question. As regards the presumed disinclination to marriage among the female relatives of eminent men generally, an exception must certainly be made in the case of those of the Divines. They consider intellectual ability and a cultured mind of small importance compared with pious professions, and as religious society is particularly large, owing to habits of association for religious purposes, the necessity of choosing a pious husband is no material hindrance to the marriage of a near female relation of an eminent divine.

N

There is a common opinion that great men have remarkable mothers. No doubt they are largely indebted to maternal influences, but the popular belief ascribes an undue and incredible share to them. I account for the belief, by the fact that great men have usually high moral natures, and are affectionate and reverential, inasmuch as mere brain without heart is insufficient to achieve eminence. Such men are naturally disposed to show extreme filial regard, and to publish the good qualities of their mothers, with exaggerated praise.

I regret I am unable to solve the simple question whether, and how far, men and women who are prodigies of genius, are infertile. I have, however, shown, that men of eminence, such as the Judges, are by no means so, and it will be seen, from my point of view of the future of the human race, as described in a subsequent chapter, that the fertility of eminent men is a more important fact for me to establish, than that of prodigies. There are many difficulties in the way of discovering whether genius, is, or is not, correlated with infertility. One—and a very serious one—is that people will not agree upon the names of those who are pre-eminently men of genius, nor even upon the definition of the word. Another is, that the men selected as examples are usually ancients, or at all events those who lived so long ago that it is often impossible, and always very difficult, to learn anything about their families. Another difficulty lies in the fact, that a man who has no children is likely to do more for his profession, and to devote himself more thoroughly to the good of the public, than if he had them. A very gifted man will almost always rise, as I believe, to eminence; but if he is handicapped with the weight of a wife and children in the race of life, he cannot be expected to keep as much in the front as if he were single. He cannot pursue his favourite subject of study with the same absorbing passion as if he had no other pressing calls on his attention, no domestic sorrows, anxieties, and petty cares, no yearly child, no periodical infantine epidemics, no constant professional toil for the maintenance of a large family.

There are other obstacles in the way of leaving descendants

in the second generation. The daughters would not be so likely as other girls to marry, for the reasons stated a few pages back; while the health of the sons is liable to be ruined by over-work. The sons of gifted men are decidedly more precocious than their parents, as a reference to my Appendices will distinctly show; I do not care to quote cases, because it is a normal fact, analogous to what is observed in diseases, and in growths of all kinds, as has been clearly laid down by Mr. Darwin. The result is, that the precocious child is looked upon as a prodigy, abler even than his parent, because the parent's abilities at the same age were less, and he is pushed forward in every way by home influences, until serious harm is done to his constitution.

So much for the difficulties in the way of arriving at a right judgment on the question before us. Most assuredly, a surprising number of the ablest men appear to have left no descendants; but we are justified, from what I have said, in ascribing a very considerable part of the adduced instances to other causes than an inherent tendency to barrenness in men and women of genius. I believe there is a large residuum which must so be ascribed, and I agree thus far with the suggestion of Prosper Lucas, that, as giants and dwarfs are rarely prolific, so men of prodigiously large or small intellectual powers may be expected to be deficient in fertility. On the other hand, I utterly disagree with the assertion of that famous author on heredity, that true genius is invariably isolated.

There is a prevalent belief somewhat in accordance with the subject of the last paragraph but one, that men of genius are unhealthy, puny beings—all brain and no muscle—weak-sighted, and generally of poor constitutions. I think most of my readers would be surprised at the stature and physical frames of the heroes of history, who fill my pages, if they could be assembled together in a hall. I would undertake to pick out of any group of them, even out of that of the Divines (see pp. 323, 324), an "eleven" who should compete in any physical feats whatever, against similar selections from groups of twice or thrice their numbers, taken at haphazard from equally well-fed classes. In the notes I made, previous to writing this book,

I had begun to make memoranda of the physical gifts of my heroes, and regret now, that I did not continue the plan, but there is even almost enough printed in the Appendices to warrant my assertion. I do not deny that many men of extraordinary mental gifts have had wretched constitutions, but deny them to be an essential or even the usual accompaniment. University facts are as good as any others to serve as examples, so I will mention that both high wranglers and high classics have been frequently the first oarsmen of their years. The Hon. George Denman, who was senior classic in 1842, was the stroke of the University crew. Sir William Thompson, the second wrangler in 1845, won the sculls. In the very first boat-race between the two Universities, three men who afterwards became bishops rowed in one of the contending boats, and another rowed in the other. It is the second and third-rate students who are usually weakly. A collection of living magnates in various branches of intellectual achievement is always a feast to my eyes; being, as they are, such massive, vigorous, capable-looking animals.

I took some pains to investigate the law of mortality in the different groups, and drew illustrative curves in order to see whether there was anything abnormal in the constitutions of eminent men, and this result certainly came out, which goes far to show that the gifted men consist of two categories— the very weak and the very strong. It was, that the curve of mortality does not make a single bend, but it rises to a minor culminating point, and then, descending again, takes a fresh departure for its principal arc. There is a want of continuity in the regularity of its sweep. I conclude that among the gifted men, there is a small class who have weak and excitable constitutions, who are destined to early death, but that the remainder consists of men likely to enjoy a vigorous old age.

This double culmination was strongly marked in the group of Artists, and distinctly so in that of the Poets, but it came out with most startling definition when I laid out the cases, of which I had made notes, 92 in number, of men remarkable for their precocity. Their first culmination was at the age of 38, then the death-rate sank till the age of 42; at 52 it had again risen to what it was at 38, and it attained its maximum at 64. The mortality of the men who did not appear to have been eminently precocious, 180 cases in all, followed a perfectly normal curve, rising steadily to a maximum at 68 years, and then declining as steadily. The scientific men lived the longest, and the number of early deaths among them was decidedly less than in any of the other groups.

The last general remark I have to make is, that features and mental abilities do not seem to be correlated. The son may resemble his parent in being an able man, but it does not therefore follow that he will also resemble him in features. I know of families where the children who had not the features of their parents inherited their disposition and ability, and the remaining children had just the converse gifts. In looking at the portraits in the late National Exhibitions I was extremely struck with the absence of family likeness, in cases where I had expected to find it. I cannot prove this point without illustrations; the reader must therefore permit me to leave its evidence in an avowedly incomplete form.

In concluding this chapter, I may point out some of the groups that I have omitted to discuss. The foremost Engineers are a body of men possessed of remarkable natural qualities; they are not only able men, but are also possessed of singular powers of physical endurance and of boldness, combined with clear views of what can and what cannot be effected. I have included Watt and Stephenson among the men of science, but the Brunels, and the curious family of Mylne, going back for nine, if not twelve generations,—all able and many eminent in their professions,—and several others, deserve notice. I do not, however, see my way to making a selection of eminently gifted engineers, because their success depends, in a very great degree, on early opportunities. If a great engineering business is once established, with well-selected men at the heads of its various departments, it is easy to keep up the name and credit for more than one generation after the death of its gifted originator.

The Actors are very closely connected—so much so as to form a caste; but here, as with the Engineers, we have great difficulty in distinguishing the eminently gifted from those whose success is largely due to the accident of education. I do not, however, like to pass them over without a notice of the Kemble family, who filled so large a space in the eyes of the British world, two generations ago. The following is their pedigree:—

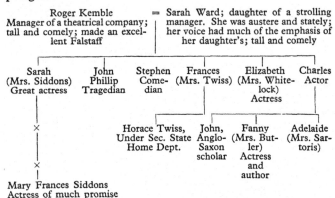

I was desirous of obtaining facts bearing on heredity from China, for there the system of examination is notoriously strict and far-reaching, and boys of promise are sure to be passed on from step to step, until they have reached the highest level of which they are capable. The first honour of the year in a population of some 400 millions—the senior classic and senior wrangler rolled into one—is the "Chuan-Yuan." Are the Chuan-Yuans ever related together? is a question I have asked, and to which a reply was promised me by a friend of high distinction in China, but which has not reached me up to the time I am writing these lines. However, I put a question on the subject into the pages of the Hong-Kong *Notes and Queries* (Aug. 1868), and found at all events one case, of a woman who, after bearing a child who afterwards became a Chuan-Yuan, was divorced from her husband, but marrying again, she bore a second child, who also became a Chuan-Yuan, to her next husband.

I feel the utmost confidence that if the question of hereditary genius were thoroughly gone into by a competent person, China would be found to afford a perfect treasury of facts bearing upon it. There is, however, a considerable difficulty in making these inquiries, arising from the paucity of surnames in China, and also from the necessity of going back to periods (and there are many such) when corruption was far less rife in China than it is at present.

The records of the Olympian Games in the palmy days of Greece, which were scrupulously kept by the Eleans, would have been an excellent mine to dig into for facts bearing on heredity; but they are not now to be had. However, I find one incidental circumstance in their history that is worth a few lines of notice. It appears, there was a single instance of a married woman having ventured to be present while the games were going on, although death was the penalty of the attempt. She was found out, but excused, because her father, brothers, and son had all been victors.

THE COMPARATIVE WORTH OF DIFFERENT

RACES

I have now completed what I had to say concerning the kinships of individuals, and proceed, in this chapter, to attempt a wider treatment of my subject, through a consideration of nations and races.

Every long-established race has necessarily its peculiar fitness for the conditions under which it has lived, owing to the sure operation of Darwin's law of natural selection. However, I am not much concerned, for the present, with the greater part of those aptitudes, but only with such as are available in some form or other of high civilisation. We may reckon upon the advent of a time when civilisation, which is now sparse and feeble and far more superficial than it is vaunted to be, shall overspread the globe. Ultimately it is sure to do so, because civilisation is the necessary fruit of high intelligence when found in a social animal, and there is no plainer lesson to be read off the face of Nature than that the result of the operation of her laws is to evoke intelligence in connexion with sociability. Intelligence is as much an advantage to an animal as physical strength or any other natural gift, and therefore, out of two varieties of any race of animal who are equally endowed in other respects, the most intelligent variety is sure to prevail in the battle of life. Similarly, among intelligent animals, the most social race is sure to prevail, other qualities being equal.

Under even a very moderate form of material civilisation a vast number of aptitudes acquired through the "survivorship of the fittest" and the unsparing destruction of the unfit, for hundreds of generations, have become as obsolete as the old mail-coach habits and customs, since the establishment of railroads, and there is not the slightest use in attempting to preserve them; they are hindrances, and not gains, to civilisation. I shall refer to some of these a little further on, but I will first speak of the qualities needed in civilised society. They are, speaking generally, such as will enable a race to supply a large contingent to the various groups of eminent men, of whom I have treated in my several chapters. Without going so far as to say that this very convenient test is perfectly fair, we are at all events justified in making considerable use of it, as I will do, in the estimates I am about to give.

In comparing the worth of different races, I shall make frequent use of the law of deviation from an average, to which I have already been much beholden; and, to save the reader's time and patience, I propose to act upon an assumption that would require a good deal of discussion to limit, and to which the reader may at first demur, but which cannot lead to any error of importance in a rough provisional inquiry. I shall assume that the *intervals* between the grades of ability are the *same* in all the races—that is, if the ability of class A of one race be equal to the ability of class C in another, then the ability of class B of the former shall be supposed equal to that of class D of the latter, and so on. I know this cannot be strictly true, for it would be in defiance of analogy if the variability of all races were precisely the same; but, on the other hand, there is good reason to expect that the error introduced by the assumption cannot sensibly affect the off-hand results for which alone I propose to employ it; moreover, the rough data I shall adduce, will go far to show the justice of this expectation.

Let us, then, compare the Negro race with the Anglo-Saxon, with respect to those qualities alone which are capable of producing judges, statesmen, commanders, men of literature and science, poets, artists, and divines. If the negro race in America had been affected by no social disabilities, a comparison of their achievements with those of the whites in their several branches of intellectual effort, having regard to the total number of their respective populations, would give the necessary information. As matters stand, we must be content with much rougher data.

First, the negro race has occasionally, but very rarely, produced such men as Toussaint l'Ouverture, who are of our class F; that is to say, its X, or its total classes above G, appear to correspond with our F, showing a difference of not less than two grades between the black and white races, and it may be more.

Secondly, the negro race is by no means wholly deficient in men capable of becoming good factors, thriving merchants, and otherwise considerably raised above the average of whites —that is to say, it cannot unfrequently supply men corresponding to our class C, or even D. It will be recollected that C implies a selection of 1 in 16, or somewhat more than the natural abilities possessed by average foremen of common juries, and that D is as 1 in 64—a degree of ability that is sure to make a man successful in life. In short, classes E and F of the negro may roughly be considered as the equivalent of our C and D—a result which again points to the conclusion, that the average intellectual standard of the negro race is some two grades below our own.

Thirdly, we may compare, but with much caution, the relative position of negroes in their native country with that of the travellers who visit them. The latter, no doubt, bring with them the knowledge current in civilised lands, but that is an advantage of less importance than we are apt to suppose. A native chief has as good an education in the art of ruling men as can be desired; he is continually exercised in personal government, and usually maintains his place by the ascendency of his character, shown every day over his subjects and rivals. A traveller in wild countries also fills, to a certain degree, the position of a commander, and has to confront native chiefs at every inhabited place. The result is familiar enough—the white traveller almost invariably holds his own in their presence. It is seldom that we hear of a white traveller meeting with a black chief whom he feels to be the better man. I have often discussed this subject with competent persons, and can only recall a few cases of the inferiority of the white man,—certainly not more than might be ascribed to an average actual difference of three grades, of which one may be due to the relative demerits of native education, and the remaining two to a difference in natural gifts.

Fourthly, the number among the negroes of those whom we should call half-witted men is very large. Every book alluding to negro servants in America is full of instances. I was myself much impressed by this fact during my travels in Africa. The mistakes the negroes made in their own matters were so childish, stupid, and simpleton-like, as frequently to make me ashamed of my own species. I do not think it any exaggeration to say, that their c is as low as our e, which would be a difference of two grades, as before. I have no information as to actual idiocy among the negroes—I mean, of course, of that class of idiocy which is not due to disease.

The Australian type is at least one grade below the African negro. I possess a few serviceable data about the natural capacity of the Australian, but not sufficient to induce me to invite the reader to consider them.

The average standard of the Lowland Scotch and the English North-country men is decidedly a fraction of a grade superior to that of the ordinary English, because the number of the former who attain to eminence is far greater than the proportionate number of their race would have led us to expect. The same superiority is distinctly shown by a comparison of the well-being of the masses of the population; for the Scotch labourer is much less of a drudge than the Englishman of the Midland counties—he does his work better, and "lives his life" besides. The peasant women of Northumberland work all day in the fields, and are not broken down by the work; on the contrary they take a pride in their effective labour as girls, and, when married, they attend well to the comfort of their homes. It is perfectly distressing to me to witness the draggled, drudged, mean look of the mass of individuals, especially of the women, that one meets in the streets of London and other purely English towns. The conditions of their life seem too hard for their constitutions, and to be crushing them into degeneracy.

The ablest race of whom history bears record is unquestionably the ancient Greek, partly because their master-pieces in the principal departments of intellectual activity are still unsurpassed, and in many respects unequalled, and partly because the population that gave birth to the creators of those master-pieces was very small. Of the various Greek sub-races, that of Attica was the ablest, and she was no doubt largely indebted to the following cause for her superiority. Athens opened her arms to immigrants, but not indiscriminately, for her social life was such that none but very able men could take any pleasure in it; on the other hand, she offered attractions such as men of the highest ability and culture could find in no other city. Thus, by a system of partly unconscious selection, she built up a magnificent breed of human animals, which, in the space of one century—viz. between 530 and 430 B.C.—produced the following illustrious persons, fourteen in number:—

Statesmen and Commanders—Themistocles (mother an alien), Miltiades, Aristeides, Cimon (son of Miltiades), Pericles (son of Xanthippus, the victor at Mycale).

Literary and Scientific Men—Thucydides, Socrates, Xenophon, Plato.

Poets—Æschylus, Sophocles, Euripides, Aristophanes.

Sculptor—Phidias.

We are able to make a closely-approximate estimate of the population that produced these men, because the number of the inhabitants of Attica has been a matter of frequent inquiry, and critics appear at length to be quite agreed in the general results. It seems that the little district of Attica contained, during its most flourishing period (Smith's *Class. Geog. Dict.*), less than 90,000 native free-born persons, 40,000 resident aliens, and a labouring and artisan population of 40,000 slaves. The first item is the only one that concerns us here, namely, the 90,000 free-born persons. Again, the common estimate that population renews itself three times in a century is very close to the truth, and may be accepted in the present case. Consequently, we have to deal with a total population of 270,000 free-born persons, or 135,000 males, born in the century I have named. Of these, about one-half, or 67,500, would survive the age of 26, and one third, or 45,000 would survive that of 50. As 14 Athenians became illustrious, the selection is only as 1 to 4,822 in respect to the former limitation, and as 1 to 3,214 in respect to the latter. Referring to the table in page 75, it will be seen that this degree of selection corresponds very fairly to the classes F (1 in 4,300) and above, of the Athenian race. Again, as G is one-sixteenth or one-seventeenth as numerous as F, it would be reasonable to expect to find one of class G among the fourteen; we might, however, by accident, meet with two, three, or even four of that class—say Pericles, Socrates, Plato, and Phidias.

Now let us attempt to compare the Athenian standard of ability with that of our own race and time. We have no men to put by the side of Socrates and Phidias, because the millions of all Europe, breeding as they have done for the subsequent 2,000 years, have never produced their equals. They are, therefore, two or three grades above our G—they might rank as I or J. But, supposing we do not count them at all, saying that some freak of nature acting at that time may have produced them, what must we say about the rest? Pericles and Plato would rank, I suppose, the one among the greatest of philosophical statesmen, and the other as at least the equal of Lord Bacon. They would, therefore, stand somewhere among our unclassed X, one or two grades above G—let us call them between H and I. All the remainder—the F of the Athenian race—would rank above our G, and equal to or close upon our H. It follows from all this, that the average ability of the Athenian race is, on the lowest possible estimate, very nearly two grades higher than our own—that is, about as much as our race is above that of the African Negro. This estimate, which may seem prodigious to some, is confirmed by the quick intelligence and high culture of the Athenian commonalty, before whom literary works were recited and works of art exhibited, of a far more severe character than could possibly be appreciated by the average of our race, the calibre of whose intellect is easily gauged by a glance at the contents of a railway book-stall.

We know, and may guess something more, of the reason why this marvellously-gifted race declined. Social morality grew exceedingly lax; marriage became unfashionable, and was avoided; many of the more ambitious and accomplished women were avowed courtesans, and consequently infertile, and the mothers of the incoming population were of a heterogeneous class. In a small sea-bordered country, where emigration and immigration are constantly going on, and where the manners are as dissolute as were those of Greece in the period of which I speak, the purity of a race would necessarily fail. It can be, therefore, no surprise to us, though it has been a severe misfortune to humanity, that the high Athenian breed decayed and disappeared; for if it had maintained its excellence, and had multiplied and spread over large countries, displacing inferior populations (which it well might have done, for it was naturally very prolific), it would assuredly have accomplished results advantageous to human civilisation, to a degree that transcends our powers of imagination.

If we could raise the average standard of our race only one grade, what vast changes would be produced! The number of men of natural gifts equal to those of the eminent men of the present day, would be necessarily increased more than tenfold, as will be seen by the fourth column of the table p. 75, because there would be 2,423 of them in each million instead of only 233; but far more important to the progress of civilisation would be the increase in the yet higher orders of intellect. We know how intimately the course of events is dependent on the thoughts of a few illustrious men. If the first-rate men in the different groups had never been born, even if those among them who have a place in my Appendices on account of their hereditary gifts, had never existed, the world would be very different to what it is. Now the table shows that the numbers in these, the loftiest grades of intellect, would be increased in a still higher proportion than that of which I have been speaking; thus the men that now rank under class G would be increased seventeenfold, by raising the average ability of the whole nation a single grade. We see by the table that all England contains (on the average, of course, of several years) only six men between the ages of thirty and eighty, whose natural gifts exceed class G; but in a country of the same population as ours, whose average was one grade higher, there would be eighty-two of such men; and in another whose average was two grades higher (such as I believe the Athenian to have been, in the interval 530–430 B.C.) no less than 1,355 of them would be found. There is no improbability in so gifted a breed being able to maintain itself, as Athenian experience, rightly understood, has sufficiently proved; and as has also been proved by what I have written about the Judges, whose fertility is undoubted, although their average natural ability is F, or $5\frac{1}{2}$ degrees above the average of our own, and $3\frac{1}{2}$ above that of the average Athenians.

It seems to me most essential to the well-being of future generations, that the average standard of ability of the present time should be raised. Civilisation is a new condition imposed upon man by the course of events, just as in the history of geological changes new conditions have continually been imposed on different races of animals. They have had the effect either of modifying the nature of the races through the process of natural selection whenever the changes were sufficiently slow and the race sufficiently pliant, or of destroying them altogether when the changes were too abrupt or the race unyielding. The number of the races of mankind that have been entirely destroyed under the pressure of the requirements of an incoming civilisation, reads us a terrible lesson. Probably in no former period of the world has the destruction of the races of any animal whatever been effected over such wide areas and with such startling rapidity as in the case of savage man. In the North American Continent, in the West Indian Islands, in the Cape of Good Hope, in Australia, New Zealand, and Van Diemen's Land, the human denizens of vast regions have been entirely swept away in the short space of three centuries, less by the pressure of a stronger race than through the influence of a civilisation they were incapable of supporting. And we too, the foremost labourers in creating this civilisation, are beginning to show ourselves incapable of keeping pace with our own work. The needs of centralisation, communication, and culture, call for more brains and mental stamina than the average of our race possess. We are in crying want for a greater fund of ability in all stations of life; for neither the classes of statesmen, philosophers, artisans, nor labourers are up to the modern complexity of their several professions. An extended civilisation like ours comprises more interests than the ordinary statesmen or philosophers of our present race are capable of dealing with, and it exacts more intelligent work than our ordinary artisans and labourers are capable of performing. Our race is over-weighted, and appears likely to be drudged into degeneracy by demands that exceed its powers. If its average ability were raised a grade or two, our new classes F and G would conduct the complex affairs of the state at home and abroad as easily as our present F and G, when in the position of country squires, are able to manage the affairs of their establishments and tenantry. All other classes of the community would be similarly promoted to the level of the work required by the nineteenth century, if the average standard of the race were raised.

When the severity of the struggle for existence is not too great for the powers of the race, its action is healthy and conservative, otherwise it is deadly, just as we may see exemplified in the scanty, wretched vegetation that leads a precarious existence near the summer snow line of the Alps, and disappears altogether a little higher up. We want as much backbone as we can get, to bear the racket to which we are henceforth to be exposed, and as good brains as possible to contrive machinery, for modern life to work more smoothly than at present. We can, in some degree, raise the nature of a man to a level with the new conditions imposed upon his existence, and we can also, in some degree, modify the conditions to suit his nature. It is clearly right that both these powers should be exerted, with the view of bringing his nature and the conditions of his existence into as close harmony as possible.

In proportion as the world becomes filled with mankind, the relations of society necessarily increase in complexity, and the nomadic disposition found in most barbarians becomes unsuitable to the novel conditions. There is a most unusual unanimity in respect to the causes of incapacity of savages for civilisation, among writers on those hunting and migratory nations who are brought into contact with advancing colonisation, and perish, as they invariably do, by the contact. They tell us that the labour of such men is neither constant nor steady; that the love of a wandering, independent life prevents their settling anywhere to work, except for a short time, when urged by want and encouraged by kind treatment. Meadows says that the Chinese call the barbarous races on their borders by a phrase which means "hither and thither, not fixed." And any amount of evidence might be adduced to show how deeply Bohemian habits of one kind or another were ingrained in the nature of the men who inhabited most parts of the earth now overspread by the Anglo-Saxon and other civilised races. Luckily there is still room for adventure, and a man who feels the cravings of a roving, adventurous spirit to be too strong for resistance, may yet find a legitimate outlet for it in the colonies, in the army, or on board ship. But such a spirit is, on the whole, an heirloom that brings more impatient restlessness and beating of the wings against cage-bars, than persons of more civilised characters can readily comprehend, and it is directly at war with the more modern portion of our moral natures. If a man be purely a nomad, he has only to be nomadic, and his instinct is satisfied; but no Englishmen of the nineteenth century are purely nomadic. The most so among them have also inherited many civilised cravings that are necessarily starved when they become wanderers, in the same way as the wandering instincts are starved when they are settled at home. Consequently their nature has opposite wants, which can never be satisfied except by chance, through some very exceptional turn of circumstances. This is a serious calamity, and as the Bohemianism in the nature of our race is destined to perish, the sooner it goes the happier for mankind. The social requirements of English life are steadily destroying it. No man who only works by fits and starts is able to obtain his living nowadays; for he has not a chance of thriving in competition with steady workmen. If his nature revolts against the monotony of daily labour, he is tempted to the public-house, to intemperance, and, it may be, to poaching, and to much more serious crime; otherwise he banishes himself from our shores. In the first case, he is unlikely to leave as many children as men of more domestic and marrying habits, and, in the second case, his breed is wholly lost to England. By this steady riddance of the Bohemian spirit of our race, the artisan part of our population is slowly becoming bred to its duties, and the primary qualities of the typical modern British workman are already the very opposite of those of the nomad. What they are now, was well described by Mr. Chadwick as consisting of "great bodily strength, applied under the command of a steady, persevering will, mental self-contentedness, impassibility to external irrelevant impressions, which carries them through the continued repetition of toilsome labour, 'steady as time.'"

It is curious to remark how unimportant to modern civilisation has become the once famous and thoroughbred looking Norman. The type of his features, which is, probably, in some degree correlated with his peculiar form of adventurous disposition, is no longer characteristic of our rulers, and is rarely found among celebrities of the present day; it is more often met with among the undistinguished members of highly-born families, and especially among the less conspicuous officers of the army. Modern leading men in all paths of eminence, as may easily be seen in a collection of photographs, are of a coarser and more robust breed; less excitable and dashing, but endowed with far more ruggedness and real vigour. Such also is the case as regards the German portion of the Austrian nation; they are far more high-caste in appearance than the

Prussians, who are so plain that it is disagreeable to travel northwards from Vienna and watch the change; yet the Prussians appear possessed of the greater moral and physical stamina.

Much more alien to the genius of an enlightened civilisation than the nomadic habit, is the impulsive and uncontrolled nature of the savage. A civilised man must bear and forbear, he must keep before his mind the claims of the morrow as clearly as those of the passing minute; of the absent, as well as of the present. This is the most trying of the new conditions imposed on man by civilisation, and the one that makes it hopeless for any but exceptional natures among savages, to live under them. The instinct of a savage is admirably consonant with the needs of savage life; every day he is in danger through transient causes; he lives from hand to mouth, in the hour and for the hour, without care for the past or forethought for the future: but such an instinct is utterly at fault in civilised life. The half-reclaimed savage, being unable to deal with more subjects of consideration than are directly before him, is continually doing acts through mere maladroitness and incapacity, at which he is afterwards deeply grieved and annoyed. The nearer inducements always seem to him, through his uncorrected sense of moral perspective, to be incomparably larger than others of the same actual size, but more remote; consequently, when the temptation of the moment has been yielded to and passed away, and its bitter result comes in its turn before the man, he is amazed and remorseful at his past weakness. It seems incredible that he should have done that yesterday which to-day seems so silly, so unjust, and so unkindly. The newly-reclaimed barbarian, with the impulsive, unstable nature of the savage, when he also chances to be gifted with a peculiarly generous and affectionate disposition, is of all others the man most oppressed with the sense of sin.

Now it is a just assertion, and a common theme of moralists of many creeds, that man, such as we find him, is born with an imperfect nature. He has lofty aspirations, but there is a weakness in his disposition, which incapacitates him from carrying his nobler purposes into effect. He sees that some particular course of action is his duty and should be his delight; but his inclinations are fickle and base, and do not conform to his better judgment. The whole moral nature of man is tainted with sin, which prevents him from doing the things he knows to be right.

The explanation I offer of this apparent anomaly, seems perfectly satisfactory from a scientific point of view. It is neither more nor less than that the development of our nature, whether under Darwin's law of natural selection, or through the effects of changed ancestral habits, has not kept pace with the development of our moral civilisation. Man was barbarous but yesterday, and therefore it is not to be expected that the natural aptitudes of his race should already have become moulded into accordance with his very recent advance. We, men of the present centuries, are like animals suddenly transplanted among new conditions of climate and of food: our instincts fail us under the altered circumstances.

My theory is confirmed by the fact that the members of old civilisations are far less sensible than recent converts from barbarism, of their nature being inadequate to their moral needs. The conscience of a negro is aghast at his own wild, impulsive nature, and is easily stirred by a preacher, but it is scarcely possible to ruffle the self-complacency of a steady-going Chinaman.

The sense of original sin would show, according to my theory, not that man was fallen from a high estate, but that he was rising in moral culture with more rapidity than the nature of his race could follow. My view is corroborated by the conclusion reached at the end of each of the many independent lines of ethnological research—that the human race were utter savages in the beginning; and that, after myriads of years of barbarism, man has but very recently found his way into the paths of morality and civilisation.

INFLUENCES THAT AFFECT THE
NATURAL ABILITY OF NATIONS

Before speaking of the influences which affect the natural ability and intelligence of nations and races I must beg the reader to bring distinctly before his mind how reasonable it is that such influences should be expected to exist. How consonant it is to all analogy and experience to expect that the control of the nature of future generations should be as much within the power of the living, as the health and well-being of the individual is in the power of the guardians of his youth.

We are exceedingly ignorant of the reasons why we exist, confident only that individual life is a portion of some vaster system that struggles arduously onwards towards ends that are dimly seen or wholly unknown to us, by means of the various affinities—the sentiments, the intelligences, the tastes, the appetites—of innumerable personalities who ceaselessly succeed one another on the stage of existence.

There is nothing that appears to assign a more exceptional or sacred character to a race, than to the families or individuals that compose it. We know how careless Nature is of the lives of individuals; we have seen how careless she is of eminent families—how they are built up, flourish, and decay: just the same may be said of races, and of the world itself; also, by analogy, of other scenes of existence than this particular planet of one of innumerable suns. Our world appears hitherto to have developed itself, mainly under the influence of unreasoning affinities; but of late, Man, slowly growing to be intelligent, humane, and capable, has appeared on the scene of life and profoundly modified its conditions. He has already become able to look after his own interests in an incomparably more far-sighted manner, than in the old pre-historic days of barbarism and flint knives; he is already able to act on the experiences of the past, to combine closely with distant allies, and to prepare for future wants, known only through the intelligence, long before their pressure has become felt. He has introduced a vast deal of civilisation and hygiene which influence, in an immense degree, his own well-being and that of his children; it remains for him to bring other policies into action, that shall tell on the natural gifts of his race.

It would be writing to no practically useful purpose, were I to discuss the effect that might be produced on the population, by such social arrangements as existed in Sparta. They are so alien and repulsive to modern feelings, that it is useless to say anything about them, so I shall wholly confine my remarks to agencies that are actually at work, and upon which there can be no hesitation in speaking.

I shall have occasion to show that certain influences retard the average age of marriage, while others hasten it; and the general character of my argument will be to prove, that an enormous effect upon the average natural ability of a race may be produced by means of those influences. I shall argue that the wisest policy is that which results in retarding the average age of marriage among the weak, and in hastening it among the vigorous classes; whereas, most unhappily for us, the influence of numerous social agencies has been strongly and banefully exerted in the precisely opposite direction.

An estimate of the effect of the average age of marriage on the growth of any section of a nation, is therefore the first subject that requires investigation. Everybody is prepared to admit that it is an element, sure to produce some sensible effect, but few will anticipate its real magnitude or will be disposed to believe that its results have so vast and irresistible an influence on the natural ability of a race, as I shall be able to demonstrate.

The average age of marriage affects population in a three-fold manner. Firstly, those who marry when young have the larger families; secondly, they produce more generations within a given period, and therefore the growth of a prolific race, progressing as it does, "geometrically," would be vastly increased at the end of a long period, by a habit of early marriages; and thirdly, more generations are alive at the same time among those races who marry when they are young.

In explanation of the aggregate effect of these three influences, it will be best to take two examples that are widely but not extremely separated. Suppose two men, M and N, about 22 years old, each of them having therefore the expectation of living to the age of 55 or 33 years longer; and suppose that M marries at once, and that his descendants when they arrive at the same age do the same; but that N delays until he has laid by money, and does not marry before he is 33 years old, that is to say, 11 years later than M, and his descendants also follow his example. Let us further make the two very moderate suppositions, that the early marriages of race N result in an increase of $1\frac{1}{2}$ in the next generation, and also in the production of $3\frac{3}{4}$ generations in a century, while the late marriages of race N result in an increase of only $1\frac{1}{4}$ in the next generation and in $2\frac{1}{2}$ generations in one century.

It will be found that an increase of $1\frac{1}{2}$ in each generation, accumulating on the principle of compound interest during $3\frac{3}{4}$ generations, becomes rather more than $\frac{18}{4}$ times the original amount; while an increase of $1\frac{1}{4}$ for $2\frac{1}{2}$ generations is barely as much as $\frac{7}{4}$ times the original amount. Consequently the increase of the race of M at the end of a century, will be greater than that of N in the ratio of 18 to 7; that is to say, it will be rather more than $2\frac{1}{2}$ times as great. In two centuries the progeny of M will be more than 6 times, and in three centuries more than 15 times, as numerous as those of N.

The proportion which the progeny of M will bear at any time, to the total living population, will be still greater than this, owing to the number of generations of M who are alive at the same time, being greater than those of N. The reader will not find any difficulty in estimating the effect of these conditions, if he begins by ignoring children and all others below the age of 22, and also by supposing the population to be stationary in its number, in consecutive generations. We have agreed in the case of M to allow $3\frac{3}{4}$ generations to one century, which gives about 27 years to each generation; then, when one of this race is 22 years old, his father will (on the average of many cases) be 27 years older, or 49; and as the father lives to 55, he will survive the advent of his son to manhood for the space of 6 years. Consequently, during the 27 years intervening between each two generations, there will be found one mature life for the whole period and one other mature life during a period of 6 years, which gives for the total mature life of the race M, a number which may be expressed by the fraction $\frac{6+27}{27}$, or $\frac{33}{27}$. The diagram represents the course of three consecutive generations of race M; the middle line refers to that of the individual about whom I have just been speaking, the upper one to that of his father, and the lower to his son. The dotted line indicates the period of life before the age of 22; the double line, the period between 22 and the average time at which his son is born; the dark line is the remainder of his life.

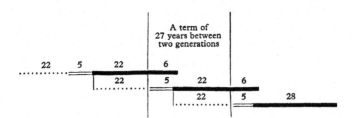

On the other hand, a man of the race N, which does not contribute more than $2\frac{1}{2}$ generations to a century, that is to say, 40 years to a single generation, does not attain the age of 22 until (on the average of many cases) 7 years after his father's death; for the father was 40 years old when his son was born, and died at the age of 55 when the son was only 15 years old. In other words, during each period of $18+15+7$, or 40 years, men of mature life of the race N are alive for only $18+15$, or

33 of them; hence the total mature life of the race N may be expressed by the fraction $\frac{33}{40}$.

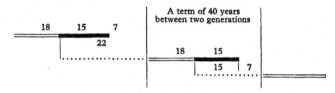

It follows that the relative population due to the races of M and N, is as $\frac{22}{27}$ to $\frac{33}{40}$, or as 40 to 271, which is very nearly as 5 to 3.

We have been calculating on the supposition that the population remains stationary, because it was more convenient to do so, but the results of our calculation will hold nearly true for all cases. Because, if population should increase, the larger number of living descendants tends to counterbalance the diminished number of living ancestry; and, conversely, if it decreases.

Combining the above ratio of 5 to 3 with those previously obtained, it results that at the end of one century from the time when the races M and N started fair, with equal numbers, the proportion of mature men of race M will be four times as numerous as those of race N[1]; at the end of two centuries, they will be ten times as numerous, and at the end of three centuries no less than twenty-six times as numerous.

I trust the reader will realise the heavy doom which these figures pronounce against all sub-sections of prolific races in which it is the custom to put off the period of marriage until middle age. It is a maxim of Malthus that the period of marriage ought to be delayed in order that the earth may not be overcrowded by a population for whom there is no place at the great table of nature. If this doctrine influenced all classes alike

[1] A little consideration of the diagram will show that the proportion in question will invariably be in the inverse ratio of the intervals between the two generations, which in the present case are 27 and 40 years.

I should have nothing to say about it here, one way or another, for it would hardly affect the discussions in this book; but, as it is put forward as a rule of conduct for the prudent part of mankind to follow, whilst the imprudent are necessarily left free to disregard it, I have no hesitation in saying that it is a most pernicious rule of conduct in its bearing upon race. Its effect would be such as to cause the race of the prudent to fall, after a few centuries, into an almost incredible inferiority of numbers to that of the imprudent, and it is therefore calculated to bring utter ruin upon the breed of any country where the doctrine prevailed. I protest against the abler races being encouraged to withdraw in this way from the struggle for existence. It may seem monstrous that the weak should be crowded out by the strong, but it is still more monstrous that the races best fitted to play their part on the stage of life, should be crowded out by the incompetent, the ailing, and the desponding.

The time may hereafter arrive, in far distant years, when the population of the earth shall be kept as strictly within the bounds of number and suitability of race, as the sheep on a well-ordered moor or the plants in an orchard-house; in the meantime, let us do what we can to encourage the multiplication of the races best fitted to invent and conform to a high and generous civilisation, and not, out of a mistaken instinct of giving support to the weak, prevent the incoming of strong and hearty individuals.

The long period of the dark ages under which Europe has lain is due, I believe, in a very considerable degree, to the celibacy enjoined by religious orders on their votaries. Whenever a man or woman was possessed of a gentle nature that fitted him or her to deeds of charity, to meditation, to literature, or to art, the social condition of the time was such that they had no refuge elsewhere than in the bosom of the Church. But the Church chose to preach and exact celibacy. The consequence was that these gentle natures had no continuance, and thus, by a policy so singularly unwise and suicidal that I am hardly able to speak of it without impatience, the Church brutalised the breed of our forefathers. She acted precisely as if she had aimed at selecting the rudest portion of the community to be, alone, the parents of future generations. She practised the arts which breeders would use, who aimed at creating ferocious, currish, and stupid natures. No wonder that club law prevailed for centuries over Europe; the wonder rather is that enough good remained in the veins of Europeans to enable their race to rise to its present very moderate level of natural morality.

A relic of this monastic spirit clings to our Universities, who say to every man who shows intellectual powers of the kind they delight to honour, "Here is an income of from one to two hundred pounds a year, with free lodging and various advantages in the way of board and society; we give it you on account of your ability; take it and enjoy it all your life if you like; we exact no condition to your continuing to hold it but one, namely, that you shall not marry."

The policy of the religious world in Europe was exerted in another direction, with hardly less cruel effect on the nature of future generations, by means of persecutions which brought thousands of the foremost thinkers and men of political aptitudes to the scaffold, or imprisoned them during a large part of their manhood, or drove them as emigrants into other lands. In every one of these cases the check upon their leaving issue was very considerable. Hence the Church, having first captured all the gentle natures and condemned them to celibacy, made another sweep of her huge nets, this time fishing in stirring waters, to catch those who were the most fearless, truth-seeking, and intelligent, in their modes of thought, and therefore the most suitable parents of a high civilisation, and put a strong check, if not a direct stop, to their progeny. Those she reserved on these occasions, to breed the generations of the future, were the servile, the indifferent, and, again, the stupid. Thus, as she—to repeat my expression—brutalised human nature by her system of celibacy applied to the gentle, she demoralised it by her system of persecution of the intelligent, the sincere, and the free. It is enough to make the blood boil to think of the blind folly that has caused the foremost nations of struggling humanity to be the heirs of such hateful ancestry, and that has so bred our instincts as to keep them in an unnecessarily long-continued antagonism with the essential requirements of a steadily advancing civilisation. In consequence of this inbred imperfection of our natures, in respect to the conditions under which we have to live, we are, even now, almost as much harassed by the sense of moral incapacity and sin, as were the early converts from barbarism, and we steep ourselves in half-unconscious self-deception and hypocrisy, as a partial refuge from its insistance. Our avowed creeds remain at variance with our real rules of conduct, and we lead a dual life of barren religious sentimentalism and gross materialistic habitudes.

The extent to which persecution must have affected European races is easily measured by a few well-known statistical facts. Thus, as regards martyrdom and imprisonment, the Spanish nation was drained of free-thinkers at the rate of 1,000 persons annually, for the three centuries between 1471 and 1781; an average of 100 persons having been executed and 900 imprisoned every year during that period. The actual data during those three hundred years are 32,000 burnt, 17,000 persons burnt in effigy (I presume they mostly died in prison or escaped from Spain), and 291,000 condemned to various terms of imprisonment and other penalties. It is impossible that any nation could stand a policy like this, without paying a heavy penalty in the deterioration of its breed, as has notably been the result in the formation of the superstitious, unintelligent Spanish race of the present day.

Italy was also frightfully persecuted at an earlier date. In the diocese of Como, alone, more than 1,000 were tried annually by the inquisitors for many years, and 300 were burnt in the single year 1416.

The French persecutions, by which the English have been large gainers, through receiving their industrial refugees, were on a nearly similar scale. In the seventeenth century three or four hundred thousand Protestants perished in prison, at the galleys, in their attempts to escape, or on the scaffold, and an equal number emigrated. Mr. Smiles, in his admirable book on the Huguenots, has traced the influence of these and of the Flemish emigrants on England, and shows clearly that she owes to them almost all her industrial arts and very much of the most valuable life-blood of her modern race. There has been another emigration from France of not unequal magnitude, but followed by very different results, namely that of the Revolution in 1789. It is most instructive to contrast the effects of the two. The Protestant emigrants were able men, and have profoundly influenced for good both our breed and our history; on the other hand, the political refugees had but poor average stamina, and have left scarcely any traces behind them.

It is very remarkable how large a proportion of the eminent men of all countries bear foreign names, and are the children of political refugees,—men well qualified to introduce a valuable strain of blood. We cannot fail to reflect on the glorious destiny of a country that should maintain, during many generations, the policy of attracting eminently desirable refugees, but no others, and of encouraging their settlement and the naturalisation of their children.

No nation has parted with more emigrants than England, but whether she has hitherto been on the whole a gainer or a loser by the practice, I am not sure. No doubt she has lost a very large number of families of sterling worth, especially of labourers and artisans; but, as a rule, the very ablest men are strongly disinclined to emigrate; they feel that their fortune is assured at home, and unless their spirit of adventure is overwhelmingly strong, they prefer to live in the high intellectual and moral atmosphere of the more intelligent circles of English society, to a self-banishment among people of altogether lower grades of mind and interests. England has certainly got rid of a great deal of refuse through means of emigration. She has found an outlet for men of adventurous and Bohemian natures, who are excellently adapted for colonising a new country, but are not wanted in old civilisations; and she has also been disembarrassed of a vast number of turbulent radicals and the like, men who are decidedly able but by no means eminent, and whose zeal, self-confidence, and irreverence far outbalance their other qualities.

The rapid rise of new colonies and the decay of old civilisations is, I believe, mainly due to their respective social agencies, which in the one case promote, and in the other case retard, the marriages of the most suitable breeds. In a young colony, a strong arm and an enterprising brain are the most appropriate fortune for a marrying man, and again, as the women are few, the inferior males are seldom likely to marry. In an old civilisation, the agencies are more complex. Among the active, ambitious classes, none but the inheritors of fortune are likely to marry young; there is especially a run against men of classes C, D, and E—those, I mean whose future fortune is not assured except through a good deal of self-denial and effort. It is almost impossible that they should succeed well and rise high in society, if they hamper themselves with a wife in their early manhood. Men of classes F and G are more independent, but they are not nearly so numerous, and therefore their breed, though intrinsically of more worth than E or D, has much less effect on the standard of the nation at large. But even if men of classes F and G marry young, and ultimately make fortunes and achieve peerages or high social position, they become infected with the ambition current in all old civilisations, of founding families. Thence result the evils I have already described, in speaking of the marriages of eldest sons with heiresses and of the suppression of the marriages of the younger sons. Again, there is a constant tendency of the best men in the country to settle in the great cities, where marriages are less prolific and children are less likely to live. Owing to these several causes, there is a steady check in an old civilisation upon the fertility of the abler classes; the improvident and unambitious are those who chiefly keep up the breed. So the race gradually deteriorates, becoming in each successive generation less fitted for a high civilisation, although it retains the external appearances of one, until the time comes when the whole political and social fabric caves in and a greater or less relapse to barbarism takes place, during the reign of which the race is perhaps able to recover its tone.

The best form of civilisation in respect to the improvement of the race, would be one in which society was not costly; where incomes were chiefly derived from professional sources, and not much through inheritance; where every lad had a chance of showing his abilities and, if highly gifted, was enabled to achieve a first-class education and entrance into professional life, by the liberal help of the exhibitions and scholarships which he had gained in his early youth; where marriage was held in as high honour as in ancient Jewish times; where the pride of race was encouraged (of course I do not refer to the nonsensical sentiment of the present day, that goes under that name); where the weak could find a welcome and a refuge in celibate monasteries or sisterhoods, and lastly, where the better sort of emigrants and refugees from other lands were invited and welcomed, and their descendants naturalised.

GENERAL CONSIDERATIONS

It is confidently asserted by all modern physiologists that the life of every plant and animal is built up of an enormous number of subordinate lives; that each organism consists of a multitude of elemental parts, which are to a great extent independent of each other; that each organ has its proper life, or autonomy, and can develop and reproduce itself independently of other tissues (see Darwin on *Domestication of Plants and Animals*, ii. 368, 369). Thus the word "Man," when rightly understood, becomes a noun of multitude, because he is composed of millions, perhaps billions of cells, each of which possesses, in some sort an independent life, and is parent of other cells. He is a conscious whole, formed by the joint agencies of a host of what appear to us to be unconscious or barely conscious elements.

Mr. Darwin, in his remarkable theory of Pangenesis, takes two great strides from this starting point. He supposes, first that each cell, having of course its individual peculiarities, breeds nearly true to its kind, by propagating innumerable germs, or to use his expression, "gemmules," which circulate in the blood and multiply there; remaining in that inchoate form until they are able to fix themselves upon other more or less perfect tissue, and then they become developed into regular cells. Secondly, the germs are supposed to be solely governed by their respective natural affinities, in selecting their points of attachment; and that, consequently, the marvellous structure of the living form is built up under the influence of innumerable blind affinities, and not under that of a central controlling power.

This theory, propounded by Mr. Darwin as "provisional," and avowedly based, in some degree, on pure hypothesis and very largely on analogy, is—whether it be true or not—of enormous service to those who inquire into heredity. It gives a key that unlocks every one of the hitherto unopened barriers to our comprehension of its nature; it binds within the compass of a singularly simple law, the multifarious forms of reproduction, witnessed in the wide range of organic life, and it brings all these forms of reproduction under the same conditions as govern the ordinary growth of each individual. It is, therefore, very advisable that we should look at the facts of hereditary genius from the point of view which the theory of Pangenesis affords, and to this I will endeavour to guide the reader, by speaking in order of TYPES—Sports of Nature, Stability, Variation, and Individuality.

TYPES

Every type of character in a living being may be compared to the typical appearance always found in different descriptions of assemblages. It is true that the life of an animal is conscious, and that the elements on which it is based are apparently unconscious, while exactly the reverse is the case in the corporate life of a body of men. Nevertheless the employment of this analogy will help us considerably in obtaining a clear understanding of the laws which govern heredity, and they will not mislead us when used in the manner I propose. The assemblages of which I speak are such as are uncontrolled by any central authority, but have assumed their typical appearance through the free action of the individuals who compose them, each man being bent on his immediate interest, and finding his place under the sole influence of an elective affinity to his neighbours. A small rising watering-place affords as good an illustration as any of which I can think. It is often hardly possible to trace its first beginnings: two or three houses were perhaps built for private use, and becoming accidentally vacant, were seen and rented by holiday folk, who praised the locality, and raised a demand for further accommodation; other houses were built to meet the requirement; this led to an inn,

o

to the daily visit of the baker's and butcher's cart, the postman, and so forth. Then as the village increased and shops began to be established, young artisans, and other floating gemmules of English population, in search of a place where they might advantageously attach themselves, became fixed, and so each new opportunity was seized upon and each opening filled up, as soon or very soon after it existed. The general result of these purely selfish affinities is that watering-places are curiously similar, even before the speculative builder has stepped in. We may predict what kind of shops will be found and how they will be placed; nay, even what kind of goods and placards will be put up in the windows. And so, notwithstanding abundant individual peculiarities, we find them to have a strong generic identity.

The type of these watering-places is certainly a durable one; the human materials of which they are made remain similar, and so are the conditions under which they exist, of having to supply the wants of the average British holiday seeker. Therefore the watering-place would always breed true to its kind. It would do so by detaching an offshoot on the fissiparous principle, or like a polyp, from which you may snip off a bit, which thenceforward lives an independent life and grows into a complete animal. Or, to compare it with a higher order of life, two watering-places at some distance apart might between them afford material to raise another in an intermediate locality.

Precisely the same remarks might be made about fishing villages, or manufacturing towns, or new settlements in the Bush, or an encampment of gold diggers, and each of these would breed true to its kind. If we go to more stationary forms of society than our own, we shall find numerous examples of the purest breed: thus, the Hottentot kraal or village of today differs in no way from those described by the earliest travellers; or, to take an immensely longer leap, the information gathered from the most ancient paintings in Egypt, accords with our observations of the modern life of the descendants of those peoples, whom the paintings represent.

Next, let us consider the nature of hybrids. Suppose a town

to be formed under the influence of two others that differ, the one a watering-place and the other a fishing-town; what will be the result ? We find that particular combination to be usually favourable, because the different elements do not interfere with but rather support one another. The fishing interest gives greater solidity to the place than the more ephemeral presence of the tourist population can furnish; the picturesque seaside life is also an attraction to visitors, and the fishermen cater for their food. On the other hand, the watering-place gives more varied conditions of existence to the fishermen; the visitors are very properly mulcted, directly or indirectly, for charities, roads, and the like, and they are not unwelcome customers in various ways to their fellow-townsmen.

Let us take another instance of an hybrid; one that leads to a different result. Suppose an enterprising manufacturer from a town at no great distance from an incipent watering-place, discovers advantages in its minerals, water power, or means of access, and prepared to set up his mill in the place. We may predict what will follow with much certainty. Either the place will be forsaken as a watering-place, or the manufacturer will be in some way or other got rid of. The two elements are discordant. The dirt and noise and rough artisans engaged in the manufactory are uncongenial to the population of a watering-place.

The moral I have in view will be clear to the reader. I wish to show that because a well-conditioned man marries a well-conditioned woman, each of pure blood as regards any natural gift, it does not in the least follow that the hybrid offspring will succeed.

SPORTS OF NATURE

I will continue to employ the same mataphor, to explain the manner in which apparent sports of nature are produced, such as the sudden appearance of a man of great abilities in undistinguished families. Mr. Darwin maintains in the theory of Pangenesis, that the gemmules of innumerable qualities, derived from ancestral sources, circulate in the blood and propagate themselves, generation after generation, still in the state of gemmules, but fail in developing themselves into cells, because other antagonistic gemmules are prepotent and overmaster them, in the struggle for points of attachment. Hence there is a vastly larger number of capabilities in every living being, than ever find expression, and for every *patent* element there are countless *latent* ones. The character of a man is wholly formed through those gemmules that have succeeded in attaching themselves; the remainder that have been overpowered by their antagonists, count for nothing; just as the policy of a democracy is formed by that of the majority of its citizens, or as the parliamentary voice of any place is determined by the dominant political views of the electors: in both instances, the dissentient minority is powerless. Let, however, by the virtue of the more rapid propagation of one class of electors, say of an Irish population, the numerical strength of the weaker party be supposed to gradually increase, until the minority becomes the majority, then there will be a sudden reversal or revolution of the political equilibrium, and the character of the borough or nation as evidenced by its corporate acts, will be entirely changed. This corresponds to a so-called "sport" of nature. Again, to make the simile still more closely appropriate to our wants, suppose that by some alteration in the system of representation, two boroughs, each containing an Irish element in a large minority, the one having always returned a Whig and the other a Conservative, to be combined into a single borough returning one member. It is clear that the Whig and Conservative party will neutralise one another, and that the union of the two Irish minorities will form a strong majority, and that a member professing Irish interests is sure to be returned. This strictly corresponds to the case where the son has marked peculiarities, which neither of his parents possessed in a patent form.

The dominant influence of pure blood over mongrel alliances is also easily to be understood by the simile of the two boroughs; for if every perfect and inchoate voter in one of them—that is to say, every male, man and child—be a radical to his backbone, the incoming of such a compact mass would overpower the divided politics of the inhabitants of the other, with which it was combined.

These similes, which are perfectly legitimate according to the theory of Pangenesis, are well worthy of being indulged in, for they give considerable precision to our views on heredity, and compel facts that appear anomalous at first sight, to fall into intelligible order.

STABILITY

I will now explain what I presume ought to be understood, when we speak of the stability of types, and what is the nature of the changes through which one type yields to another. Stability is a word taken from the language of mechanics; it is felt to be an apt word; let us see what the conception of types would be, when applied to mechanical conditions. It is shown by Mr. Darwin, in his great theory of *The Origin of Species*, that all forms of organic life are in some sense convertible into one another, for all have, according to his views, sprung from common ancestry, and therefore A and B having both descended from C, the lines of descent might be remounted from A to C, and redescended from C to B. Yet the changes are not by insensible gradations; there are many, but not an infinite number of intermediate links; how is the law of continuity to be satisfied by a series of changes in jerks? The mechanical conception would be that of a rough stone, having, in consequence of its roughness, a vast number of natural facets, on any one of which it might test in "stable" equilibrium. That is to say, when pushed it would somewhat yield, when pushed much harder it would again yield, but in a less degree; in either case, on the pressure being withdrawn it would fall back into its first position. But, if by a powerful effort the stone is compelled to overpass the limits of the facet on which it has hitherto found rest, it will tumble over into a new position of stability, whence just the same proceedings must be gone through as before, before it can be dislodged and rolled another step on-wards. The various positions of stable equilibrium may be looked upon as so many typical attitudes of the stone, the type being more durable as the limits of its stability are wider. We also see clearly that there is no violation of the law of continuity in the movements of the stone, though it can only repose in certain widely separated positions.

Now for another metaphor, taken from a more complex system of forces. We have all known what it is to be jammed in the midst of a great crowd, struggling and pushing and swerving to and fro, in its endeavour to make a way through some narrow passage. There is a dead-lock; each member of the crowd is pushing, the mass is agitated, but there is no progress. If, by a great effort, a man drives those in front of him but a few inches forward, a recoil is pretty sure to follow, and there is no ultimate advance. At length, by some accidental unison of effort, the dead-lock yields, a forward movement is made, the elements of the crowd fall into slightly varied combinations, but in a few seconds there is another dead-lock, which is relieved, after a while, through just the same processes as before. Each of these formations of the crowd, in which they have found themselves in a dead-lock, is a position of stable equilibrium, and represents a typical attitude.

It is easy to form a general idea of the conditions of stable equilibrium in the organic world, where one element is so correlated with another that there must be an enormous number of unstable combinations for each that is capable of maintaining itself unchanged, generation after generation.

VARIATION

I will now make a few remarks on the subject of individual variation. The gemmules whence every cell of every organism is developed, are supposed, in the theory of Pangenesis, to be derived from two causes: the one, unchanged inheritance; the other, changed inheritance. Mr. Darwin, in his latter work, *Variation of Animals and Plants under Domestication*, shows very clearly that individual variation is a somewhat more important feature than we might have expected. It becomes an interesting inquiry to determine how much of a person's constitution is due, on an average, to the unchanged gifts of a remote ancestry, and how much to the accumulation of individual variations. The doctrine of Pangenesis gives excellent materials for mathematical formulæ, the constants of which might be supplied through averages of facts, like those contained in my tables, if they were prepared for the purpose. My own data are too lax to go upon; the averages ought to refer to some simple physical characteristic, unmistakable in its quality, and not subject to the doubts which attend the appraisement of ability. Let me remark, that there need be no hesitation in accepting averages for this purpose; for the meaning and value of an average are perfectly clear. It would represent the results, supposing the competing "gemmules" to be equally fertile, and also supposing the proportion of the gemmules affected by individual variation, to be constant in all the cases.

The immediate consequence of the theory of Pangenesis is somewhat startling. It appears to show that a man is wholly built up of his own and ancestral *peculiarities*, and only in an infinitesimal degree of characteristics handed down in an unchanged form, from extremely ancient times. It would follow that under a prolonged term of constant conditions, it would matter little or nothing what were the characteristics of the early progenitors of a race, the type being supposed constant, for the progeny would invariably be moulded by those of its more recent ancestry.

The reason for what I have just stated is easily to be comprehended, if easy though improbable figures be employed in illustration. Suppose, for the same merely of a very simple numerical example, that a child acquired one-tenth of his nature from individual variation, and inherited the remaining nine-tenths from his parents. It follows, that his two parents would have handed down only nine-tenths of nine-tenths, or $\frac{81}{100}$ from his grandparents, $\frac{729}{1000}$ from his great-grandparents,

and so on; the numerator of the fraction increasing in each successive step less rapidly than the denominator, until we **arrive** at a vanishing value of the fraction.[1]

[1] The formula is as follows:—

G = the total number of gemmules; of which those derived unchanged through parentage = Gr; the remainder, = $G(1-r)$, being changed through individual variation. Then—

	Derived unchanged through Parents		Modified through individual variation
The gemmules in any individual consist of	Gr	$+$	$G(1-r)$
The part Gr derived through the parents is similarly composed of two parts; namely	Gr^2	$+$	$Gr(1-r)=G(r-r^2)$
The part Gr^2 derived through the grandparents is composed of	Gr^3	$+$	$Gr^2(r-r^2)=G(r^2-r^3)$
&c.	&c.		&c.
That derived from the nth ascending generation is composed of	$Grn+1$	$+$	$Gr(rn-1-rn)=$ $G(rn-rn+1)$

Hence G consists of $Grn+1$ unchanged gemmules derived from generations higher than the $n^{th} + G$ multiplied into the sum of the following series, every term of which expresses gemmules, modified by individual variation—

$$1-r+\overline{r-r^2}+\overline{r^2-r^3}+ \text{ and } +\overline{rn-rn+1}=1-rn+1$$

as r is a fraction less than 1 (it was $\frac{9}{10}$ in the imaginary case discussed in my text, and would generally be very small, but I have no conception what,—perhaps as small as $\frac{999}{1000}$, or some numbers still nearer unity), the value of $rn+1$ will vanish if n be taken sufficiently large, in which case the individual may be considered as wholly derived from gemmules modified by individual variations *posterior* to the nth generation.

It must be understood that I am speaking of variations well within the limits of stability of the race, and also that I am not speaking of cases where the individuals are selected for some peculiarity, generation after generation. In this event a new element must be allowed for, inasmuch as the average value of r cannot be constant. In proportion as the deviation from the mean position of stability is increased, the tendency of individual variation may reasonably be expected to lie more strongly towards the mean position than away from it. The treatment of all this seems well within the grasp of analysis, but we

The part inherited by this child in an unchanged form from all his ancestors above the fiftieth degree, would be only one five-thousandth of his whole nature.

I do not see why any serious difficulty should stand in the way of mathematicians, in framing a compact formula, based on the theory of Pangenesis, to express the composition of organic beings in terms of their inherited and individual peculiarities, and to give us, after certain constants had been determined, the means of foretelling the average distribution of characteristics among a large multitude of offspring whose parentage was known. The problem would have to be attacked on the following principle.

The average proportion of gemmules, modified by individual variation under various conditions preceding birth, clearly admits of being determined by observation; and the deviations from that average may be determined by the same theory in the law of chances, to which I have so often referred. Again, the proportion of the other gemmules which are transmitted in an unmodified form, would be similarly treated; for the children would, *on the average*, inherit the gemmules in the same proportions that they existed in their parents; but in each child there would be a deviation from that average. The table in page 75 is identical with the special case in which only two forms of gemmules had to be considered, and in which they existed in equal numbers in both parents.

If the theory of Pangenesis be true, not only might the average qualities of the descendants of groups A and B, A and C, A and D, and every other combination be predicted, but also the numbers of them who deviate in various proportions from those averages. Thus, the issue of F and A ought to

want a collection of facts, such as the breeders of animals could well supply, to guide us for a few steps out of the region of pure hypothesis.

The formula also shows how much of a man's nature is derived on the average from any given ancestor; for if we call the father the 1st generation, the grandfather the 2nd, and so on, as a man has 2^n parents in the nth generation, and as the formula shows that he only inherits Gr^n unchanged gemmules from all of them put together, it follows that the portion derived from each person in that generation is, as $(\frac{r}{2})^n$.

result in so and so, for an average, and in such and such numbers, per million, of A, B, C, D, E, F, G, &c., classes. The latent gemmules equally admit of being determined from the patent characteristics of many previous generations, and the tendency to reversion into any ancient form ought also to admit of being calculated. In short, the theory of Pangenesis brings all the influences that bear on heredity into a form, that is appropriate for the grasp of mathematical analysis.

INDIVIDUALITY

I will conclude by saying a few words upon what is to be understood by the phrase "individuality." The artificial breeding of fish has been the subject of so many books, shows, and lectures, that every one has become more or less familiar with its processes. The milt taken from the male is allowed to fall upon the ova that have been deposited by the female, which thereupon rapidly change their appearance, and gradually, without any other agency, an embryo fish may be observed to develop itself inside each of them. The ova may have been separated for many days from the female, the milt for many hours from the male. They are, therefore, entirely detached portions of organized matter, leading their own separate organic existences; and at the instant or very shortly after they touch, the foundations are laid of an individual life. But where was that life during the long interval of separation of the milt and roe from the parent fish? If these substances were possessed of conscious lives in the interim, then two lives will have been merged into one "individuality" by the process; which is a direct contradiction in terms. If neither had conscious lives, then consciousness was produced by an operation as much under human control as anything can be. It may not be said that the ovum was always alive, and the milt had merely an accessory influence, because the young fish inherits its character from its parents equally, and there is an abundance of other physiological data to disprove the idea. Therefore so far as fish are concerned, the creation of a new life is as unrestrictedly within the compass of human power, as the creation of any material product whatever, from the combination of given elements.

Again, suppose the breeder of fish to have two kinds of milt, belonging to salmon of different characters, each in a separate cup, A and B, and two sorts of ova, each also in a separate cup, C and D. Then he can make at his option the two sorts of fish AC and BD, or else the two sorts of fish AD and BC. Therefore not only the creation of the lives of fish, in a general sense, but also the specific character of individual lives, within wide limits, is unrestrictedly under human control. The power of the director of an establishment for breeding fish is of exactly the same quality as that of a cook in her kitchen. Both director and cook require certain elements to work upon; but, having got them, they can create a fish or a dinner, as the case may be, according to a predetermined pattern.

Now, all generation is physiologically the same,[1] and therefore the reflections raised by what has been stated of fish are equally applicable to the life of man. The entire human race, or any one of its varieties, may indefinitely increase its numbers by a system of early marriages, or it may wholly annihilate itself by the observance of celibacy; it may also introduce new human forms by means of the intermarriage of varieties and of a change in the conditions of life. It follows that the human race has a large control over its future forms of activity,—far more than any individual has over his own, since the freedom of individuals is narrowly restricted by the cost, in energy, of exercising their wills. Their state may be compared to that of cattle in an open pasture, each tethered closely to a peg by an elastic cord. These can graze in any direction, for short distances, with little effort, because the cord stretches easily at first; but the further they range, the more powerfully does its elastic force pull backwards against them. The extreme limit of their several ranges must lie at that distance from the peg where the maximum supply of nervous force which the

---

[1] The Address of the President of the Royal Society, 1867, in presenting the Copley medal to Von Baer.

chemical machinery of their bodies can evolve, is only just equivalent to the outflow required to resist the strain of the cord. Now, the freedom of humankind, considered as a whole, is far greater than this; for it can gradually modify its own nature, or, to keep to the previous metaphor, it can cause the pegs themselves to be continually shifted. It can advance them from point to point, towards new and better pastures, over wide areas, whose bounds are as yet unknown.

Nature teems with latent life, which man has large powers of evoking under the forms and to the extent which he desires. We must not permit ourselves to consider each human or other personality as something supernaturally added to the stock of nature, but rather as a segregation of what already existed, under a new shape, and as a regular consequence of previous conditions. Neither must we be misled by the word "individuality," because it appears from the many facts and arguments in this book, that our personalities are not so independent as our self-consciousness leads us to believe. We may look upon each individual as something not wholly detached from its parent source,—as a wave that has been lifted and shaped by normal conditions in an unknown, illimitable ocean. There is decidedly a solidarity as well as a separateness in all human, and probably in all lives whatsoever; and this consideration goes far, as I think, to establish an opinion that the constitution of the living Universe is a pure theism, and that its form of activity is what may be described as co-operative. It points to the conclusion that all life is single in its essence, but various, ever varying, and inter-active in its manifestations, and that men and all other living animals are active workers and sharers in a vastly more extended system of cosmic action than any of ourselves, much less of them, can possibly comprehend. It also suggests that they may contribute, more or less unconsciously, to the manifestation of a far higher life than our own, somewhat as—I do not propose to push the metaphor too far—the individual cells of one of the more complex animals contribute to the manifestation of its higher order of personality.

APPENDIX

The deviations from an average are given in the following table of M. Quételet as far as 80 grades; they are intended to be reckoned on either side of the average, and therefore extend over a total range of 160 grades. The eightieth is a deviation so extreme, that the chances of its being exceeded (upwards or downwards, whichever of the two events we please to select) is only $\frac{5,000,000 - 4,999,992}{10,000,000} = \frac{8}{10,000,000}$, or less than one in a million. That is to say, when firing at a target (see Diagram, p. 68) less than one out of a million shots, taking the average of many millions, will hit it at a greater height than 80 of Quételet's grades above the mean of all the shots; and an equally small number will hit it lower than the 80th grade below the same mean.

Column M gives the chance of a shot falling into any given grade (80 × 2 or) 160 in total number. Column N represents the chances from another point of view; it is derived directly from M, and shows the probability of a shot lying between any specified grade and the mean; each figure in N consisting cf the sum of all the figures in M up to the grade in question, and inclusive. Thus, as we see by Column M, the chance against a shot falling into the 1st grade (superior or inferior, whichever we please to select is 0·025225 to 1, and 0·025124 to 1 against its falling into the 2d, and 0·024924 to 1 against its falling into the 3d; then the chance against its falling between the mean and the third grade, inclusive, is clearly the sum of these 3 numbers, or 0·075273, which is the entry in Column N, opposite the grade 3.

These columns may be used for two purposes.

The one is to calculate a table like that in p. 75, where I have simply lumped 11 of Quételet's grades into 1, so that my classes A and *a* correspond to his grade 11 in column N, my classes B and *b* to the difference between his grades 22 and 11, my C and *c* to that between his grades 33 and 22, and so on.

TABLE **BY** QUÉTELET

Grade or Rank of the Group	M Probability of Drawing each Group	N Sum of the Probabilities, commencing at the most probable Group	Number of the Grade	M Probability of Drawing each Group	N Sum of the Probabilities, commencing at the most probable Group
1	0·025225	0·025225	41	0·0009458	0·495278
2	0·025124	0·050349	42	0·0008024	0·496081
3	0·024924	0·075273	43	0·0006781	0·496759
4	0·024627	0·099900	44	0·0005707	0·497329
5	0·024236	0·124136	45	0·0004784	0·497808
6	0·023756	0·147892	46	0·0003994	0·498207
7	0·023193	0·171085	47	0·0003321	0·498539
8	0·022552	0·193637	48	0·0002750	0·498814
9	0·021842	0·215479	49	0·0002268	0·499041
10	0·021069	0·236548	50	0·0001863	0·499227
11	0·020243	0·256791	51	0·0001525	0·499380
12	0·019372	0·276163	52	0·0001242	0·499504
13	0·018464	0·294627	53	0·0001008	0·499605
14	0·017528	0·312155	54	0·0000815	0·499686
15	0·016573	0·338728	55	0·0000656	0·499752
16	0·015608	0·344335	56	0·0000526	0·499804
17	0·014640	0·358975	57	0·0000421	0·499847
18	0·013677	0·372652	58	0·0000334	0·499880
19	0·012726	0·385378	59	0·0000265	0·499906
20	0·011794	0·397172	60	0·0000209	0·499927
21	0·010887	0·408060	61	0·0000164	0·499944
22	0·010008	0·418070	62	0·0000128	0·499957
23	0·009166	0·427236	63	0·0000100	0·499967
24	0·008360	0·435595	64	0·0000077	0·499974
25	0·007594	0·443189	65	0·0000060	0·499980
26	0·006871	0·450060	66	0·0000046	0·499985
27	0·006191	0·456251	67	0·0000035	0·499988
28	0·005557	0·461809	68	0·0000027	0·4999912
29	0·004968	0·466776	69	0·0000021	0·4999933
30	0·004423	0·471199	70	0·0000016	0·4999948
31	0·003922	0·475122	71	0·0000012	0·4999960
32	0·003464	0·478586	72	0·0000009	0·4999969
33	0·003047	0·481633	73	0·0000007	0·4999976
34	0·002670	0·484304	74	0·0000005	0·4999981
35	0·002330	0·486634	75	0·0000004	0·4999984
36	0·002025	0·488659	76	0·0000003	0·4999987
37	0·001753	0·490412	77	0·0000002	0·4999989
38	0·001512	0·491924	78	0·00000014	0·4999990
39	0·001298	0·493222	79	0·00000011	0·4999991
40	0·001110	0·494332	80	0·00000004	0·4999992

The other is as a test, whether or no a group of events are due to the same general causes; because, if they are, their classification will afford numbers that correspond with those in the table; otherwise they will not. This test has been employed in pp. 70, 71, and 73. The method of conducting the comparison is easily to be understood by the following example, the figures of which I take from Quételet. It seems that 487 observations of the Right Ascension of the Polar Star were made at Greenwich between 1836 and 1839, and are recorded in the publications of the Observatory, after having been corrected for precession, nutation, &c., and subject only to errors of observation. If they are grouped into classes separated by grades of 0·5 sec. the numbers in each of these classes will be as shown in Column III, page 432. We raise them in the proportion of 1,000 to 487 in order to make the ratios decimal, and therefore comparable with the figures in Quételet's table, and then insert them in Column IV. These tell us that it has been found by a pretty large experience, that the chance of an observation falling within the class of −0·5 sec. from the mean, is 150 to 1,000; of its falling within the class of −1·0 sec. is 126 to 1,000; and so on, for the rest. This information is analogous to that given in Column M of Quételet's table, and we shall now proceed to calculate from IV the Column V, which is analogous to Quételet's N. The method of doing so is, however, different. N was formed by adding the entries in M from the average outwards; we must set to work in the converse way, of working from the outside inwards, because the exact mean is not supposed to have been ascertained, and also because this method of working would be more convenient, even if we had ascertained the mean. Now, wherever the mean may lie in a symmetrical series, the chance is 500 to 1,000 against an observation being on one specified side of it—say the *minus* side. Therefore Column IV by showing that no observation lies outside the class −3·5 sec. tacitly states that it is 500 to 1,000 (or 0·500 to 1·00) that any observation will lie between −3·4 sec. and the mean; 0·500 is therefore written in Column V opposite −3·5 sec. Again, as according to IV there are only 2 cases in the class −3·5 sec. it is (500−2=) 498 to 1,000 that any observation will lie between class −3·0 sec. and the average, and 0·498 is written in Column V opposite to −3·0 sec. Similarly (498−12=) 0·486 is written opposite to −2·5 sec. and we proceed in this way until we fall within the observations that form part of the group of the mean, 168 in number. Our remainder is 68; it ought, strictly speaking, to be equal to one half of 168, or 84; we therefore may conclude that the mean has been taken a trifle too high.

A calculation made in exactly the same way, from +3·5 sec.

I	II	III	IV	V	VI	VII	VIII	IX	X
Classes	Range included in each Class	No. of Observations in each Class	Events per 1000 by experience. Ditto raised as 1000 to 487	Probabilities derived from Experience	Corresponding Grade in N	Differences	Revised Grades	Probabilities derived from Calculation	Events per 1000 by calculation. Differences in previous Columns
sec.									
All below		0	0						⎫ 4
−3·5	−3·25 to −3·75	1	2	0·500	45·5		41·5	0·500	⎬
−3·0	−2·75 „ −3·25	6	12	0·498	35·0	10·5	35·0	0·496	10
−2·5	−2·25 „ −2·75	12	25	0·461	28·0	7·0	28·5	0·486	22
−2·0	−1·75 „ −2·25	21	43	0·418	22·0	6·0	22·0	0·418	46
−1·5	−1·25 „ −1·75	36	74	0·344	16·6	5·4	15·5	0·341	81
−1·0	−0·75 „ −1·25	61	126	0·218	9·3	7·3	9·0	0·215	126
−0·5	−0·25 „ −0·75	73	150	0·68	2·6	6·7	2·5	0·063	152
Mean 0·0	+0·25 „ −0·25	82	168			6·6			163
+0·5	+0·25 „ +0·75	72	148	0·100	4·0	6·5	4·0	0·100	147
+1·0	+0·75 „ +1·25	63	129	0·248	10·5	8·0	10·5	0·247	112
+1·5	+1·25 „ +1·75	38	78	0·377	18·5	8·5	17·0	0·359	72
+2·0	+1·75 „ +2·25	16	33	0·455	27·0	8·5	23·5	0·431	40
+2·5	+2·25 „ +2·75	5	10	0·488	35·5		30·0	0·471	19
All above		1	2	0·500				0·500	10
		487	1000						1000

inwards to the mean, will take in the other portion of the mean group, namely, 100. Now we compare our results with Quételet's Column N, and see to which of his grades the numbers in our Column V are severely equal; the grades in question are written in Column VI. In proportion as these observations are strictly accordant with the law of deviation from a mean, so the intervals between the grades in Column VI will approach to equality. What they actually are, is shown in Column VII. We cannot expect the two extreme terms to give results of much value, because the numbers of observations are too few; but taking only the remainder into consideration, we find that the average interval of 6·5 is very generally adhered to. Now, then, let us see what the numbers in the classes would have been by theory if, starting either from 2·5 (a little lower than 2·6, as we agreed it ought to be) above the average, or from 4, below it, we construct a series of classes, according to Quételet's grades, having a common interval of 6·5. Column VIII shows what these classes would be; Column IX shows the corresponding figures taken directly from Quételet's N, and Column X gives the difference between these figures, which are so closely accordant with the entries in Column IV, as to place it beyond all doubt that the errors in the Greenwich observations are strictly governed by the law of a deviation from an average.

It remains that I should say a very few words on the principle of the law of deviation from an average, or, as it is commonly called, the law of Errors of Observations, due to La Place. Every variable event depends on a number of variable causes, and each of these, owing to the very fact of its variability, depends upon other variables, and so on step after step, till one knows not where to stop. Also, by the very fact of each of these causes being a variable event, it has a mean value, and, therefore, it is (I am merely altering the phrase), an even chance in any case, that the event should be greater or less than the mean. Now, it is asserted to be a matter of secondary moment to busy ourselves in respect to these minute causes, further than as to the probability of their exceeding or falling short of their several mean values, and the chance of a larger or smaller number of them doing so, in any given case, resembles the chance, well known to calculators, of the results that would be met with when making a draw out of an urn containing an equal quantity of black and white balls in enormous numbers. Each ball that is drawn out has an equal chance of being black or white, just as each subordinate event has an equal chance of exceeding or falling short of its mean value. I cannot enter further here into the philosophy of this view; it has been discussed by many writers, and the subject is still inexhausted.

A table, made on the above hypothesis, has been constructed by Cournot, and will be found in the Appendix, p. 267, of Quételet's *Letters on Probabilities* (translated by Downes; Layton & Co., 1849), but it does not extend nearly so far as that of M. Quételet. The latter is calculated on a very simple principle, being the results of drawing 999 balls out of an urn, containing white and black balls in equal quantities and in enormous numbers. His grade No. 1 is the case of drawing 499 white and 500 black, his 2 in 498 white and 501 black, and so on, the 80th being 420 white and 579 black. It makes no sensible difference in the general form of the results, when these large numbers are taken, what their actual amount may be. The value of a grade will of course be very different, but almost exactly the same *quality* of curve would be obtained if the figures in Quételet's or in Cournot's tables were protracted. All this is shown by Quételet in his comparison of the two tables.

INDEX

Abbott, 335–6
Ability, 26–7, 77–8
Abinger, *see* Scarlett
Abney, 128
Actors, 50*n.*
Adams, 170–1
Addington, 150
Addison, 221
Æschylus, 279, 281–2, 380
Africans, 32, 39, 40
Aikin, 221
Alderson, 63, 128
Alexander, 188, 196–200, 376, 380
Alibone, 128
Alison, 221–2
Allegri, 293, 304
Amati, 293
Ameinas, 281
America, United States of, 38–9, 47, 79–80
Ampère, 63, 249–50
Anderson, 265–6
Arago, 63, 249, 250
Argyll, *see* Stuart
Ariosto, 282, 380
Aristophanes, 282, 380
Aristotle, 250–1, 380
Arniston, *see* Dundas
Arnold, 222
Arteveldt, 86, 171
Artists, 50*n.*; *see also* Painters, Musicians, Actors
Atkyns, 128–9
Augustus, 203
Augustus II (King of Poland), 212–13

Austen, 240
Aylesford, *see* Legge

Bach, 293–6
Bache, 263
Bacon, 97, 251–2, 380
Badile, 304
Baillie, 269
Barbauld, 221
Barry, 64
Bassano, 308
Bathurst, 106, 129
Batty, 129
Bedford, 157
Bedingfield, 129
Beethoven, 296
Bellini, 304
Benda, 296–7
Bentham, 222
Bentinck, 150, 157
Béranger, 278
Bernoulli, 252–4
Berwick, *see* Churchill
Best, 129
Bickersteth, 129
Bion, 281
Birch, 129
Blackburn, 129
Blackstone, 129
Blair, 366–7
Boat Races, Oxford and Cambridge, 54–5
Boccaccio, 278
Boileau, 218, 222
Bolingbroke, 157
Bonaparte, 188–9, 201–2, 376

Bononcini, 297
Bossuet, 222, 380
Bouillon, 215
Boulton, 244, 276
Boyle, 254–6
Bradshaw, 138
Bramston, 129
Brodie, 132, 256
Bromley, 345
Brontë, 217, 218, 223
Brougham, Lord, 78, 121, 130, 150
Brown-Séquard, 31
Browne, 130
Brunel, 389
Buckingham, 160
Buckland, 257
Buffon, 257
Buller, 106, 130
Bunbury, 159, 354
Burchell, 357
Burleigh, *see* Cecil
Burnet, 114–15, 130
Burns, 278
Bussy-Rambutin, 234
Bute, *see* Stuart
Butler, 63, 354–5
Byron, 282

Cæsar, 189, 203–4, 376, 380
Cagliari, 304–5
Calderon, 278, 380
Cambridge: Senior Classics, 63–4, 353–8; Wranglers, 58–64; Boat Races, 54–5
Camden, *see* Pratt
Campbell, 114–15, 130, 167
Candlish, 362–3
Canning, 151, 157–8, 183
Canterbury, *see* Sutton
Caracci, 305

Casaubon, 239–40
Cassini, 257–8
Castlereagh, *see* Stewart
Cavendish, 258
Cecil, 171, 252
Celsius, 258
Chamberlain, 166
Champernoun, 212
Champollion, 223
Chancellors, 96, 127
Charlemagne, 189, 196, 204, 380
Charles Martel, 196, 204
Charles XII (of Sweden), 189, 207
Châteaubriand, 217, 218, 223–4
Chatham, *see* Pitt
Chaucer, 283
Chelmsford, *see* Thesiger
Chenier, 283
Chinese, 32, 35
Christina (Queen of Sweden), 206
Chuan-Yuan, 390–1
Church, 410–11
Churchill, 130, 189, 200–1, 210
Clarendon, *see* Hyde
Clarke, 130, 321, 336
Clasper, 363–4
Classics scholars, 353–8
Claude, 306
Cleopatra, 199
Clive, 130, 204
Cobham, 160
Cockburn, 130
Colbert, 172
Coleridge, 111, 131, 283–4
Coligny, 204–5
Colonius, 337
Colpepper, 179

Commanders, 84–7, 188–215, 384; appendix to, 197–215
Comte, 379–81
Condorcet, 63, 258–9
Conduit, 274
Cooke, 251–2
Coombes, 364
Cooper, 125, 131, 179, 318, 364
Copley, 63, 131
Corday, 285
Cork, *see* Boyle
Corneille, 284–5, 380
Correggio, 304
Cottenham, *see* Pepys
Cowley, 169
Cowper, 106, 111, 125, 131, 162, 278, 285
Cramond, *see* Burnet
Cranmer, 314
Cranworth, *see* Rolfe
Cromwell, 142, 172–3, 205, 337, 380
Culverel, 341
Cuvier 259
Cynægeirus, 281

D'Alembert, 63, 83, 259–60
Daley, 367
Dampier, 131
Dante, 278, 380
Dartmouth, *see* Legge
Darwin, 9–10, 12, 14–17, 31, 36, 45, 244, 260–1, 416–28
Davy, 261–2, 277
De Candolle, 262
De Dieu, 336–7
De Grey, 131
Denison, 132
Denman, 132, 256, 355, 388
Derby, *see* Stanley

Deviation from an average, 28–9, 66–76
Dibdin, 285–6
Disraeli, 158, 217
Divines, 50n., 312–52, 385; appendix to, 335–52
Dod, 319, 337
Dolben, 111, 132
Donne, 337–8
Doria, 205
Dowdeswell, 142
Downe, 320, 338, 346–7
Draper, 129
Dryden, 240, 286
Dudevant, 213
Dudley, 107, 112, 235
Dufferin, 167
Dundas, 158
Dussek, 297–8

Edgeworth, 137, 224
Eichhorn, 298
Eldon, *see* Scott
Ellenborough, *see* Law
Ellis, H. Leslie, 62
Engineers, 50n., 389–90
Erle, 132
Erskine, 96, 106, 132, 150, 338
Etienne, 238–40
Eugene (Austrian Prince), 189, 205–6
Euler, 262
Euphorion, 281
Evans, 316, 338–9
Ewbank, 367
Eyck, 305–6
Eyre, 132

Fénelon, 217, 224
Fenton, 254
Feriol, 260

Fertility, 36–8
Fielden, 225
Fielding, 133, 218, 224–5
Finch, 106, 115, 132–3, 179, 267
Finnieux, 112
Fitzroy, 167
Floyd, 163
Fontanelle, 260, 284
Forbes, 263
Forster, 133
Fox, 151, 159, 183
Francis, 160
Franklin, 263
Frenchmen, 47; height of, 71–2

Gabrielli, 298
Galilei, 263–4, 380
Garvagh, *see* Canning
Gelée, 306
Genghis Khan, 196
Genius, 26–7, 46
Geoffroy, 264
Gerhard, 352
Germans, 47
Gibbon, 144, 150
Gilbert, 211–12
Gillies, 129
Gilpin, 339
Glaister, 367
Gmelin, 264–5
Goderich, *see* Robinson
Goethe, 286–7
Goldoni, 278
Goldsmith, 218
Golightly, 367
Gordon, 367
Gouge, 316, 339–41
Goulburn, 63, 355

Gould, 125, 133, 225
Gracchus, 86
Grafton, 167, 183
Gramont, 218, 225
Grant, 151, 196
Grattan, 160
Greeks, 396–7
Gregory, 222, 265–6
Grenville, 151, 160–1, 183
Grey, 162
Grotius, 217, 225–6
Grynæus, 175, 341–3
Guilford, *see* North
Guise, 173, 320
Gurney, 134
Gustavus Adolphus, 189
Guyse, 343

Halford, 145
Hall, 318, 350, 357
Hallam, 226–7
Haller, 265
Hamilcar, 207
Hampden, 145, 172, 205
Hannibal, 189, 207–8
Harcourt, 134, 179–80
Hardinge, 142–3
Hardwicke, *see* Yorke
Harrington, 112, 367
Harvey, 265–7, 320
Hasdrubal, 208
Hatherley, *see* Wood
Hatton, 119–20, 139
Haydn, 298
Hawkins, 145, 355–6
Hawks, 364
Heath, 134
Heine, 287–8
Helvetius, 227
Henley, 134, 180

Henry, 320, 343–4
Herbert, 106, 107, 134, 320, 344–5
Herschel, 267–8
Hewitt, 134
Hildersham, 345
Hiller, 299
Holland, *see* Fox
Homel, 314–15
Hook, 288
Hooker, 145, 268, 318, 346
Hooper, 345
Hornby, 167
Horner, 162
Hospinian, 345
Hotham, 134
Huguenots, 413
Humboldt, 268–9
Hunter, 269
Hutton, 273–5
Huyghens, 269
Hyde, 106, 111, 121, 134–5, 180
Hyder Ali, 208

Idiots, 26–7, 65–6, 76
Illegitimate families of Judges, 177–8
Illustrious, definition of, 46, 53
Imbecile, *see* Idiots
Irving, 218, 228, 367
Italians, 47
Ivison, 367–8

Jamieson, 368
Jaw, human, 31–2
Jeffreys, 107, 136, 138, 180
Jenkinson, 162
Jervis, 136, 151, 162
Jewell, 338, 345–7
Jews, 35, 47

Jonson, 278
Judges, 29–30, 46, 50*n*., 95–148, 177–8, 384; appendix to, 127–48
Junius, 319–20, 347
Jussieu, 269–71

Kaye, Dr. (Bishop of Lincoln), 63
Keating, 136
Keats, 278
Keiser, 299
Kemble, 390
Kennedy, 356–7
Kenyon, 180
Kimbolton, *see* Montagu
King, 106, 136, 150
Knox, 347
Köningsmark, 213

Lamb, 162, 228
Langdale, *see* Bickersteth
Lansdowne, *see* Petty
Lasco, à, 347
Laud, 335–6
Law, 136, 150, 357
Lawrence, 137, 196, 208
Lechmere, 125, 137
Lee, 137
Legge, 137
Leibnitz, 63, 271, 380
Leicester, *see* Dudley
Leighton, 324, 348
Lessing, 217, 228
Lewis, 144
Lifford, *see* Hewitt
Linley, 166
Linnæus, 271–2
Literary men, 216–42, 384; appendix to, 221–42

Little, 368
Liverpool, *see* Jenkinson
Locke, 106, 136
Lombroso, 26
Londonderry, *see* Stewart
Long, 368
L'Ouverture, 394
Lovelace, 283
Lovell, 137
Lowthian, 367
Lushington, 97, 357–8
Lyndhurst, *see* Copley
Lyttleton, 107, 137–8
Lytton, 217

Macaulay, 64, 114–16, 228–9
Macclesfield, *see* Parker
Mackenzie, 168
Maddison, 364
Maddox, 357
Mago, 208
Malthus, 36
Manchester, *see* Montagu
Mancini, 206
Manners, *see* Sutton
Mansfield, 125, 138, 150
Manufacturers, 50*n.*
Marius, 204
Mark Antony, 204
Marlborough, *see* Churchill
Marley, 160
Matfin, 364
Mathematicians, 50*n.*, 58–64
Mather, 348
Matthew, 326, 348
Maurice of Nassau, 189, 196, 208–9
Mazarin, 206
Mazzuoli, 306
Mede, 323, 324

Melbourne, *see* Lamb
Melville, *see* Dundas
"Men of the Time", 50–1
Mendelssohn, 299
Metastasio, 278
Meyerbeer, 299
Mieris, 307
Mill, 229
Milman, 288
Milton, 111, 138, 288, 380
Mirabeau, 86, 173
Monsey, 143
Montagu, 107, 111–14, 120, 138–41, 168, 236
Moore, 210, 278
More, 174–5, 338
Mornington, 169
Moth, 320
Mozart, 300, 380
Muirhead, 277
Musicians, 50*n.*, 291–300, 384; appendix to, 293–300
Mylne, 389

Napier, 159, 196, 210–11, 272
Napoleon, *see* Bonaparte
Nares, 139
Necker, 237
Negroes, 27, 38–9, 40, 394–5
Nelson, 143, 151, 191–3, 211, 376
Newton, 272–4, 380
Nichol, 368
Nicomachus, 251
Niebuhr, 217, 218, 229
Normans, 38
North, 111–21, 139, 150, 163, 180
Northington, *see* Henley
Nottingham, *see* Finch

Nowell, 319, 348–50

Oarsmen, 359–65; appendix to, 362–5; in University Boat Races, 54–5
Oersted, 274
Olympias, 198
Opie, 128
Orford, *see* Walpole
Orrery, *see* Boyle
Overbury, 111, 137
Ovid, 278

Painters, 50*n*., 301–11, 384; appendix to, 303–11
Palestrina, 300
Palgrave, 145, 229, 268
Palmer, 321, 368
Palmerston, *see* Temple
Pangenesis, 416–28 *pass*.
Parker, 142, 180–1, 196
Parmegiano, 306
Patteson, 142
Peel, 163
Peerages, their influence on race, 177–87
Pembroke, 236
Pengelly, 142
Penzance, *see* Wilde
Pepin, 196, 204
Pepys, 142
Percival, 163
Petty, 163–4
Philip of Macedon, 196–8
Philocles, 281
Phillimore, 97
Pitt, 151, 164
Plato, 380

Pliny, 274–5, 380
Poets, 50*n*., 278–90, 384
Pollock, 142
Ponte, 307–8
Pope, 278
Popes, the, 81–2
Porson, 64, 218, 230
Porta, 275
Portland, *see* Bentinck
Potter, 308, 320
Powis, 142
Praed, 288–9
Pratt, 106, 124, 142–3, 150, 181
Premiers, 150
Prestley, 340
Protestant refugees, 38, 413
Ptolemy, 196, 198–200
Pyrrhus, 196, 200

Quételet, 28, 66–7, 69–71

Racine, 289
Raleigh, 211
Rastall, 338
Raymond, 143, 181
Redesdale, 163
Renforth, 364
Reputation as a test of ability, 49–55, 77–88
Reynolds, 143
Richelieu, 175–6, 380
Richmond, *see* Fox
Ripon, *see* Robinson
Rivet, 322
Roberts, 226
Robertson, 130
Robinson, 165
Robley, 368
Robson, 368

Robusti, 308
Rochester, *see* Hyde
Rockingham, 184
Rolfe, 143
Romanes, 35
Romilly, 143, 151, 165
Roper, 112, 174
Roscoe, 218, 230–1
Rossi, 289
Rousseau, 218
Runjeet Singh, 212
Russell, 157
Ruysdael, 308

Sadler, 364
Sage, Le, 218, 231
St. Beuve, 258
St. John, Sir O., 130, 157
St. Leonards, 96
St. Vincent, *see* Jervis
Salisbury, *see* Cecil
Sand, *see* Dudevant
Sandhurst, 72–3
Sandwich, 120
Sanzio, 309
Saurin, 350
Saussure, 275
Saxe, 212
Scaliger, 83, 218, 231–2
Scarlett, 143
Sceptics, 331
Schiller, 279
Schlegel, 232, 287
Schmuck, 271
Science, Men of, 50*n.*, 243–77, 384; appendix to, 249–77
Scipio, 189, 213–14, 380
Scotchmen, 56; chests of, 70–2; ability of, 395
Scott, 96, 97, 106, 144, 150, 165, 184

Seguin, Dr., 65
Selwyn, 97, 358
Seneca, 64, 233
Senior Classics of Cambridge, 353–8; appendix to, 354–8
Sévigné, 218, 233–4
Sewell, 144
Seymour, 167
Shaftesbury, *see* Cooper
Shakespeare, 278–9, 380
Shannon, *see* Boyle
Shelburne, *see* Petty
Sheridan, 165–7
Sidgwick, 358
Sidmouth, 184
Sidney, 107, 111–12, 217, 234–7
Small, 244
Socrates, 380
Somers, 106, 144
Sophocles, 279, 281
Soult, 191
Spelman, 144
"Sports" of Nature, 34–5, 419–21
Staël, de, 232, 237
Stanhope, 164
Stanihurst, 351
Stanley, 167
Statesmen, 50*n.*, 84–7, 149–76, 384; appendix to, 155–76
Stephen, 238
Stephens, 238–40
Stephenson, 275, 389
Stewart, 167, 183
Stowell, *see* Scott
Stratford de Redcliffe, *see* Canning
Stuart, 168, 183
Suckling, 211
Sutton, 144

Swift, 218, 240
Sydney, *see* Sidney

Talbot, 144, 181
Talleyrand, 85
Tasso, 289, 380
Taylor, 240–2, 365
Temple, 160, 168–9
Tençin, 260
Teniers, 309
Tenterden, 96
Thesiger, 96, 144
Thompson, 388
Thurlow, 144, 150
Timurlane, 196
Tinian, 368–9
Tintoretto, 308
Tippoo, Saib, 208
Titian, 309–10
Titus, 214
Tonstall, 339
Torrington, 345
Tracy, 128–9
Treby, 145
Trevelyan, 229
Trevor, 107, 145, 169, 181
Trimnell, 130
Trollope, 242
Tromp, 214
Trosse, 324, 325
Truro, *see* Wilde
Turenne, 189, 196, 214–15
Turner, 145, 268
Tweddell, 369
Twisden, 133, 145
Tyne Rowing Club, 360–1

Usher, 351

Vandyck, 309
Variation, 34–5

Vaughan, 145, 355–6
Vecelli, 309–10
Vega, 289
Velde, 310–11
Verney, 146
Veronese, 304–5
Volta, 276
Vossius, 347

Wallace, A., 35
Waller, 111, 134, 172, 205
Walpole, 151, 163, 169, 184
Walsingham, *see* De Grey
Walter, 107, 137
Warwick, *see* Dudley
Watson, 359–62 *pass.*, 366
Watt, 83, 244, 276–7, 380, 389
Watts, 321–2, 336
Wearmouth, 369
Wedderburn, 181
Weissmann, 31
Welch, 324, 351–2
Weldon, 28
Wellesley, 151–2, 169–70
Wellington, 150, 151, 169–70, 189, 193, 215
Whewell, 244
Whitaker, 321, 349–50
Wigram, 146
Wilberforce, 170
Wilde, 96, 107, 146
Wilkins, 337
Willes, 146
William the Silent, 189, 195–6, 208–9, 380
William III, 189, 196, 209
Williams, 111, 132
Wilmot, 125, 146
Winship, 365
Witsius, 352

Witt, de, 176
Wollaston, 277
Wolphius, 345
Wood, 146
Wordsworth, 289–90, 358
Wrestlers, 366–9; appendix to, 366–9

Writers, *see* Literary Men
Wyndham, 125, 146–7
Wynford, *see* Best

Yorke, 96, 106, 124, 125, 147–8, 181
Young, 289

COSIMO CLASSICS

COSIMO is an innovative publisher of books and publications that inspire, inform and engage readers worldwide. Our titles are drawn from a range of subjects including health, business, philosophy, history, science and sacred texts. We specialize in using print-on-demand technology (POD), making it possible to publish books for both general and specialized audiences and to keep books in print indefinitely. With POD technology new titles can reach their audiences faster and more efficiently than with traditional publishing.

> ➤ **Permanent Availability:** Our books & publications never go out-of-print.

> ➤ **Global Availability:** Our books are always available online at popular retailers and can be ordered from your favorite local bookstore.

COSIMO CLASSICS brings to life unique, rare, out-of-print classics representing subjects as diverse as *Alternative Health, Business and Economics, Eastern Philosophy, Personal Growth, Mythology, Philosophy, Sacred Texts, Science, Spirituality* and much more!

COSIMO-on-DEMAND publishes your books, publications and reports. If you are an Author, part of an Organization, or a Benefactor with a publishing project and would like to bring books back into print, publish new books fast and effectively, would like your publications, books, training guides, and conference reports to be made available to your members and wider audiences around the world, we can assist you with your publishing needs.

Visit our website at www.cosimobooks.com to learn more about Cosimo, browse our catalog, take part in surveys or campaigns, and sign-up for our newsletter.

And if you wish please drop us a line at info@cosimobooks.com. We look forward to hearing from you.

Lightning Source UK Ltd.
Milton Keynes UK
UKOW04f0058140917
309168UK00001B/3/P

9 781596 057692